Clinical Gerontological Social Work Practice

Robert Youdin, PhD, LCSW, is an independent scholar at the Princeton Research Forum. He has been in private practice for the past 31 years in Princeton, New Jersey. For 20 years, Dr. Youdin was an adjunct associate professor at the Fordham University Graduate School of Social Service in New York City. From 2007 to 2008, he was a project director for a Gero Innovations Grant for the Master's Advanced Curriculum Project funded by the John A. Hartford Foundation and Council on Social Work Education. From 2005 to 2007, Dr. Youdin was a participant in the Curriculum Development Institute (Gero-Ed) sponsored by the John A. Hartford Foundation and Council on Social Work Education. He is a past assistant research scientist at the Biometrics Unit of the New York State Psychiatric Institute in New York City. In 1977, he was elected a member of Sigma Xi, the Scientific Research Society of North America. In addition, he has appeared on numerous public service radio programs discussing older adult substance abuse and eating disorders. Dr. Youdin's website can be visited at http://www.youdin.net/

Clinical Gerontological Social Work Practice

Robert Youdin, PhD, LCSW

SPRINGER PUBLISHING COMPANY

Springer Publishing Company, LLC
11 West 42nd Street
New York, NY 10036
www.springerpub.com

Acquisitions Editor: Sheri W. Sussman
Production Editor: Shelby Peak
Composition: Graphic World

ISBN: 978-0-8261-2989-5
e-book ISBN: 978-0-8261-2992-5
Instructor's Manual ISBN: 978-0-8261-2732-7
Instructor's PowerPoints ISBN: 978-0-8261-2739-6

Instructor's Materials: Qualified instructors may request supplements by emailing textbook@springerpub.com

14 15 16 17 / 5 4 3 2 1

The author and the publisher of this Work have made every effort to use sources believed to be reliable to provide information that is accurate and compatible with the standards generally accepted at the time of publication. The author and publisher shall not be liable for any special, consequential, or exemplary damages resulting, in whole or in part, from the readers' use of, or reliance on, the information contained in this book. The publisher has no responsibility for the persistence or accuracy of URLs for external or third-party Internet websites referred to in this publication and does not guarantee that any content on such websites is, or will remain, accurate or appropriate.

Library of Congress Cataloging-in-Publication Data

Youdin, Robert, author.
  Clinical gerontological social work practice / Robert Youdin.
    p. ; cm.
  Includes bibliographical references and index.
  ISBN 978-0-8261-2989-5 — ISBN 978-0-8261-2992-5 (e-book)
  I. Title.
  [DNLM: 1. Mental Disorders. 2. Social Work—methods. 3. Aged.
4. Psychotherapy. 5. Sexuality. WT 150]
  HV1451
  362.6--dc23
                              2014002983

Printed in the United States of America by McNaughton & Gunn.

The creation of this book was inspired by the loving memory of Esther Youdin. Her sensitivity and experience with mental health concerns of older adults provided the foundation for this text.

Esther Youdin (1894–1981)

Contents

Foreword

Clinical Gerontological Social Work Practice by Dr. Robert Youdin represents a timely and important contribution to the field of social work practice. Social work with older adults has lagged behind practice with families and children. However, with the rapid aging of the population, sometimes referred to as a "silver tsunami," this must change for social work to remain relevant today and in the future.

Although the relatively few books available on social work practice with older adults tend to reflect a social gerontology perspective, Dr. Youdin integrates advanced clinical social work practice with in-depth knowledge of evidence-based practice as well as geriatric medicine, psychiatry, and gerontology. This book is a forward-looking orientation that reflects the reality of social work today with older adults throughout the aging life course. It also anticipates the future needs of baby boomers, who are moving toward old age with knowledge and interest in psychological interventions and the expectation of accessing age-appropriate therapeutic treatment.

Between 2010 and 2050, the United States is projected to experience a rapid growth in its aging population. By 2050, the number of Americans age 65 and above will more than double from over 40 million in 2010 to over 88 million in 2050. This group already controls a large proportion of the wealth in the nation and, at the same time, is increasingly diverse with dramatic income and health disparities. The baby boomers are sometimes portrayed in the media as a monolithic age cohort, but this is far from accurate.

Starting in 2011, the vanguard of the baby boom generation celebrated its 65th birthday. Often portrayed as the best educated, healthiest, and most entitled generation of older adults to date, the baby boomers arrive at old age at a time when there are more older adults living than ever before, and they are likely to experience longevity beyond that of any prior generation. Given their impact on social values, culture, gender roles, sexual orientation, and racial and ethnic biases in their youth, the baby boomers are not just aging; they are redefining the process.

This change has already begun. The feminist movement inspired many women to stay single and to not fear divorce. Newly available birth control methods led to smaller families. The Stonewall riots represented the empowerment of lesbian, gay, bisexual, and transgender (LGBT) people to demand freedom from silence and oppression, and greater freedom in sexual expression. The Vietnam War tragically led to drug addiction in many returning veterans and greater acceptance of drug and alcohol use by society as a whole. Advances in medicine are extending life for many individuals into extreme old age. Changes in attitudes and practices related to death and dying give more options for control to the individual client and, at the same time, more ethical and legal challenges to individual practitioners. The baby boomers are riding the crest of these and other social changes, and are bringing with them a different sense of what it means to grow old.

Dr. Youdin's book lays out the impact of these and other trends on contemporary older age in the United States, and the ways in which clinical social work practitioners can respond to these changes in order to meet the challenges of serving older adult clients' needs, both today and in the future. Social work practitioners must incorporate knowledge of new medical and social challenges, such as AIDS, recreational prescription drug use, alternative lifestyles, and more diverse service options as never before in work with older adult clients.

Dr. Youdin provides a comprehensive overview of clearly articulated theoretical frameworks that are recognized in the field of practice with aging adults as relevant to life course development practice strategies: He addresses the diversity of age cohorts in later life instead of simply presenting old age as a monolithic construct. He also presents a framework that allows readers to imagine the myriad ways in which age interacts with environment, physical and behavioral health, family structure, race and ethnicity, gender and sexual identity, spirituality, and other variables that make each individual unique. This is complemented by a comprehensive overview of intervention theories that cover clinical practice with older adults and their families.

The book contains vignettes representing situations in which older people work with social workers to solve problems associated with the aging process; these vignettes provide concrete examples for practitioners and excellent discussion points for students. The inclusion of LGBT older adults is enlightened and helpful. The book is organized in a way that reflects the process of engagement between a clinical social worker or helping professional and an older adult client, as well as the planning and implementation of interventions. It focuses on different client populations and life course development issues, culminating in death and dying, about which a clinical social worker must be knowledgeable in order to engage in competent and ethical practice with older adult clients.

In addition, Dr. Youdin addresses a very important issue in practice with older adults: stigma. He discusses common aspects of practitioners' countertransference, including fear of illness and death and discomfort with older adult sexuality, which social work practice with older adults might trigger in a social work practitioner. Dr. Youdin also provides a good discussion of ageism that older adults will inevitably experience in their later years. He frankly addresses other aspects of the lives of older adults such as sex, thereby challenging the still-common notion that older people are not sexual beings. Throughout the book, he integrates discussions of relevant policy issues, including one linked to stigma, and challenges the belief that older adults are costly burdens on society.

An in-depth chapter on psychotherapy with older adults serves to make the distinction between normative and inevitable stressors of aging and pathological aging. It provides excellent content regarding possible interactions between psychotropic drugs and medication taken for typical medical conditions such as heart disease, arthritis, diabetes, and other conditions linked to aging. This is an important assessment area that students of social work are rarely acquainted with in the classroom. The author also discusses the impact of a wider range of psychological conditions on the older adult client, including depression, personality disorders, psychoses, and delusional disorders. Dr. Youdin also provides expert knowledge on distinguishing between irreversible forms of dementia and treatable mental health disorders.

Although Dr. Youdin focuses attention on theory, practice, and advanced mental health issues, he does not neglect to include medical and social issues, which are of increasing importance in work with older adults. Chronic pain, family and gender differences, and interactions among medical and psychiatric illnesses, medications, and treatments are carefully and extensively discussed. The discussion on older adults in prison settings reflects a broadly inclusive human rights perspective. In addition, the author uses a scholarly approach to the subject matter, using multiple citations linked to an extensive bibliography, which makes *Clinical Gerontological Social Work Practice* an advanced reading opportunity for clinical students at the master's and doctoral levels, as well as for practiced clinical practitioners.

I congratulate Dr. Youdin on this excellent, timely, and comprehensive contribution to the professional literature on clinical social work and advanced practice with older adults. All social work practitioners, particularly those with practices that include older adult clients, should read this important book. It is also an excellent text for advanced client social work courses in which content on practice with older adult clients is included. Finally, university and agency libraries should include it in their collections. I highly recommend this book to social work practitioners, students, and professors alike.

Patricia Brownell, PhD
Associate Professor Emerita of Social Service
Fordham University

Preface

AIMS AND FOCUS

Perkinson (2013) indicates that there is a global need for gerontological practice specialization across existing health and social service professions because of the ever-increasing population of older adults. Walker (2005) cautions that with the retiring baby boomers, there is a coming "demographic tidal wave or tsunami" (p. 43) that once arrived will never depart. According to Potter (2010), by 2020 there will be more than 53 million people over the age of 65 and about 7 million over the age of 85.

Hidden within these statistics are some demographic segments of older people in the current cohort who face prospects that are more dismal. Walker (2005) indicates that within the "demographic tidal wave or tsunami" are women and people living alone, who are primarily Latino and Black. Of the older women, 10% are White, 21.4% are Latina, and 27.4% are Black. This increasing older population experiences conflicts arising from retirement and living longer, financial stressors, substance abuse, dementia, coping with chronic illness, stigma, caregiving stress and, in some cases, multiple chronic illnesses (Oliver & DeCostero, 2006; Sisco, Volland, & Gorin, 2005; Wieland, 2005).

Therefore, with the continued stressors of poverty affecting vulnerable older people and the ever-persistent threats of disease, financial stress, stigma, and isolation, the social work profession must address the clinical needs of older people. Additional gerontological training must be instituted in undergraduate and graduate social work programs. Aside from educating students, there needs to be a retraining of social workers whose prior training is devoid of gerontological curriculum.

The aim of this book is to provide social work students with a treatment focus that integrates theory, technique, concrete services, advocacy, and social policy. This is consistent with strength-based, empowerment theoretical approaches that are human rights focused. Hagestad and Dannefer (2001) warn of *microfication of gerontology*, in which clinical micro practice dominates research and theory. This book takes an integrated approach to combat microfication of gerontological social work practice by integrating theoretical perspectives with individual, family, group, community, and governmental perspectives. Social workers do not practice in a rarified environment; they practice in an environment that is affected by and connected with mezzo and macro influences.

Clinical Gerontological Social Work Practice has a global perspective. It is important to understand the culture of others in the context of their international roots. In addition, it is important, as a social worker, to have a global perspective because of encounters with transient populations, which mandates an understanding of gerontology from other cultural perspectives.

FEATURES

Each chapter ends with a summary and discussion questions/topics. A case example is presented in each chapter to humanize the text material. Content and case examples reflect diversity. This book covers a range of diversity issues by including multiculturalism, sexual orientation, socioeconomic issues, gender, and other subcategories of vulnerable populations.

Part I gives the reader an overview of theoretical lenses of aging, various treatment approaches to the older client, assessment techniques, and stigma considerations.

Part II provides the reader with specialized knowledge about psychopathology, dementia, medical issues, substance abuse, and sexual problems and their social work interventions. In addition, gay, lesbian, bisexual, and transgender issues are discussed, including how to integrate this information for successful social work intervention. Care settings that are commonly seen in social work practice are discussed, highlighting environmental, institutional, and social considerations and how they influence social work practice. Part II concludes with a comprehensive chapter on social work intervention with issues of death and dying.

PART I

Chapter 1, Theories to Inform the Social Worker Practicing With Older Adults, introduces theories of aging that help clinicians to understand the older adults they are treating. In addition, this chapter contrasts the strength-based person-in-environment theory with the pathologically based medical model of psychological problems. The reader learns the importance of addressing reduction in an older adult's resilience to environmental stressors. This understanding enables the reader to comprehend how the older adult recognizes his or her strengths and functions more positively by enjoying the benefits of his or her current life stage, and to recognize and reduce psychopathology and morbidity.

Chapter 2, Assessing an Older Adult, gives the reader a unique understanding of how to engage with an older client and learn who the client is, what he or she feels, and what he or she has experienced in a lifetime. It is suggested that social workers should advocate eliminating the intake worker from mental health agency settings. The social worker who will be continuing with the older client's counseling should assess the older client.

Many mental health agencies use a checklist assessment form that enables a social worker to gather demographic information, mental status information, and psychiatric and substance-use history. These forms end with a *Diagnostic and Statistical Manual of Mental Disorders* (5th ed.; *DSM-5*; American Psychiatric Association, 2013a) diagnosis and a treatment plan or disposition to another agency. Though efficient for a rapid collection of information, these forms do a disservice to an older client. Little or no engagement occurs between social worker and older client, and developmental history is rarely explored during the assessment session. In addition, in many agencies an intake worker performs the assessment and then refers the older client to another social worker for treatment. Because of time constraints, many social workers rely on the diagnosis and treatment plan established during the assessment session by the intake worker. In addition, making a *DSM-5* diagnosis thrusts the social worker into the theoretical dissonance of viewing the older client from a person-in-environment perspective while simultaneously using the medical model perspective of diagnosing a psychiatric disease.

Chapter 3, Intervention Theories Informing the Clinician Treating Older Adults, introduces clinical orientations and techniques useful to the practicing social worker and social work student. These include ageism theories, empowerment and strength perspective theories, constructivist theory, existential theory, cognitive behavioral theory, narrative theory, reminiscence therapy, and feminist theory.

Chapter 4, Stigma and Older Adults, teaches the reader about the oppressive effects of stigma on older adults. Stigma is a psychosocial construct that is multidimensional, containing many different elements that oppress individuals. Stigma causes spoiled identities that in turn become the chronic oppression of an individual or a group of people. People are stigmatized by others or, paradoxically, stigmatize themselves. This is called autostigmatization. People have many dimensions that may be a focus for stigma. Examples include physical deformities, psychological problems, medical illnesses, race, religion, gender, poverty, sexual orientation, and age. In most cases, an individual is found in the intersection of two or more stigmas. Common culprits who can cause stigma include people from majority populations, health care providers, law enforcement personnel, and governmental policies—in other words, any person or social institution that has power over others.

PART II

Chapter 5, Psychopathological Problems in Older Adults, introduces the reader to the various psychological disorders affecting older adults. When interacting with an older adult who is suffering from psychological problems, a social worker must decide between two basic orientations—the medical model or the person-in-environment model. This is a critical choice, because each model leads the older adult down a different treatment path. The medical model invariably subjects the older adult to pharmacotherapy, electroconvulsive treatment, brain stimulation, and/or psychosurgery.

Chapter 6, Alzheimer's Disease and Other Dementias, emphasizes that although Alzheimer's disease is a serious problem, there are other types of dementia commonly seen in social work practice. These include mild cognitive impairment (MCI), vascular dementia, dementia with Lewy bodies (DLB), Korsakoff syndrome, and frontal lobe dementia (including Pick's disease). Parkinson's disease is often misunderstood as producing a dementia unique to Parkinson's disease. In fact, a subgroup of older adults with Parkinson's disease experiences dementia, but contemporary thought is that the rate of dementia is equal to the older population at large, and therefore occurs independent from the Parkinson's disease process.

In addition, this chapter introduces the problem of older adults experiencing dementia who are incarcerated. This underserved population raises many ethical and human rights issues.

Chapter 7, Medical Problems in Older Adults, educates the reader on the medical problems that older adults experience. This is critical for social workers because many older adults with chronic medical conditions have co-occurring psychological problems. In addition, older adults with chronic medical conditions have a dearth of knowledge about their conditions and how to care for themselves. Coordination with family members and caregivers around self-care issues, medicine compliance, safety issues, socialization, and exercise is important because health care providers often overlook psychoeducation. Therefore, social workers need to initiate and coordinate psychoeducational programs, psychotherapeutic interventions, and basic health care information. In addition, social workers need to seek continued education about medical disorders in order to understand the process an older adult experiences when suffering from a chronic medical condition.

Chapter 8, Older Adult Substance Abusers, instructs the reader about older adult substance abusers. Contrary to conventional wisdom, there is an escalating incidence of substance abuse in older adults. The current cohort of older adults, the baby boom generation, is making a profound change in the culture of substance abuse in older adults. Unlike prior cohorts whose primary substance-abuse problem was alcohol abuse and dependency, the baby boom generation brings polysubstance-abuse behaviors. Projections indicate that the incidence of substance abuse will more than double by the year 2020.

This brings a special challenge to social workers, who are the primary gatekeepers on the front line, to recognize substance abuse and dependency in the older adults they serve and to implement treatment interventions. All social workers need additional training in substance-abuse treatment with older adults.

Chapter 9, Older Adult Sexuality, educates the reader about sexuality in older adults. Although most people recognize adolescent and adult sexuality as a normal basic drive, the stereotype of older adults is their sex drive is nonexistent. In reality, older people do enjoy a sexual life, want to engage in sexual activity, and feel a loss when functional problems or social stressors such as divorce or death of a spouse or partner intervene. Biological factors causing sexual decline include chronic illness, dementia, and surgery, as well as pharmacy and polypharmacy side effects. Unfortunately, when older adults experience a decline in sexual desire or sexual activity, they also experience fear, anxiety, depression, boredom, and disenfranchised grief.

Chapter 10, Older Adult Abuse, describes how elder abuse is a hidden epidemic in the United States. Caretakers, including adult children, a spouse or partner, a hired home companion, staff at an institutional setting, or other family members or friends, may abuse older adults. Abuse may be physical, financial, emotional, or sexual. Most older adults are too frightened, embarrassed, demented, medically ill, or depressed to report abuse. In addition, many older adults fear that reported abuse would result in limiting what freedom they have by causing them to be placed in a more restrictive setting.

Another form of older adult abuse occurs when an older adult causes self-harm or self-neglect. Unfortunately, an older adult often is not aware of his or her self-harm or self-neglect behaviors. Therefore, vigilance is required from health care providers, family members, friends, and staff members of institutions to recognize signs and symptoms of self-abuse and self-neglect. This is an ideal opportunity for social workers to provide psychoeducational training for recognition of these self-abuses.

Chapter 11, Gay Male, Lesbian, Bisexual, and Transgender Older Adults, instructs the reader about issues specifically relevant to this population. Being old and a gay male, lesbian, bisexual, or a transgender person places an older adult at the intersection of older age and LGBT issues, making one vulnerable to discrimination and stigmatization. Adding race, medical illness, mental health problems, or other vulnerabilities to the intersection creates a very difficult life experience for an LGBT older adult. This difficulty demands the need for ongoing research on the older LGBT population and the development of psychoeducational training for social workers about the special needs of the older LGBT population. In addition, social workers need to take the lead on advocating for policy changes that would ensure that the human rights of older LGBT people are protected.

Chapter 12, Care and Residential Settings for Older Adults, informs the reader about many housing opportunities for older adults. These include aging-in-place and living in a retirement community, a continuing care community, or a nursing home. Clinical gerontological social work practice with older adults requires that the social worker have a comprehensive knowledge of these housing opportunities in order to be able to advise older adults and their families of what type of housing is the best fit for themselves or their loved ones. For some older adults, there is no choice of residence because they are incarcerated. Another imperative for social workers is to advocate for appropriate housing of older adult inmates to provide a more humanistic environment that addresses their special needs. Alternatively, social workers may advocate for release of some older adult inmates who no longer represent a threat to society.

Chapter 13, Dying and Death, helps prepare the reader to deal with issues older adults face when dying and to assist their survivors, who must deal with loss. Dying and death are normal aspects of life but phenomena that most people avoid thinking about. It is imperative for clinicians to become familiar with the various aspects of dying and death that cause older people concern. These include end-of-life palliative care, terminal illness, intensive hospital care, euthanasia, and where they may die.

An Instructor's Manual and PowerPoint slides are also available to supplement the text. **To obtain an electronic copy of these materials, faculty should contact Springer Publishing Company at textbook@ springerpub.com.**

TERMINOLOGY

In gerontology there is controversy and confusion about what to call people who are over 65 years of age. Are they *older, older people, older adults, elder people, elder adults, seniors*? There are no clear guidelines for a single correct label. In this book, the terms *older person, older people,* and *older adults* will be the labels of choice, unless referring to works of other authors who have used other labels. A few years ago, when speaking to a middle school class about what social workers do, I mentioned that I was a gerontologist and worked with older people. A student asked me, "What about high school students was interesting to you?" This is an example of how terminology may cause difficulty and is a relative problem for the receiver as well as the deliverer.

Hooyman and Kiyak (2010) suggest that *Hispanic* be replaced by *Latino* because *Hispanic* implies an association with colonialism and its devastating consequences on Spanish-speaking people of the Americas. Similarly, this book will use the term *Black* instead of *African American* whenever people of color are referred to unless they are Americans of African descent or another descent is identified by an author. The term *Caucasian* implies a specific origin of Europe, North Africa, western Asia, and India for all White people, which is not all encompassing. Instead, the term *White* will be used, unless an author identifies a specific descent.

Acknowledgments

First and foremost, I would like to thank Naomi Sarah Brower, MSW, LCSW, whose insights into clinical gerontology have been most informative, and whose love and support was and is extraordinary. I am grateful to my daughter Donna and stepson Teddy for their support and interest in my writing projects. In addition, I would like to acknowledge the many colleagues who lent support and guidance before and during the process of writing this book: Raymond Fox, PhD; Patricia Brownell, PhD; James Salwitz, MD; Benito Mustine, MD; Rhea Tuxen, MD; Theodore Reich, MD; the late Harold C. Urey, PhD; the late Milton H. Erickson, MD; the late Arnold M. Mordkoff, PhD; the late Eric Nash, MD; and the late Samuel Sutton, PhD. I acknowledge the many past students at Fordham University's Graduate School of Social Service, who consistently impressed me with their intellectual curiosity, which was most inspiring. Finally, I thank the many patients, both past and present, who allowed me the privilege of entering their lives for brief moments; you have consistently taught me to appreciate the trials, tribulations, and dignity inherent in the life process.

Last, but not least, I would like to thank Sheri W. Sussman, Executive Editor, and her colleagues at Springer Publishing Company for their unrelenting support and encouragement in the development of this text. Sheri Sussman consistently provided enlightening editorial input and a proverbial *kick in the ass* when needed.

Clinical Gerontological Social Work Practice

OVERVIEW OF THEORIES, ASSESSMENT TECHNIQUES, AND TREATMENT APPROACHES TO THE OLDER ADULT CLIENT

CHAPTER 1

Theories to Inform the Social Worker Practicing With Older Adults

The road is everything, the destination nothing.
—Bertha Pappenheim, The Story of Anna O

Clinical gerontological social work practice with older adults is a rapidly growing field encompassing many practice venues. A social worker working with older adults needs specialized knowledge about older adult multicultural issues, sexuality, and medical and psychological problems; the different types of dementia, substance abuse, death-and-dying issues, housing concerns, and the different types of care settings. Perkinson (2013) indicates that there is a global need for gerontological practice specialization across existing health and social service professions because of the ever-increasing population of older adults.

The social work mission with older adults encompasses micro practice, mezzo practice, and overriding macro policies affecting an older adult. The danger of not combining micro, mezzo, and macro practices is highlighted by Resser and Epstein (1990) and Kaufman, Segal-Engelchin, and Huss (2012), who indicate that most incoming social work students are interested in micro practice and consequently view issues through a restrictive lens that causes them to see and explain all social problems through psychological interpretations. Most social work students enter social work programs with a micro practice preference, putting little significance on broader social issues (Weiss, Gal, Cnaan, & Maglajlic, 2002; Weiss & Kaufman, 2006; Weiss-Gal, 2008). In contrast, other studies show that the social work curriculum is now moving toward a more holistic goal of viewing individual problems as a consequence of multiple environmental factors, from individual psychological issues to social policies and multicultural factors (Csikai & Rozensky, 1997; Limb & Organista, 2006).

Gerontological social work specialization tracks in current master's in social work (MSW) degree programs offer a unique opportunity to return social work training to a holistic approach to older adults combining micro, mezzo, and macro perspectives. However, there is no significant evidence of social work students taking advantage of this opportunity. This is in contrast with nursing education curriculum, which stresses the importance of gerontological specialization (Buchannan, 2012; Harris, Mayo, Balas, Aaron, & Buron, 2013) and interprofessional teams to enhance practice effectiveness (West, Holmes, Zidek, & Edwards, 2013). This interprofessional collaboration model has significant potential to enhance gerontological knowledge across all levels of experience, from student to seasoned practitioner, and may be adaptable across health and social service professions serving older adults, whether providing synchronous or asynchronous services. The accounting profession currently recognizes the importance of future accountants preparing themselves to serve the ever-increasing older adult population with estate planning guidance, financial planning, and relevant elder care services (Corkem, Parks, & Morgan, 2013).

Because of the increasing population of older adults, gerontological social work education must be expanded to meet the needs of this population. According to Potter (2010), by 2020 there will be more than 53 million people over the age of 65 and about 7 million over the age of 85 years. Jungers and Slagel (2009) indicate that between 2008 and 2050, the American population over the age of 85 years is expected to more than triple from 5.4 to 19 million. In addition, starting in 2012 an average of 10,000 older adults from the baby boom cohort began retiring each day. These older adults are more likely than previous cohorts to seek counseling for mental health issues because of increased levels of education and a climate of reduced stigma about seeking counseling services. Conflicts include those arising from retirement and living longer, financial stressors, substance abuse, dementia, coping with chronic illness, caregiving stress, and, in some cases, multiple chronic illnesses (Oliver & DeCostero, 2006; Sisco, Volland, & Gorin, 2005; Wieland, 2005). However, most social workers find themselves devoid of gerontological knowledge and are compelled by circumstance to seek evidence-based knowledge, workshops, and university-based continuing education training to guide their treatment of older adults.

THE NEED FOR A UNIFYING GERONTOLOGICAL SOCIAL WORK THEORETICAL ORIENTATION

Unfortunately, the field of gerontological social work lacks a unifying theory for psychological and social aging to help social work professionals navigate the road to understanding the unique aspects of older adults. Research on treating older adults has produced multiple studies that have generated reams of data, but a theoretical foundation to support these studies has not arisen from the studies (Bass & Ferraro, 2000; Biggs, Lowenstein, & Hendricks, 2003; Longino, 2005). Aging is an active process that occurs from the moment of conception until death. An older adult simultaneously experiences conflicts and problems unique to the final developmental stages of life while also experiencing problems of anticipated death, the final stage of life. This is a process called *gerody-namics* (Schroots & Birren, 1988). Social work professionals treating older adults are concerned with age-related changes that occur in adults who are 65 years of age and older. From a systems perspective, these changes involve a combination of biology, individual functioning, interpersonal functioning, social policies, cultural influences, and historical influences. This orientation mandates a gerontological social worker to have a holistic view of the older adult as a fundamental guiding principle (Lerner, 2006; Overton, 2006; Witherington, 2007). Because of the lack of a unifying gerontological social work theory, practitioners and students in social work must refer to and integrate several psychosocial theories to understand psychological and social changes that occur in adults after 65 years of age.

THEORY CIRCLE

Collingwood, Emond, and Woodward (2008) propose a theoretical orientation that is adaptable to a social worker assisting older adults. The first aspect of this *theory circle* model (described in this chapter) orients the social worker to how he or she chooses theoretical perspectives to guide his or her perception of older adults. The second aspect (see Chapter 3, Intervention Theories Informing the Clinician Treating Older Adults) applies other theoretical models that guide the social worker to evidence-based interventions when working with an older adult. Practice interventions are implemented after the older adult client is comprehensively assessed. Chapter 2, Assessing an Older Adult, details all aspects of a comprehensive assessment of an older adult that informs the gerontological social worker's selection of interventions described in Chapter 3. The theory circle model follows the logic that social workers need to employ evidenced-based theory when practicing, rather than relying on intuition or anecdotal experience.

This chapter follows the first aspect of the theory circle model by describing theories that inform the social worker about the older adult in order to set a lens in the social worker for subsequent assessment and clinical intervention with the older adult. The case example of Georgina at the end of this chapter is an introductory case that presents an older adult without obvious psychopathology yet in need of gerontological social work counseling. In this case the theory that informed the social worker (person-in-environment theory) served an informing function as well as an intervention function (Figure 1.1). Therefore, the theory circle does not necessarily need two aspects—theory to inform and theory to assess and intervene—but it may also be understood that the theory to inform may have a dual purpose by also being a theory to assess and intervene. In other cases dealing with psychopathological reactions to the reduction of resilience in the person-in-environment model, additional clinical theories to assess and to intervene become necessary; these theories are discussed in Chapter 2, Assessing an Older Adult, and Chapter 3, Intervention Theories Informing the Clinician Treating Older Adults.

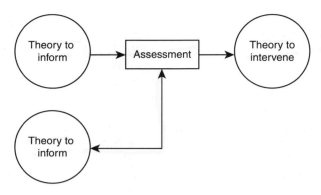

FIGURE 1.1 Variations of the theory circle.

SUGGESTED THEORIES TO INFORM THE SOCIAL WORKER TREATING OLDER ADULTS

In the text that follows, age stages and Erikson's stage theory (1982; Erikson & Erikson, 1997) are the first theoretical theories to highlight the nonhomogeneity of older adults. In addition, there is a discussion of person-in-environment theory (Wapner & Demick, 2005; Weiss-Gal, 2008) that helps explain age-related changes in older adults and support current clinical perspectives on gerontological counseling of older adults. These theories are contrasted with the medical model, which makes use of a pathological perspective of an older adult's psychological problems. This model is problematic for gerontological social workers because it is devoid of a strength-based perspective and lacks an empowerment problem-solving orientation. Combined, these theories, aside from the medical model, lay a foundation for the clinical techniques discussed in subsequent chapters. This is by no means exhaustive, yet it leaves room for social workers to expand their theoretical understanding of psycho-social phenomena in late life by incorporating or formulating additional theories of late-life development.

Age Stages

Researchers often study cohorts of individuals who are identified at a certain life stage. These individuals are followed through subsequent life stages. This is a convenient way to follow an age cohort and understand the numerous changes they go through during subsequent stages of development. However, the life-stage lens is not all encompassing and does not explain the differences that exist within age cohorts (Dannefer, 1988; Maddox, 1987). Nevertheless, the demarcation between the young-old and later life stages is significant because an older adult living past 75 years is living past what is considered normal life expectancy. Linn and Linn called this phenomenon the "biological elite" (1980).

Young-old (65–74 years of age)

Neugarten (1975) suggests the first grouping of older people should be between the ages of 55 to 75 years of age, giving this group of older people the name young-old. Since Neugarten's research, contemporary thought has compressed this age group to 65 to 74 years of age. This age group tends to be healthier than the middle-old and the old-old. In addition, the ratio of men to women is greater in this life stage than in subsequent life stages, which find lower ratios of men to women.

Middle-old (75–84 years of age)

Various researchers have defined middle-old adults as being between the ages of 75 years and 85 years old (Becker, 1994; Halpert & Zimmerman, 1986; Parker, Thorslund, & Nordstrom, 1992). This age group suffers from more physical disabilities and medical problems than older adults younger than 75 years (Parker et al., 1992). However, a middle-old adult, although suffering more medical consequences of aging, through therapeutic intervention is able to experience an improvement in any existing psychological problem. A middle-old adult experiences less depression and anxiety than those older adults younger than 75 years (Halpert & Zimmerman, 1986) and is generally in need of a holistic approach by the social worker to help cope with environmental challenges.

Old-old (86 years of age and older)

In the year 2000, the old-old numbered 70 million people, and this population is expected to increase to 153 million people in the year 2025. The majority of old-old in 2025 is anticipated to be found in developing countries, with the greatest concentration in China (*World Population Ageing 1950-2050*, 2002). This increasing population of the old-old faces medical illness and functional challenges (Zeng & Vaupel, 2002). Consequently, this phenomenon affects how the social worker must approach the treatment of an old-old adult client. The old-old adult must find solutions to accommodate increasing experiences with illness, both acute and chronic. The gerontological social worker must understand these changes in the old-old, how they differ from the young-old (Smith et al., 2002), and how to adapt clinical techniques to this population. In addition, the social worker is faced with the challenge of facilitating services to the old-old in a reality of overburdened health resources for older adults. The social worker must adapt to supporting preventative strategies to help lessen an old-old adult's incidence of disease and help an old-old adult reframe his or her orientation to an orientation of healthy aging (Fries, 1990; McCarthy, Ling, & Carini, 2013). This is an ethical issue that is part of a gerontological social worker's mandate to be an advocate for an old-old client because most health care institutions and social service agencies frown on clients directing or taking initiatives for their own health care.

Centenarians

Centenarians currently number 180,000 worldwide and are projected to increase in number to 3.2 million by the 2050 (Krach, 1999). Most centenarians are women who outlive their male cohort. Consequences of illness and functional limitations are greater with centenarians when compared with the old-old or the young-old. Knight and Ricciardelli (2003) report that an older adult's ability to adjust to his or her expectations of health and functioning decreases with age. However, a healthy adjustment with these changes in health and functioning occurs when an older adult has a high degree of acceptance of these life-stage changes (Erikson & Erikson,

1997; McCarthy, 2011; McCarthy et al., 2013). This is why centenarians are capable of reporting a positive satisfaction with life equal to those of young-old adults or old-old adults.

Super-centenarians

Super-centenarians are defined as older adults who have lived to be 110 years of age or older. In the United States recent annual averages of super-centenarians number less than 50, which is a population considerably smaller than centenarians, who currently number approximately 180,000 worldwide (Krach, 1999). Coles (2004) feels that the number of super-centenarians in the United States is somewhat greater, approximating 75 to 100 older adults. Super-centenarians often present with significant deficits in their sensorium, poor dental health, significant functional limitations, proneness to dermatological injury, and problems in orientation (person, place, time; Coles, 2004).

PSYCHOLOGICAL AND SOCIAL AGING THEORIES

Erikson's Stages Theory

Erikson postulates that psychological development occurs throughout one's lifetime through successful adjustments to psychological, biological, and social environments at eight different stages in life through an intergenerational process. Each stage is grounded to previous stages in what Erikson calls the epigenetic principle (1982, p. 59). These stages are *Basic Trust vs. Basic Mistrust, Autonomy vs. Shame and Doubt, Initiative vs. Guilt, Industry vs. Inferiority, Identity vs. Role Confusion, Intimacy vs. Isolation, Generativity vs. Stagnation, Ego Integrity vs. Despair*. This author finds it useful to think of these stages as a continuum rather than a zero sum problem in which one side must win over the other side. Therefore, instead of looking at a stage such as Ego Integrity vs. Despair, one may look at this stage as a continuum of issues and conflicts, one side to embrace and the other to release. A person in the process of transitioning through a stage maximizes his or her experience through the degree of acceptance of the strength of the stage and the degree of release of the conflicted aspects of the stage.

In the first seven stages of Erikson's postulation, each stage is about the development of the individual. However, underlying this individual development is the dynamic of intergenerational interaction with other people. This intergenerational interaction facilitates the accomplishment of a successful resolution of his or her life stage. For example, an infant achieving a successful stage of trust cannot do so without an adult caretaker who has successfully left a self-centered stage of youth and is able to provide the nurturing and validation needed by the infant. A weakness in Erikson's theory is the lack of accounting for environmental influences outside in addition to interpersonal interaction. For example, environmental factors such as war, disease, physical deformity, and poverty may also interfere with nurturing and validation.

In Erikson's eighth stage, *Ego Integrity vs. Despair*, achieving ego integrity requires a reverse intergenerational interpersonal interaction. Instead of achieving ego integrity through interpersonal relationship with an older person, the older adult now achieves ego integrity by focusing on the needs of others younger than he or she. This requires that an older adult make a transformation from achieving gratification of his or her needs through interaction with others, to achieving growth and gratification of the self though commitment on focusing on the needs of others, such as family, friends, and community. In order to accomplish this acceptance, an older adult must be able to look back on his or her life and accept the successes and limitations experienced as a process of growth and change. This enables the older adult to detach from life and accept death as the final aspect of his or her life. This process of accepting death enables the older adult not to fear death.

Erikson and Erikson later indicate that spiritual transcendence is an additional developmental stage in late life that is active beyond the *Ego Integrity vs. Despair* stage (1997). In this final stage, a transcendence is created in the ego, body, and role of the older adult, whereby the older adult moves to acceptance of one's self-worth rather than engaging in preoccupation with disease, disability, and loss of professional identity. This is accomplished by focusing on satisfaction with one's accomplishments. In addition, life satisfaction and acceptance of one's accomplishments are shown to be necessary components for successfully progressing through the process of aging (McCarthy, 2011; McCarthy et al., 2013).

The reciprocal process occurs in which an older adult becomes despondent about prior life experiences, viewing choices made as causing missed opportunities, which in turn causes him or her to view death with a sense of despair. A gerontological social worker must address this despair as an existential dilemma and help the older adult move toward a more positive reframing of his or her life successes, failures, and conflicts in order to balance the tension between integrity and despair experienced by the older adult. This achieves what Aserr, Milillo, Long, and Horne-Moyer (2004) indicate as an older adult's experiencing lower levels of anxiety about death when compared with younger adults.

The Medical Model

The medical model of psychological problems (Figure 1.2) is based on how physicians are trained to diagnose disease. This model proposes the categorization of mental illnesses by identifying predictable constellations of symptoms. These symptoms are identified by clinical observation and are not based on the scientific methodology used for other medical conditions. Once categorized, a direct path is created to intervention with medications, electroconvulsive therapy, psychotherapy, or psychosurgery. Andreasen (2007) indicates that there are many problems with the medical model, such as the following:

1. Using any psychiatric diagnostic manual developed by the American Psychological Association forces a social worker to identify a person's psychological problem by observing a small number of aggregate symptoms that prevent the social worker from developing a comprehensive understanding of the internal experiences, as well as the environmental stressors converging on the older client, which are not addressed by the manuals.

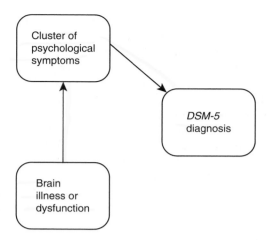

FIGURE 1.2 The medical model using minimum symptoms to describe a mental illness that originates from an illness or dysfunction in the brain.

2. By using minimum symptoms to diagnose a client, the social worker is in effect dehumanizing the client. Many agencies, hospitals, and treatment centers use checklists to diagnose a client, causing the social worker to miss the depth of information that is attained with a comprehensive biopsychosocial assessment. (In-depth information is discussed in Chapter 2, Assessing an Older Adult.)
3. Andreasen claims that "validity has been sacrificed for reliability" (p. 111). Andreasen feels that social workers and researchers share a common nomenclature, probably the "wrong one" (p. 111).

It is important to note that a social worker treating an older adult with a medical model orientation will tend to pathologize and at times infantilize an older adult. This occurs because the medical model omits a strength perspective. By following such a model, the social worker misses an opportunity to facilitate an older adult in increasing his or her feeling of empowerment when dealing with the numerous conflicts of life that are not necessarily psychopathological.

Person-in-Environment Theory and Resilience: A Good Partnership

One can envision the *person-in-environment theory* and *resilience* as a weakness of an older adult to bounce back to a normal state when confronted with environmental stressors. This is called *passive accommodation* (Wapner & Demick, 2005), meaning an older adult is viewed by a social worker as giving in to environmental stressors A gerontological social worker takes a contrary position called a *differentiated and integrated* (2005) person-in-environment state in which an older adult actively engages in problem solving. This approach integrates service providers across disciplines with friends, relatives, and care providers (Hebblethwaite, 2013) under the direction of the gerontological social worker to facilitate problem solving with the older adult. The gerontological social worker helps an older adult use his or her strengths to initiate problem solving, which breaks the dis-engaged state where the older adult was stuck. This act of bouncing back to a normal state is called *resilience*.

To understand the concept of resilience, think of a rubber ball held high in your hand. When you release the rubber ball from your hand and let it drop to the floor, it does something magical. On striking the floor the roundness of its shape becomes depressed. However, the rubber ball immediately restores its shape back to a sphere by having the depression in the ball caused by the ball striking the floor spring back to a normal shape. The energy in this spring-back motion propels the ball back to your hand, ready to be dropped again. When an older adult has weakened resilience, the older adult will drop to a minimal state of mental health, never reaching the original starting position that occurred before the intervention of the environmental stressor. Borden (1992, p. 125) feels that resilience is a person's ability to "maintain continuity of one's personal narrative, and a coherent sense of self following traumatic events." Weakened resilience enables an older adult to have maladaptive reactions to internal and external environmental stimuli. Some social workers consider these maladaptive reactions as psychopathology resulting from a disease within the brain (the medical model), whereas most social workers, who are strength oriented, consider these reactions as maladaptive choices made by an older adult that neglect the repertoire of positive solutions to environmental stimuli used in his or her past (a person-in-environment perspective).

When psychological, social, biological, or economic forces come at the older adult, his or her degree of resilience (Figure 1.3) determines whether the response to these forces is positive and adaptive or negative and maladaptive. Resilience is an older adult's ability (the ball bouncing back) to consistently recover from traumatic events across each developmental stage. Becker (1997) feels that a therapist must recognize elements in the assessment of an older adult that identify resilient dynamics. Greene (2002) feels that resilient dynamics are comprised of prior biological recoveries,

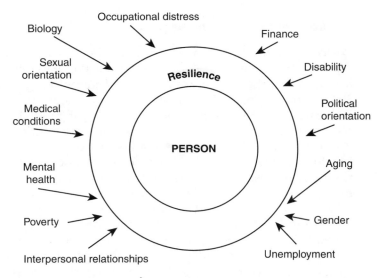

FIGURE 1.3 The protective role of resilience in person-in-environment theory.

the degree of goodness of fit in interpersonal relationships, prior coping experiences with stressful situations, current ability to function in everyday activities, membership in one or more diverse categories (racial, ethnic, gay male, lesbian, poverty, etc.), coping history with being stigmatized, what environmental resources are available, and social policies that have a direct effect on the older adult and his or her response to them. By reinforcing existing resilience dynamics and teaching the older adult new positive coping strategies, the older adult will be in a successful position to overcome environmental trauma (White, Driver, & Wrren, 2010).

When an older person's resilience is weakened by poverty, illness, isolation, or other life circumstances that make him or her vulnerable, this weakened vulnerability causes his or her resilience to be overrun. This weakening of resilience causes the older adult to react to psychosocial/economic/health pressures in a maladaptive way that often is given a pathological label, which in turn further stigmatizes the older adult. Ironically the very people who are attempting to provide help to the older person give him or her this label. Most of these stressors converging on an older adult are a product of diversity, an umbrella term that is composed of numerous constructions produced by power differentials (Stoller & Gibson, 1994). Williams and Wilson (2001) feel that there is a need for more diversity research because there is a dearth of research on the intersection of social, political, cultural and ethnic stigmas with ageism, and the consequence of this intersection with physical and psychological health. This holistic view is important because one's life experience is a complex composite of various subsystems interacting with each other as well as contributing to the gestalt of one's existential experience (Overton, 2006).

However, there are numerous examples of older people in hardship positions overcoming these pressures and demonstrating a high degree of resilience. For example, in older deaf communities and older Jewish communities, members developed strong resilience to converging pressures that were a product of experiences with hardship, losing one's hearing, or being a victim of the Holocaust (Becker, 1980; Myerhoff, 1978).

Person-in-Environment Theory: The Beginning

Person-in-environment theory originated with Lawton's ecological model (Lawton & Nahemow, 1973; Nahemow, 2000). Lawton's model is seen as a foundation theory for environmental gerontology (Wahl & Weisman, 2003), which is also related to home environments and activities-of-daily-living research (Iwarsson & Stahl, 2003). Starting with Lawton's model, the older person is seen as a person with certain capabilities and strengths, and the environment has certain demands that converge on the older person. Lawton's model is criticized because it does not deal with an older adult's needs, attitudes, perceptions, or access to resources, causing researchers to expand Lawton's model to encompass many variables that converge on older people (Scheidt & Norris-Baker, 2003). Capabilities are determined by the status of an older adult's health, finances, family relationships, being in a partnership or marriage, gender, race/ethnicity, sexual orientation, degree of independent living, cognitive capabilities, and other social constructs. Examples of demands are diseases, debt service, physical impediments in the home environment, lack of community supports, governmental policies, racism, gender discrimination, and other external forces. In addition, person-in-environment theory is viewed as the interaction of an older person's ever-changing biology and psychological dynamics and the interaction of these changing aspects of the person with the environment, which also is constantly changing.

This complex interactional view of the person-in-environment theory is called a dialectical approach to personality development (Levinson, 1986; Levinson, Darrow, Klein, Levinson, & McKee, 1978). The dialectical approach (Figure 1.4) looks at resilience as an older person's ability to sense and understand his or her changes in biology and psychological dynamics and the ability of the older person to understand the ever-changing environmental demands that are converging on him or her. Person-in-environment theory is also viewed as a complex system that is a gestalt of many subsystems interacting with each other to form multiple feedback loops (Glipin & Murphy, 2008).

Perception of Control

The person-in-environment interaction is also influenced by an older adult's perception of control over his or her life. Rodin and Langer (1985) suggest that an older adult, as a consequence of being older, is vulnerable because of negative perceptions he or she may harbor about controlling his or her interaction with his or her environment. The older adult feels that this is a consequence of physiological changes that occur with aging when he or she interacts with various environmental barriers. This phenomenon has the potential to intensify as an older adult continues to age. Many times this phenomenon of an older adult having a changing perception of control over his or her life occurs when an older adult is deciding where to live out the rest of his or her life (see Chapter 12, Care and Residential Settings for Older Adults). Although most older adults prefer to remain

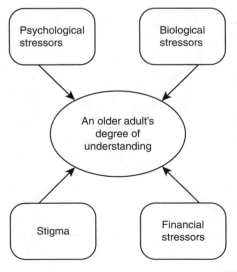

FIGURE 1.4 The dialectical approach of person-in-environment theory.

in the community in which they have been living, some older adults are forced to make choices of a new residential location as a result of physical changes caused by aging or medical conditions. This is an opportunity for the gerontological social worker to help the older adult choose an environment that is supportive and restorative of his or her perception of control over oneself. The social worker harnessing prior problem-solving skills in the older adult and facilitating their use by joining the older adult in the process of choosing a new living condition achieves stability in the older adult's interaction with his or her environment.

An older adult who perceives a strong sense of control over his or her environment demonstrates resilience, allowing a positive adjustment to life-threatening health problems. It is this phenomenon that facilitates an older adult's adjustment to, among others, cancer, HIV/AIDS, cardiac illness, and autoimmune diseases such as rheumatoid arthritis (Affleck, Tennen, Pfeiffer, & Fifield, 1987). However, perceived control does not show any significant effect on older adults who have positive prognoses (Helgeson, 1992) or little or no functional impairments (Zautra, Reich, & Newsom, 1995). Menec and Chipperfield (1997) found that perceived control had a greater effect on resilience to functional impairment in old-old adults (86 years of age and older) when compared with young-old adults (65–74 years of age). The current aging baby boom generation contains many survivors of the polio epidemic of the 1940s and 1950s. Many of these survivors report a paradoxical experience of control over their environment by having to learn new ways to control their muscles and movements to overcome the dysfunctions in movements and paralysis of muscles caused by polio. By learning new ways to control their muscles and movements, they subsequently extended this new sense of control to other environmental obstacles, such as work and school. This enabled these older adults to experience a greater success interacting with environmental stressors than comparable cohorts who did not experience polio (Oshinsky, 2005).

THE CASE OF GEORGINA

The case of Georgina* is an example of how a social worker must understand and implement knowledge of developmental stage theory, environmental influences, and resilience theory when working with an older adult in crisis (Figure 1.5). This case is an example of how clinical practice with an older adult is not limited to psychotherapy. Many social workers who are unfamiliar with gerontological counseling restrict their thinking of clinical practice. They actualize this by only providing psychotherapy services (see Chapter 5, Psychopathological Problems in Older Adults). Although psychotherapy is an important aspect of clinical gerontological social work practice, more often than not a holistic environmental approach is needed when treating an older adult.

Georgina is an 86-year-old African American woman who just entered an assisted living facility 27 miles from the home she had resided in for the past 45 years. Georgina is a retired bookkeeper and has no close relatives living near her. She is a lesbian, and 6 years ago she lost her partner of 31 years. Georgina claims that she has adjusted to the death of her partner

---

*Names and other identifying information have been changed to preserve confidentiality.

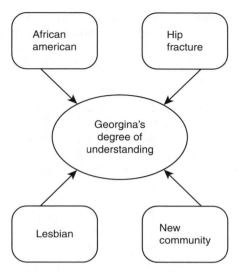

FIGURE 1.5 Psychosocial–health stressors converging on Georgina, causing a reduction in resilience.

as a direct result of the support she received from a close network of friends in her previous community. This was a special community for her because it was a retirement community created for lesbians and gay men, although she indicated that the community included some heterosexual members who expressed complete acceptance of the gay and lesbian lifestyle.

Georgina entered a new facility because 6 months ago she fractured her hip and subsequently underwent a hip-replacement operation. After a 4-month stay at a rehabilitation facility she returned home and found that she was unable to cope well, being bound to a wheelchair most of the time, aside from very short walks (a step or two) from her chair to her bed or her chair to the toilet, two of many environmental obstacles. Her community's buildings were constructed before the requirement for accessibility for handicapped persons became law. Therefore the clubhouse, which is three stories high, does not have an elevator, and the sidewalk curbs do not have a depressed lip to accommodate a wheelchair. Even though the apartment's front and rear doors were wide enough to accommodate a wheelchair, many of the interior doors were not. The kitchen counters were too high to reach from a sitting position, and the bathrooms, whether public or in her residence, were not equipped for a handicapped person.

Because of these environmental barriers, Georgina felt forced to make a decision to enter this assisted living facility. On arrival, Georgina was struck by the absence of a homosexual community. To complicate matters, she was the only African American resident. The only other African Americans were members of the nursing and custodial staff. All the doctors, physical therapists, occupational therapists, and administration were either White or Latino. Georgina reported that her initial reaction to this facility was panic, which quickly morphed into symptoms of depression. Georgina felt hopeless and helpless about her new living situation and began to experience difficulty sleeping. In addition, she began losing weight, which alarmed the medical staff when it was discovered that she'd lost 14 pounds in a 10-day period.

Georgina was assessed by the facility's social worker using a person-in-environment perspective to understand Georgina's problems transitioning to her new home. Over a period of 3 weeks, Georgina and the social worker developed different strategies to facilitate a positive adjustment to this facility:

- The social worker arranged for a local transportation company that specializes in transporting older people with medical conditions to health care appointments and grocery shopping to transport Georgina to her old community once per week so that she may maintain her long-term relationships there. In addition, Georgina alerted the people at her old community that they could use the service to visit Georgina whenever they chose.
- Realizing the importance of interprofessional collaboration when serving an older adult (West et al., 2013), the social worker enlisted the help of an occupational therapist and a physical therapist for Georgina. The physical therapist provided physical therapy on an intensive basis to increase her muscle strength so that eventually she would be able to spend more time out of her wheelchair, whether standing for short periods or walking short distances. Fortunately, Georgina's apartment has an adjoining kitchen that is shared with three other residents. The occupational therapist is most important in this case, by helping Georgina learn to overcome environmental barriers (Liu, Brost, Horton, Kenyon, & Mears, 2013). The occupational therapist helped Georgina learn to use the kitchen, which was designed to be handicapped accessible, with short cabinets, enough space for a wheelchair to maneuver, special gadgets that enable gripping items that are not reachable by a resident, utensils that reduce pressure on finger and hand joints, automatic lighting, and a telephone system that allows remote talking.
- The social worker, in consultation with a friend of Georgina's who helps Georgina with her financial arrangements and is an accountant who specializes in working with older adults (Corkem et al., 2013), coordinated, with Georgina's permission, the sale of her prior residence and the move of some of her furniture, pictures, and personal items into her new apartment. This residential care facility encourages residents to furnish their rooms with personal items rather than being forced to have furnishings provided by the institution. Once Georgina's possessions arrived, she reported a sense of "being home again."

By taking this person-in-environment approach, the social worker was able to help Georgina develop a comprehensive understanding of the changes that occurred in her external and internal environments. Gradually she developed a greater ability to ambulate in her environment, using the wheelchair on an as-needed basis when she felt fatigued. She became proficient with a walker, feeling an increasing sense of independence. Having a handicapped-accessible kitchen enabled Georgina to return to cooking, an activity she thoroughly enjoyed.

Using the transportation service enabled Georgina to maintain relationships with friends from her old community. By reconnecting, she gradually lost the self-stigma of being the only African American resident in this facility. In her prior residence, she had many African American friends. Over time, many of her friends began visiting her using the same transportation service Georgina uses to visit them once per week. This frequent contact with old friends enabled Georgina to come out to the new residents and be open about her sexual orientation (see Chapter 11, Gay Male, Lesbian, Bisexual, and Transgender Older Adults). To her surprise, one of the residents came to visit her one night and expressed how grateful he was with her arrival. He indicated his gratitude was because he was gay and experienced painful feelings of isolation, feeling that he was the "only gay person in the world" since his world was limited to this facility, having lost his partner and all his close friends recently. This man just celebrated his 102nd birthday and told Georgina that she was his best present ever.

SUMMARY

This chapter introduced theories of aging that help social workers to understand the older adults they are treating. In addition, this chapter contrasted the strength-based person-in-environment theory with the pathologically based medical model of psychological problems. This chapter stressed the importance of addressing reduction in an older adult's resilience to environmental stressors. This understanding enables an older adult to recognize his or her strengths and function more positively by enjoying the benefits of his or her current life stage and to recognize and reduce psychopathology and morbidity. The case of Georgina is an example of how a social worker must understand and implement knowledge of developmental stage theory, environmental influences, and resilience theory when working with an older adult in crisis. This case is an example of how clinical practice with an older adult is not limited to psychotherapy. A social worker working with older adults must employ advocacy skills and provide concrete services, as well as psychotherapeutic interventions.

DISCUSSION TOPICS

1. Discuss the many factors that would increase resilience in an older adult; for example, making health-related changes such as smoking cessation, initiating an exercise program, availing oneself of psychotherapy services, and so on. Choose five resilience-related topics for discussion.
2. After interviewing six older adults about how they cope with stresses in their life, discuss your findings and how they relate to the theories discussed in this chapter.
3. Present your own theory of aging and describe its application to gerontological social work.

CHAPTER 2

Assessing an Older Adult

It is more important to know what sort of person has a disease than to know what sort of disease a person has.

—Hippocrates, BrainyQuote

The process of assessing an older adult occurs on two levels. The first level takes place when an older client presents for assessment. This is usually the first contact the social worker has with the older adult. This may occur with an intake worker who then makes a referral to a social worker, or may occur with a social worker who will continue providing service to the older client. This initial contact presents an opportunity to begin engagement with the client by showing an empathic understanding of his or her feelings and thoughts and an acknowledgment of his or her presenting problem. Empathy plays a critical role in a psychotherapeutic relationship and is essential for the success of the therapy (Gibbons, 2011).

Ghaemi (2007) suggests that "without a systemically accurate description and understanding of a patient's inner and outer experience, clinicians cannot know how to accurately diagnose and make a prognosis of a patient's condition" (p. 122). Encouraging an older adult to tell a life story, guided by the structural aspects of a clinical assessment, enables the social worker to develop a culturally sensitive engagement with the older client (Millender, 2011). This type of engagement sets a foundation for a person-in-environment evaluation of an older adult. Despite distortions of an older adult's interpretation of his or her reality, the story is an accurate window into the inner dynamics, personal conception of reality, and history of the older adult client (Frank, 2012). The older adult's story indicates what the older adult feels that the social worker may find significant (2012). McQuaide and Ehrenreich (1997) feel that a comprehensive assessment is necessary to determine a client's potential strengths, coping skills, and resilience. In addition, an older person sharing his or her reality facilitates an engagement between social worker and client that supports the ethic of caring, which is fundamental to social work (Dybicz, 2012; Maidment, 2006).

The second level of the assessment process is used for gathering facts that are analyzed for diagnosis, treatment planning, and disposition. Treatment plans and dispositions are discussed in subsequent chapters. There are many protocols used by agencies and private practitioners. Any assessment of an older person requires a multidimensional observation of the client ranging from aspects located within the individual to person-in-environment interaction. In addition, it is necessary for the social worker to have a comprehensive knowledge of policies and procedures of health and social agencies and how these policies affect the older client. The older client may be directly involved with one or more agencies or one or more agencies' policies may indirectly affect a client.

PART 1: ENVIRONMENTAL AND COMMUNICATION CHALLENGES TO BE OVERCOME BY THE SOCIAL WORKER AND OLDER CLIENT

Office Assessment Setting

Even though in many agencies the therapist has little control over the therapeutic setting, many small details need attention to facilitate successful engagements with clients. Ideally the color of the office where the assessment occurs should be soft tones. Where agencies might insist on white or gray, color can be added with pictures, books, and, if outside light is available, through a window, skylight, or plants. If the agency office has fluorescent lights, turn them off and put a few incandescent or light-emitting diode (LED) lamps in the office where the assessment occurs. The ambiance created by this type of lighting will create a relaxed environment. The level of lighting should be bright enough to accommodate vision problems experienced by older adult clients. The social worker should make sure the reception area has magazines that appeal to older adults.

Most social workers treating older adults will be younger than their clients. Therefore, clinical authority and respect may become an issue. Dressing professionally, having diplomas displayed, and having a bookcase with clinical texts can address this issue. These external cues will help an older adult feel comfortable with a younger social worker.

Chairs are another problematic issue. Acknowledging the dignity and respect due to an older client, there should be no distinction between seating for a client and seating for the social worker. Chairs should be of equal height and equal comfort. When entering the room for the assessment, the social worker should let the client choose his or her seating first and then select a seat that is within a distance that keeps the client comfortable, not too close to invade his or her personal space and not too far to appear distant and making it hard for the client to hear. In addition, the entrance to the office building must be wheelchair accessible as must be the office itself. Seating must accommodate a wheelchair and follow the same contingencies listed for the placement of chairs.

A Matter of Speaking

Hearing loss in varying degrees is a presenting problem in most older adults (Levy, Slade, & Gill, 2006). It is common to treat older adults experiencing hearing deficits who have trouble perceiving high frequencies. Therefore, a social worker must be prepared to speak slower and louder, and female social workers must consider speaking in a lower, deeper tone.

Home, Nursing Home, Assisted Care Facility, or Hospital Assessment Setting

Sometimes an assessment will occur outside the social worker's office. This requires the social worker to enter the client's environment, whether an older adult's home or an institutional setting. Psychologically the social worker is entering the older client's personal setting. Whenever possible, the social worker should let the client guide where to sit. The social worker should engage the client about the setting, validating that this is where the older client is living at the time of assessment. This initial engagement is an opportunity for the social worker to gather information from the setting the client is in that would not necessarily surface during a formal interview process in the social worker's office. Photographs displayed can prompt discussion about the client's interpersonal relationships, past or present. The cleanliness and order of the client's home are instructive. Is the client hoarding? Is the home environment in disarray? Is the client overly fastidious about his or her environment? Many questions can be asked and answered by simple focused observations by the social worker.

Working the Clock

An assessment session is analogous to a therapeutic session. It has a beginning, a middle, and an end (Figure 2.1). The social worker must be aware of the time in order to accomplish a preliminary engagement, collect information, and close the appointment in a way that will make sense to the older client and give the client an opportunity to have questions answered about the assessment process or the therapeutic process they may be entering, or the disposition assigned. In some cases an assessment may occur over two or three sessions. Each of these sessions has a beginning, middle, and an end, and, if more than one session, an additional beginning, middle, and end, from the first session to the last session.

When keeping track of time, the social worker should never look at a wristwatch, even though the social worker might be wearing one. By diverting his or her eyes, the social worker inadvertently may give the client a message that the social worker is bored, wants the session to be over, or perhaps is thinking about something other than the older client. This problem can be overcome by placing one or more clocks at strategic locations in the assessment room so that the social worker may see the

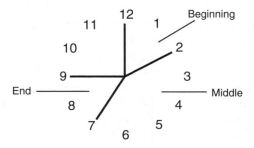

FIGURE 2.1 Making a 45-minute session a process for the social worker and older adult client.

time while still looking at the client, and the client may also see the time. Many clients like to know where they are with the time in order to judge how much time is left and how much time they have to address issues that might not have been addressed by the social worker.

To Take or Not Take Notes

There are conflicting opinions about taking notes during an assessment. Many social workers feel that the quantity of information collected requires one to take notes during the assessment session. An opposing argument is that taking notes distances the social worker from the client, subtly influences the client's perception of what the social worker might be looking for, and sometimes causes the social worker to sit at a desk while talking with the client. This author recommends that the social worker write notes immediately after the assessment session. This enables the social worker to directly engage the client during the assessment, and by retrospective processing and reflecting about the session the social worker tends to identify themes and ideas that are not readily apparent during the assessment session. By not taking notes, the social worker has the opportunity to closely observe the client's body language, which at times may be missed when focusing on note taking.

PART 2: ASSESSMENT CATEGORIES

What follows is a generic outline that can be applied or modified in most agency and private practice settings. In addition to the commonly used assessment categories, additional assessment categories or modifications of generic categories specific to older people are discussed.

Gender, Age, Ethnicity, Sexual Orientation

Gender and age are obvious categories with the exception of transgender. Identification of transgender individuals is essential because this population is consistently underserved by health care providers (Bockting, Robinson, & Rosser, 1998; Kenagy, 2005). In addition, dichotomizing gender to male and female actively supports the oppression of transgender individuals by relegating them to a no-gender status (Burdge, 2007). For example, from a survey administered to 113 male-to-female individuals and 69 female-to-male individuals, Kenagy (2005) finds that about three fifths of respondents had engaged in unprotected sexual activity during the past 12 months, the risk for HIV infection from unprotected sex was significantly higher among respondents of color than among White respondents, and 30.1% of respondents had attempted suicide. More than half of respondents had been forced to have sex, 56.3% had experienced violence in their homes, and 51.3% had been physically abused. Twenty-six percent of respondents had been denied medical care because they were transgender. These findings suggest that screening for transgender individuals (whether or not they have undergone genital transition) as a gender category is essential because of the vulnerability of this population.

Race as a category is controversial. Many agencies have substituted ethnicity for race as a useful tool for research and practice rather than for surveillance (Cooper, 1994). According to the Office of Management and Budget the traditional racial/ethnic groupings of American Indian/ Alaska native, Asian/Pacific Islander, Black/African American, White not of Hispanic origin, and Hispanic are categories that do not have a genetic basis (Thomas, 2001). Although it is important for the social worker to have multicultural sensitivity and knowledge, some authors feel that the identification of race promotes racism, is unnecessary in a mental health assessment (Mallon, 2006), and may contribute to problems in cross-racial practice (Davis & Gelsomino, 1994). In addition, Lee and Bean (2004) indicate that by the year 2050 one in five Americans will have a mixed racial background, complicating understanding of the multicultural experience of a client being assessed by a social worker.

A contrary view is that most social workers do not have a comprehensive knowledge of the nuances of different cultures (Jackson & Samuels, 2011). For example, Joo, Morales, de Vries, and Gallo (2010) indicate that African Americans are less likely to use psychotherapy services. Therefore the clinician assessing an African American client in need of psychotherapy must spend some time educating the client on the benefits of psychotherapeutic intervention. If assessing ethnicity, the social worker should attend to the degree of acculturation, how the client's perception of ethic identification has been helpful or hurtful, and what conflicts have been experienced related to ethnic issues.

Presenting Problem

The presenting problem is the complaint that brought the client to the agency or the social worker's private practice. The presenting problem is not a diagnosis. If the client is unable to communicate clearly, then this information should be taken from the person who provided the information to the agency or the person who accompanied the client to the agency or to the social worker's office. The reason for presentation should be written with patient quotes. This will help the social worker assess the older client's perception of his or her problem. The client's perception of the problem may be coherent or may be bizarre. In either case, this is the first step in information gathering that will lead to diagnosis, treatment plan, and disposition.

A complete history of the presenting problem should include whether the problem is recurring, long-standing, or recently established. What are the frequency, duration, and intensity of the problem? Were there any antecedent events that the client can relate to the presenting problem? What, if any, were the consequences the client experienced or is experiencing from the presenting problem? From a strength perspective, the social worker should determine what measures the older client has used in the past to solve similar problems. The social worker should determine the client's motivation for change. Is the client presenting voluntarily or on a mandated basis?

Environmental and Demographic Information

The social worker must evaluate the status of the client's housing, transportation, food, clothing, recreation opportunities, social supports, access to medical care, kinship, contact with neighbors, and other environmental resources that the client or social worker considers important. Attention should be directed to what environmental resources exist but are not being used by the client. An advocacy imperative for the social worker is to determine what needed resources do not exist and need to be developed.

Psychosocial status composed of environmental and demographic information provides identifying data that complete the client's profile. Age, gender, and ethnicity were covered in the first section of the assessment. Demographic data include marital status or relationship status, level of education, occupational history, family members, family history, persons living with the client, caretakers, friends, financial status, health insurance (private, Medicaid, or Medicare), and other social service support. This gives the social worker the opportunity to assess the quality of social relationships the client is engaged in and the client's intellectual ability and to identify psychosocial stressors that may be converging on the client.

Developmental History

During the collection of this data, the opportunity will arise while discussing social relationships to collect historical information on the client's psychosocial development. This includes knowledge of events surrounding his or her birth, childhood, adolescence, young adulthood, middle adulthood, and late adulthood (Gidman, 2013; Tonrey, 2007).

Birth

Events surrounding birth include problems the client's mother experienced during pregnancy, any trauma experienced or defect noted during or after birth, maternal medical and psychological health, and maternal substance-use history, as well as information about the degree to which the father or partner were participatory in this early stage of the client's development.

Childhood

Information regarding the client's childhood should include the quality of the mother–father (partner)–child relationship, any stories remembered about the client's infancy, toilet training, sleep and appetite status, developmental landmarks that were late in achieving, experiences starting school, childhood friendships, developmental landmarks such as when the client began to read or write, any remembrance of psychological difficulties, family interaction, how behaviors were punished, and any history of verbal, physical, or sexual abuse.

Adolescence

Assess the client's view of his or her education; sexual development; social relationships; intimate relationships; any history of verbal, physical, or sexual abuse; relationships with teachers or other persons of authority; family relationships; any occupational history; special interests for future vocation; hobbies; client's body image perception during adolescence; substance-use history; or any other significant recollections the client has.

Young and middle adulthood

The therapist has the client articulate his or her occupational history; history of parenthood; family history; marital or relationship history; education history; sexual history; history of verbal, physical, or sexual abuse; military history; history of substance use; and any remarkable perception the client has of young and middle adulthood.

Late adulthood, after 65 years of age

The client describes his or her history with the same adult categories described earlier and includes feelings from when he or she anticipated retirement and reactions to any physical or mental limitations that may have been experienced.

For all developmental stages

Special attention should be placed on the identification of feelings or emotional states that the client remembers experiencing during each of these developmental periods.

Medical Status

Social workers are not physicians and are not qualified to perform a medical examination. However, the gathering of medical information from the client, a collateral contact, or treating physicians may provide information about disease states that mimic psychiatric states, disease states that produce psychological symptoms, or medications that are taken by the client that may be producing psychological side effects. It is helpful to have the client bring in all medications, whether over the counter or prescribed, that he or she is taking. This is often called a *brown bag assessment*. Some agencies use electronic checklists to determine what medications a client is taking. Often this section of the assessment is reviewed by a psychiatrist, who may determine whether the older client needs to be referred for a medical examination or who may find this information helpful if prescribing psychotropic medications.

BROWN BAG ASSESSMENT	FEATURE 2.1

The social worker must ask the older client to put all the medication he or she is taking in a bag and bring the bag of medications to the next session to verify the following:

- What medications is he or she taking?
- What dosage?
- What frequency?
- Who is the prescribing physician?

Sexual Assault History

When assessing an older person, sexual assault history is often over-looked by social workers (Burgess & Morgenbesser, 2005; Manzer, 2003). It is important to determine whether the client has been assaulted or has a history of sexually assaulting another. Trauma related to sexual assault is an important consideration in the process of differential diagnosis. This is an important role for the therapist in detecting elder sexual abuse (see Chapter 10, Older Adult Abuse).

Sexual History

The social worker should explore the client's present sexual activity (mas-turbation, extra-relationship affairs, interest in sex (libido), sexual activity history, sexual orientation, and any pathological sexual symptoms or sex-ually transmitted diseases (present or past). Many older adults welcome this discussion because it releases them from the stereotype that older people are not sexually active or interested in sex (see Chapter 9, Older Adult Sexuality).

Substance Use

All substances that have abuse or addictive potential must be identified during the assessment. The use of *substance* rather than *drug* is important. *Drug* implies a compound that is manufactured for human consumption. This narrow identification of compounds manufactured for human con-sumption omits substances like cleaning fluids, spray paints, correction fluid, nitrous oxide or other propellants, and so on. Often when questioned about drugs, a client will identify with a prescribed drug or an illicit drug that is associated with addiction. Alcohol is another category that must be investigated. Many clients do not view alcohol as a "drug," and often deny labeling their consumption as abusing alcohol, or being dependent on alcohol.

When taking a substance-use history, the client must not be intoxi-cated. If a client presents in an intoxicated state, the assessment must be terminated, to be continued only after the client is medically cleared for substance intoxication. Information is gathered on type of substance, recent intoxication, frequency of use, dosage, and route of administration. This analysis must be done separately for each substance the client is consum-ing. Once a current history is taken, then a history of prior substance use is taken, including type of substance, intoxication experience, frequency of use, dosage, and route of administration.

In addition, a comprehensive history of substance-related diagnoses and treatment must be taken, including dates of diagnosis and treatment, place of treatment, duration of treatment, and, where possible, contact information from the treating therapist or institution. Treatment history should include twelve-step programs, self-help groups, faith-based sup-port groups, and any other intervention deemed relevant by the client (see Chapter 8, Older Adult Substance Abusers).

Psychiatric History

An evaluation needs to be made of any current psychiatric or psycho-therapeutic treatment, including dates of service, the contact information of the provider of services, the name and dosages of any psychotropic medications, and any recent hospitalizations, partial hospitalizations, or attendance at agency-based day programs. In addition, a comprehensive history of these categories must be investigated. It is often helpful to identify a collateral source to confirm the accuracy of the information taken from the client because some psychological problems in older adult clients can cause confusion or poor recall.

Appearance

The appearance of the client must not be overlooked. It is important to assess whether the client is well groomed, unkempt, has any obvious body odors, and is dressed appropriately or bizarrely. Descriptive notation of the social worker's observations along with any patient quotes must be included in the client's assessment record.

Attitude

It is important to note the client's attitude toward his or her problem, the interview, and the social worker. This includes the willingness of the client to share information and feelings, the degree of withholding information and feelings, and the quality of information that the client is willing to share.

Motor Status

The social worker should observe the level of physical activity that the client engages in. Does the client show hyperactivity in his or her gestures, moving extremities, changing his or her position in the room, or pacing? Alternatively, is the client showing retardation in movements, being mostly still or immobile? Are the client's movements, or lack of movement, congruent with the client's mood?

Ecopraxia

Is the client imitating the social worker's movements, or that of other persons in the waiting room, or staff members observing the assessment interview?

Catatonia

Is the client immobile, staying in a constantly maintained position (catalepsy)? Is the client showing agitated movements with no purpose (catatonic excitement)? Is the client immobile, in a rigid position, resisting any effort from the social worker to change his or her position (catatonic rigidity)? Is the client in a bizarre or inappropriate posture (catatonic posturing)? Is the client showing exaggerated slow movements or no movement at all while seemingly unaware of his or her surroundings (catatonic stupor)? Is the client frozen in one position but can be moved into another position that then freezes (waxy flexibility)? Is there a lack of any movement by the client (akinesia)?

Speech Quality

The social worker must evaluate the tone of voice of the client and the rate and pitch of his or her speech. This includes an assessment of whether the rate is rapid or pressured and the pitch high. Alternatively, is the speech low, muted, or slow? Notation should be made regarding the degree of congruence between the speech observations and the reported mood. It is important for the social worker to distinguish the quality of the client's speech, not whether the client is difficult to understand because of an accent or difficulty in speaking a language that is not native to the assessment setting. Sometimes a client will refuse to speak or does not have the ability to speak. The social worker must differentiate between the inability to speak and mutism without any structural abnormalities.

Echolalia

Is the client repeating words or phrases of the social worker, people in the waiting room, or other staff members?

Thought Process

There are many aspects of the client's thought content that the social worker must question and observe. Do the client's thoughts seem to flow with a logical connection from one to the other? Do ideas expressed from the client seem to fly from one to another without a strong, logical connection (flight of ideas)? Are the connections within normal limits? Are they loosely connected? How rapidly does the client move from association to association? Are the client's thoughts interrupted by either being blocked (derailed) or interrupted by an interfering thought? Is the content of the client's thoughts fraught with unnecessary detail and minutiae? Are the client's thoughts tangential, never seeming to get to a point?

A client's thoughts must be reality tested. Does the client tend to view his or her world within normal limits, or does the client have a narcissistic focus to his or her social world? Does the client seem to persevere and become preoccupied with obsessions? Are the client's thoughts delusional? If delusional, are the delusions persecutory, grandiose, or paranoid?

Mood/Affect

Mood refers to the internal feelings that the patient is experiencing. The social worker must assess the intensity, duration, and frequency of the mood or moods that are experienced by the older client. In the case in which a client is unable to identify a feeling he or she is experiencing, a feeling chart can be shown to the client. This enables the client to point to the word or picture describing what he or she is feeling. The social worker should determine whether the mood is labile. Is it fluctuating slowly, remaining the same, or rapidly shifting from one extreme to another?

Affect refers to the client's projection, through body language, of what he or she is feeling. The therapist must determine whether the client's affect is within normal range, constricted, flat, congruent with the client's mood, or incongruent with the client's mood. When the client's affect is incongruent with his or her reported mood, or when the affect is incongruent with what the client is communicating, the clinician must detail the inappropriateness of the client's affect. Labile affect should be noted. Are there rapid shifts in affect and is this shifting consistent with labile mood reported by the client?

Sleep/Appetite Status

Is the client sleeping less than or more than usual during the past few weeks? Is the client eating less or more than usual during the past few weeks? Has the client lost (without trying) or gained weight during the past few weeks?

Suicide Assessment

Social workers are usually the first contact for suicidal older adults. Feldman and Freedenthal (2006) warn that social work programs offer little education or training in suicide assessment or intervention. With this in mind, whether or not the social worker suspects suicidality, it is mandatory that a complete suicidal assessment be carried out and documented. Barr, Leitner, and Thomas (2004) recommend that older adults presenting to a hospital emergency room with suspected evidence of self-harm should receive a mandatory suicide assessment. In the case of an older adult, he or she will often not disclose suicidal feelings, plan, or intent unless asked by the social worker. Asking is critical because an older adult intent on killing him or herself will usually act on intent without warning others. Therefore, asking the following set of questions is critical. Each category is independent from the others. Therefore, an older client can experience one or more categories at any given time, in any given order.

Ideation

Suicidal ideation is identified when an older adult has thoughts of dying that are experienced as acceptable and rational. Cheavens and Lynch (2004) found that there is no difference between older adults and younger people in their reports of suicidal ideation. A client may say, "If I didn't wake up tomorrow it would be OK because I would no longer have to deal with the pain in my life." These thoughts are general, without any identified plan or intent to hurt him or herself. If the client reports suicidal ideation, the social worker should use client quotes for the description of his or her ideation. If the client denies suicidal ideation, the social worker should document that the client denies suicidal ideation.

Plan

When an older client has a plan to kill him or herself, this signals the possibility of a dangerous situation that may require hospitalization. Many beginning social workers are reluctant to ask a client whether he or she has a plan to kill him or herself because the beginning social worker may feel that this might put the idea or suggestion in the client's mind. The opposite is true. An older client normally welcomes a social worker asking whether he or she has a plan to kill him or herself and feels a sense of relief from having the ability to talk about this painful aspect of his or her life. If the client has a plan, the social worker should use client quotes for the description of the plan. If there is no plan, the social worker should document that the client denies having a plan. According to Abrams, Marzuk, Tardiff, and Leon (2005), a plan that has a high degree of success in an older adult is falling from a height. These authors analyzed all medical examiner–certified suicides in New York City from 1990 to 1998 to compare suicide methods used by elderly and younger adults. They found that older people were more likely than younger people to use falling from a height as a plan for a successful completion of suicide.

Intent

A client having intent to kill him or herself is a serious event, especially if coupled with a well-thought-out plan. Depending on the seriousness of the intent (*I will kill myself on Thursday*), hospitalization is most likely necessary. Erlangsen, Bille-Brahe, and Jeune (2003) found that clients in the oldest-old categories (80 years of age and above) use more determined suicide methods than clients 65 to 79 years of age. This is critical when an oldest-old client reports a loss of a partner/spouse within the year before presentation for assessment (Erlangsen, Jeune, Bille-Brahe, & Vaupel, 2004). Therefore, special attention should be employed when interviewing clients from oldest-old categories. A client usually welcomes questions by the social worker about having the intent to kill him or herself. This brings relief to the client and offers an opportunity for help. If the client has intent, the social worker should use client quotes for the description of the intent. If there is no intent, the social worker should document that the client denies having intent.

Means

The means by which the individual plans to commit suicide is an important aspect for the social worker to question the client about. In many cases a client may not have a conscious plan or intent but is hoarding pills just in case, buying ammunition for a gun, buying razor blades, coveting a knife, or purchasing some sturdy rope. By asking whether the client has the means to hurt him or herself, a therapist may open a discussion that leads to a client disclosing a plan or intent. If not, an older adult securing means to commit suicide must be prompted and assessed, causing a clinical judgment to determine whether there is an immediate threat to the client. If the client has been accumulating means, the social worker should use client quotes for the description of the means. If there are no means, the therapist should document that the client denies having means.

History

Similar to the current suicide assessment, a social worker must gather a detailed history of any prior suicidal ideation, plan, means, or intent. As before, the social worker should document with client quotes that either describe or deny past ideation, plan, means, or intent.

Special considerations

If the social worker determines that there is an immediate risk for a suicide attempt, hospitalization is necessary. In an agency setting, the social
worker must follow agency protocol for protecting the client. In a private
practice setting, the social worker may notify the local police or first aid
squad to assist transporting the older adult to a hospital or emergency
room for assessment and treatment. If the client seems to have the potential for a suicide attempt but the danger is not immediate, then an arrange-
ment must be made with the client for follow-up. This can be a scheduled
telephone contact a few hours later and repeated until the threat of a suicide attempt disappears. An alternative plan would be to enlist a relative,
roommate, or friend who can check in on the client and has permission
from the client to call the social worker with progress reports. Either plan
would reassure the client that he or she is not alone and would bring stability to the client until client–social worker contact may return to regularly scheduled appointments.

Rational Suicide

The concept of whether a client has the right and ability to rationally
determine to end his or her life is an ethical dilemma facing many health
professionals. Valente and Trainor (1998) suggest several considerations a
health care professional needs to assess in order to determine whether an
older client is making a rational decision for ending his or her life because
of a terminal illness. These authors suggest that a client must demonstrate
a rational process of thinking by having an adequate understanding of
medical facts concerning his or her illness, understanding the impact of
suicide on loved ones, demonstrating that alternative treatment options
have been explored, and presenting funeral and estate arrangements.
The client should be informed of hospice and home care alternatives (see
Chapter 12, Care and Residential Settings for Older Adults) and demonstrate a coherent understanding of alternative choices. The social worker
should evaluate the suicide plan with medical consultation in terms of
means and outcomes and evaluate the client's decision within the client's
culture, values, and beliefs. A rational decision for suicide should never
be coerced, is voluntary, and whenever possible is discussed with kin or
loved ones.

Valente and Trainor (1998) indicated that there are few practice
guidelines for a health care professional to evaluate ethical dilemmas.
Rogers, Gueulette, Abbey-Hines, Carney, and Werth (2001) indicate that
most medical students receive little or no information on suicide and the
differentiation between suicide and rational suicide. Rational suicide is the
controversial dilemma an older person faces when wanting to end his or
her life while in a painful, terminal disease state. Feldman and Freedenthal
(2006) stress that social work education provides inadequate exposure to
suicide education and prevention, causing social workers dealing with
suicidal clients to act out of instinct rather than training. Therefore, there
is an urgent need for all health care practitioners to receive vigorous training in suicide identification and prevention and differentiation between
suicide and rational suicide.

Homicidal Assessment

Similar to a suicide assessment, a homicidal assessment is required whether a social worker suspects homicidality or not. All subcategories of the homicidal assessment must be asked and documented with client quotations. In most jurisdictions, if a client has a homicidal plan or intent, the social worker is mandated to make a best effort to notify the intended victim or victims and notify the local police authorities. Therefore, the following set of questions is critical. Each category is independent from all others. An older client can experience one or more categories at any given time, in any given order.

Homicidal ideation

Homicidal ideation is evidenced by general thoughts of wanting to hurt or kill someone without identification of a specific victim. A client may say, "I feel like killing someone, I'm really pissed off, no one better get in my way." On questioning, the client denies any intended victim. If the client experiences homicidal ideation, the social worker should use client quotes for the description of his or her ideation. If the client denies homicidal ideation, the social worker should document that the client denies ideation.

Homicidal plan

It is important to determine whether an older client has a plan to hurt or kill another person or persons. Because this is a criminal act, many clients will not disclose a homicidal plan on questioning. Nevertheless, a social worker is obligated to ask. If the client discloses a plan, the social worker must detail the plan with client quotes. In addition, the worker must attempt to get as much information as possible about the intended victim or victims. If a plan is disclosed, the social worker is obligated to notify the intended victim or victims, as well as the local police authority. Most agencies should have an established protocol for notifying the police and, if possible, having the client on premises until the authorities arrive. If the agency does not have this type of protocol, then the social worker must advocate for it. This increases the margin of safety for the intended victim or victims, the client, and the social worker. If the client has a plan, the social worker should use client quotes for the description of his or her plan. If there is no plan, the worker should document that the client denies having a plan.

Homicidal intent

A client presenting with a homicidal intent creates a dangerous situation. As with a homicidal plan, there should be an agency protocol on how to reach police authorities, whether or not to retain the client at the agency until the police arrive, and how to reach the intended victim or victims. Many agencies have on-site security, whose presence during the assessment often limits the immediate danger of the situation.

In a private practice setting, the social worker should arrange seating in the office by placing the client farthest from the door, enabling the social worker to leave the room if the client becomes threatening. An emergency telephone, or preferably a cell phone, or alarm system should be made available so that the social worker may contact the police in a violent or potentially violent situation.

If a client has an intent to hurt or kill someone, details should be gathered with client quotations, including when, how, where, and who. If there is no intent discovered through questioning, then the social worker should document that the client denies having intent.

Means

The questioning of an older client about whether he or she has the means to hurt or kill someone is a delicate but necessary task. If there is a perceived threat, or if the social worker feels that the client has dangerous tendencies, the identification of means becomes necessary. In many instances, where there is no plan or intent, the social worker can often negotiate with the client to have the potential homicidal means removed from the client's possession or access. Many clients understand the dangerous aspect of having access to a gun, knife, or other weapon and will welcome making arrangements to have a friend or relative remove the means from the client's access. If the client has means, the social worker should use client quotes for the description of the available means. If there are no means, the social worker should document that the client denies having means.

If the client is armed when arriving at the assessment, the social worker must insist that the client surrender his or her weapon. In an agency setting, the surrender of a weapon is usually to a security guard. In a private setting, if the weapon is surrendered, it should be place in a locked room and the police should be notified. If the client refuses to surrender his or her weapon, the social worker should terminate the interview in a nonthreatening manner, telling the client that he or she cannot be interviewed while armed.

History

Similar to the current homicidal assessment, a social worker must gather a detailed history of any prior homicidal ideation, plan, means, or intent. As before, the social worker should document with client quotes that either describe or deny past ideation, plan, means, or intent.

Special considerations

If the social worker feels that there is a potential for violence, the therapist must engage in several behaviors. If the client appears agitated or threatening, often a short wait in the reception area can have a calming effect on an agitated client. The social worker should never engage the client in a threatening, angry, or patronizing way. The social worker should never touch the client or approach the client without warning. The social worker should be aware of escape routes. When possible, have another person (usually a security guard) present at the assessment or outside the room with the door opened. An emergency protocol for notifying security, or in a private setting, the police, should be established in advance.

Mental Status Exam

Orientation

The social worker assesses the older adult's orientation to person, place, and time. Disorientation to these parameters should be noted with a detailed description of the client's confusion. The social worker should avoid using shorthand such as *oriented x3*. Even though *x3* indicates that the client is oriented to person, place, and time, this shorthand leads to confusion when the therapist uses shorthand when the client is oriented to only one or two spheres. The shorthand *oriented x2* or *x1* has no meaning because the reader of the chart note does not know what sphere or spheres the clients is disoriented to.

Memory

The social worker should ask an older client what he or she experienced in the past 24 hours, what he or she ate, whom the client was with, what he or she did, and so on, to assess recent memory. Giving the client a digit span, usually consisting of 7 digits, to remember tests immediate recall. The social worker starts with 3 digits and asks the client to repeat them in forward and reverse orders. Then the therapist continues asking for 4, 5, 6, and 7 digits, respectively. In addition, a social worker may ask a client to count by 7s starting with the number 7 (serial sevens) and then subtracting from 100 by 7s. Each counting process should take place during a period of 30 seconds. The therapist should note errors or confusion evidenced by the client. Another method is to present three objects to the client, ask the older client to remember them, and then distract the client for a few minutes. After a short period, the social worker asks the client what three objects were presented before, whether he or she remembers the order they were presented, and whether he or she can tell the social worker the reverse order in which they were presented.

Perception

The social worker must assess whether an older client's view of reality evidences distortions, which may include hallucinations, illusions, experiencing depersonalization, derealizaton, or déjà vu. It must be determined whether these phenomena are instigated by a substance or medication, are hypnagogic (on falling asleep) or hypnopompic (on awakening). Are these perceptual disturbances disturbing to the client? Are they persistent?

General knowledge

Questioning an older client on general knowledge should be consistent with the client's level of education. Basic questions on state capitals, or naming two or more countries, or asking the client to group recalled items into predetermined categories such as fruits, types of cars, or animals, will determine a general fund of knowledge and offer an additional insight into the client's thought processes.

Abstractions

Abstract thinking is assessed by asking the older client to interpret several common proverbs (e.g., "A rolling stone gathers no moss"), or how she or he would solve a problem such as what she or he would do if she or he had a flat tire on a busy highway.

Sensorium

It is important to screen older clients for sensory deficits. Some aspects of diminished sensory capacity can be ascertained during the assessment interview. However, a complete assessment should be made through consultation with the client's family physician or geriatrician. Clinicians whose focus is on determining a diagnosis based on the *Diagnostic and Statistical Manual of Mental Disorders* (5th ed.; *DSM-5*; American Psychiatric Association, 2013), often overlook this aspect of the assessment. Review of the sensorium is critical for client safety.

This is particularly true for the sense of smell. Nordin, Monsch, and Murphy (1995) report that clients with Alzheimer's disease (see Chapter 6, Alzheimer's Disease and Other Demetias) as well as nondemented older patients have little awareness of diminished sense of smell (hyposmic) or loss of smell (anosmic). Lack of or diminished sense of smell may be an early indicator of Alzheimer's disease in the young-old (Burns, 2000). Because of this lack of awareness, it is recommended that their family physicians or geriatricians perform formal testing of smell thresholds. This is critical because loss of the sense of smell, or diminished ability to smell, makes an older client vulnerable to not detecting spoiled food, leaking gas, or smoke conditions, all of which may be life threatening. Smell is intimately linked to the sense of taste (Murphy, Cain, & Bartoshuk, 1977). Therefore, older adults complaining that food does not seem to taste the same might indicate hyposmic or anosmic problems. Having a diminished sense of taste presents a risk for older adults not having the ability to detect spoiled food, which puts them in danger of food poisoning or consuming large amounts of salt (to increase taste sense), which may affect preexisting medical conditions. Ageusia (loss of taste) is a rarely seen condition (Beers, Porter, Jones, Kaplan, & Berkwits, 2006).

Most older adults have some degree of hearing loss (Levy et al., 2006). It is important to discriminate between hearing loss and hallucination. Levy et al. report that older adults, especially those suffering from some form of dementia, may misinterpret common sounds. For example, "the sound of a telephone may be perceived as a small dog barking" (Bakker, 2003, p. 48). Some therapists may misinterpret this as a psychotic symptom rather than a sensory deficit.

Visual impairments are a common presentation in older adults. These impairments include macular degeneration, cataracts, complications from stokes, diabetic retinopathy, and other medical conditions (see Chapter 7, Medical Problems in Older Adults). Collateral confirmation of visual impairments is important because of concerns for older clients' safety. Are they safe to drive? Does their home environment need modification to accommodate their visual impairments? Clients with Alzheimer's disease, because of the anatomical changes in their brains, experience sensitivity to glare and visual misinterpretations (Bakker, 2003). As with hearing misinterpretations, a therapist must be careful to discriminate between a visual misinterpretation and a psychotic hallucination.

The main issue with the sense of touch is personal. Because of needed assistance with bathing and dressing, some older adults feel a sense of violation being touched by strangers in settings or activities that are considered intimate. This is worthy of exploration to evaluate whether there is a need for counseling, or whether some form of physical or sexual abuse is occurring

Spirituality/Religion

The social worker should explore a client's sense of spirituality, religion, or lack of religion. Spirituality is defined as "a quest for understanding answers to ultimate questions about life, meaning, and one's relationship to the sacred," and religion as "an organized system of beliefs, practices, rituals, and symbols designed to facilitate closeness to God or a higher power and to foster an understanding of one's relationship to others" (Koenig, McCullough, & Larson, 2001, p. 18). Erikson (see Chapter 1, Theories to Inform the Clinician Practicing With Older Adults) notes that this exploration is important for older adults who are in a process of integrating maturing forms of *hope, will, purpose, competence, fidelity, love,* and *care,* which complete a comprehensive sense of *wisdom* (Erikson, Erikson, & Kivnick, 1986). This helps prepare an older adult for resolution of the existential dilemma of an oncoming process of dying and death (see Chapter 13, Dying and Death). This assessment provides an opportunity to help a client link to clergy if religious counseling is needed.

Older Adult Abuse

Older adults are at high risk for abuse from family members (see Chapter 10, Older Adult Abuse). The 1996 U.S. National Elder Abuse Incidence Study reports that older children or spouses represent two thirds of perpetrators of elder abuse. In addition, older adults are abused in hospitals, nursing homes, and other service-related institutions (Brownel & Berman, 2004; Nelson, 2002). This is a difficult problem for the social worker to identify. Through direct questioning and collateral consultation with family members, friends, neighbors, and caregivers, the social worker should look for signs of neglect, isolation, financial decisions being made by others for the client, abandonment by family, signs of physical abuse, poor nutrition, and associated psychological problems such as depression, anxiety, or posttraumatic symptoms. Clients should be screened for possible sexual abuse perpetrated by family members, sex offenders, or health care personnel.

Goals for change

The social worker and older adult should make a contract of the goals of treatment and a timeframe for treatment.

Collateral Interviews

Teri and Wagner (1991) stress the important of collateral informers to the clinical assessment. This is critical when an older adult is experiencing Alzheimer's disease or other cognitive impairments. Collateral contacts may be family members, neighbors, caregivers, clergy, family physicians, or geriatricians.

DSM-5 Diagnosis

A *DSM-5* diagnosis, using the current version of the *Diagnostic and Statistics Manual of Mental Disorders,* published by the American Psychiatric Association (2013), is required for treatment planning, medication administration, and insurance reimbursement. This includes listing the diagnosis or diagnoses in order of importance. It must be noted that there is a potential problem with diagnosing an older adult who recently (within 2 months) experienced a loss of a loved one. The bereavement exclusion that was previously in the fourth edition, text revision (*DSM-IV-TR*; American Psychiatric Association, 2000) is not in the *DSM-5*. Therefore, symptoms during the first 2 weeks of bereavement that normally dissipate within 2 months may be misdiagnosed as a major depression (Pomeroy & Parrish, 2012). This change found in the *DSM-5* is one example of many that are included in a *black box warning*. This warning states that the *DSM-5* (Frances, 2012) may lead to overdiagnosing the population, which may lead to increased stigma (see Chapter 4, Stigma and Older Adults) for those older adults diagnosed with a psychiatric problem, and increased use of psychiatric medication (see Chapter 5, Psychopathological Problems in Older Adults).

THE CASE OF DR. FRANK

Gender, Age, Ethnicity, Sexual Orientation

Dr. Frank* is an 81-year-old White, Jewish, heterosexual male.

Presenting Problem

Mr. Berns, who is a good friend of Dr. Frank, brought Dr. Frank to the emergency room. Dr. Frank indicated that Mr. Berns convinced him to be evaluated because he has not been sleeping well, has lost his appetite, and has been feeling sad and depressed for the past 3 weeks. His feelings of sadness and depression have occurred nearly every day for the past 3 weeks and have been increasing in intensity.

Environmental and Demographic Information

Dr. Frank is living alone in the apartment he shared with his wife, which is located in the Upper West Side area of Manhattan, in New York City. Dr. Frank reported that his wife died 3 years ago. Dr. Frank reports having an adequate amount of food that is periodically replenished by a local food market for which he arranged delivery service. Living in the borough of Manhattan, he has adequate access to public transportation, which eliminates any concern about his ability to drive an automobile. Dr. Frank reports that he has a network of doctors and a dentist within a half hour of travel from his apartment. He indicates that he is friendly with his neighbors and has a chess partner (Mr. Berns) whom he meets for games three times per week. Dr. Frank reports little contact with family members. He has no children and periodically speaks to some cousins of his wife who live in another state. He said, "My family are the friends that I have met and keep contact with, mostly people from my building or colleagues from the medical school years."

Dr. Frank has health insurance coverage with Medicare and a supplemental policy with a private insurance company. In addition, he has a long-term extended care policy with a private insurance company.

*Names and other identifying information have been changed to preserve confidentiality.

Developmental History

Birth

Dr. Frank was born in Vilna, Lithuania. He is a middle child, with a brother 3 years older (now deceased) and a sister 4 years younger (now deceased). Dr. Frank indicated that "as far as I know there was nothing special about my birth except for the fact that I was born on our kitchen table, delivered by a cousin." He indicated that he was unsure of any other details about his birth and infancy except that he was relatively healthy and happy according to stories told to him by his mother and father before they died during the Holocaust. Greene (2010) indicates that survivors of the Holocaust are an excellent example of extreme distress and the experience of survival and resilience to such distress. This example underlies the importance of social workers to extend their education to the cultural and historical experiences of their clients.

Childhood

Dr. Frank's father was a physician in the city of Vilna, which meant his family lived in relative comfort and status. He remembers being a good student and, "much to my parents' disappointment," had ambitions to become a rabbi. He indicated that he had many friends and "even a girlfriend or two." Dr. Frank indicated that none of his childhood friends survived the Holocaust.

Adolescence

Dr. Frank indicated that as an adolescent he experienced anti-Semitism that seemed to get worse as he approached young adulthood. He remembers how the authorities closed his religious school and how he had to study in secret at a farm located outside the city limits. He described how his father was forced to stop practicing medicine, causing the family, for the first time, to experience financial hardship.

Young and middle adulthood

Dr. Frank indicated that his family sent his brother, sister, and himself into hiding with a Catholic family who had a farm in the countryside. This event heralded his young adulthood. He said that he remembered feeling angry and scared most of the time, experienced periods during which he lost his appetite, hardly slept, and had thoughts that "being dead would be better than living like this." During this period, he found out from a cousin that his parents were arrested and transported to a location of unknown origin. Dr. Frank indicated that his feelings of hopelessness and helplessness worsened during this time.

When the war ended, Dr. Frank reported returning to Vilna, where he found a non-Jewish family living in his house. When he complained to the authorities he was rebuffed and told that it would be better for him not to stay in Vilna. Seeing no future, Dr. Frank met with his siblings, and as a group they decided to journey to England, where they knew of a cousin who was living in London. When they reached London, after a difficult transit by foot, wagon, train, and boat, they finally reached their destination. Dr. Frank does not remember any details of his journey or his brief stay in London. He does remember feeling lonely and isolated, "not connected to anything."

Dr. Frank indicated that a relative in New York paid for his passage to America, where he entered a yeshiva in Brooklyn, New York, to continue his rabbinical studies. Again, he indicated remembering few details about this time. He did recall becoming disillusioned with religion and longing for his family members, long since dead "from the Nazi killers." Feeling a spiritual connection to his father, Dr. Frank enrolled in City College in New York City and began his premedical studies. After graduation, he attended Queens Medical School in Queens, New York, and became a successful surgeon and professor of medicine. He characterized this period of his life as all work and no play.

Dr. Frank indicated that he continued to remain socially isolated, spending 16 hours a day working and teaching at the medical center. When he was 45, he met his wife-to-be, who helped him "come out of his shell and be more human." Over time and with his wife's encouragement they developed a small social network, and for the first time in his adult life, he indicated that he felt a sense of balance. They never had children, but he feels that the closeness he had with his wife made up for not having children.

Dr. Frank indicated that when he was 51 years old he experienced what he learned was his second major depression. After a brief hospitalization, Dr. Frank was able to return to practicing medicine and led a relatively uneventful life.

Late adulthood, after 65 years of age

Dr. Frank indicated that he retired from practicing and teaching medicine when he was 72 years old. He said, "By that time I had it with medicine, was tired, and needed a rest." He and his wife decided to spend several years traveling around the world. He indicated that this plan worked for 3 years, but then his wife was diagnosed with chronic lymphocytic leukemia. This forced them to stop their ambitious travel plans and to resettle into an apartment they kept in New York City. Dr. Frank indicated that his wife's illness progressed slowly, causing their life to gradually become more limited. He said that "in the end, my time was mainly custodial," they stopped seeing friends, and once again he experienced being isolated and losing his only family. His wife died 3 years ago.

Medical Status

As taken from the emergency room (ER) chart, Dr. Frank reported to the ER physician performing the medical screening that he suffers from systolic hypertension and that his blood pressure is currently being controlled with medication (verapamil). He reported having high cholesterol and triglycerides, which are being treated with Lipitor. He reported taking a "baby" aspirin once daily. In addition, he indicated that he suffers from osteoarthritis in both hands, which has disabled him from playing the piano on a frequent basis. He indicated that he treats pain arising from his osteoarthritis with over-the-counter Tylenol and a glucosamine/chondroitin supplement. Two weeks ago, he was diagnosed with non-Hodgkin's lymphoma, small cell, beta type. Dr. Frank indicated that "this is a watch-and-wait disease which does not get treated until, or and if, it puts me in jeopardy for major infections."

DR. FRANK'S BROWN BAG ASSESSMENT	FEATURE 2.2

Dr. Frank was asked to return for a follow-up session and to bring with him any medication, whether prescribed or over the counter, that he is taking. He was asked to put all the medications in a bag. Dr, Frank's bag contained the following:

- Verapamil, 240 mg each evening, prescribed by Dr. M
- Lipitor, 60 mg once per day, prescribed by Dr. M
- Aspirin, 81 mg once per day, suggested by Dr. M
- Tylenol, 500 mg as needed, purchased at local drugstore
- Glucosamine/chondroitin, 1500 mg/1500 mg three times per day, purchased at a local health food store
- Xanax, 1 mg four times per day as needed, prescribed by Dr. O.
  (This medication was not reported to the emergency room physician or to the therapist during the initial assessment.)

Sexual Assault History

Dr. Frank denied any history of sexual assault or being sexually assaulted.

Sexual History

Dr. Frank indicated that he does not engage in any sexual activity and has not engaged in any sexual activity since his wife became ill 6 years ago. Before that he had an active sexual life with his wife that he found satisfactory. He indicated that currently he does not have any desire for sex, does not masturbate, but often wishes that his interest in sex would return. He denied having any sexually transmitted disease or any history of sexually transmitted diseases.

Substance Use

Dr. Frank denied any substance intoxication, abuse, or dependency. He indicated that his experience with alcohol was an occasional drink when socializing. He said, "I like to be in control of myself, so using drugs or alcohol to get high is the last thing that I would ever be interested in."

Psychiatric History

Dr. Frank indicated that when he was 51 he was diagnosed with a recurrent major depression and was hospitalized at the Empire State Psychiatric Institute in Manhattan, New York. He said that his treatment included antidepressant medication of which he cannot recall, electroconvulsive therapy, and psychotherapy. He said he was hospitalized for 6 weeks and on release entered therapy with a psychoanalyst for a period of 6 years. He was unable to recall the name of the psychoanalyst. He and his social worker surmised that his first major depression occurred when in hiding during the Holocaust.

Appearance

Dr. Frank was dressed appropriately yet his clothing looked rumpled, as though he had been wearing his shirt and pants for several days. When questioned, he said that he had lost his desire to change his clothes and for the past 3 days had worn the same clothing during the day and while sleeping. He made little eye contact with the social worker and sat with a stooped posture.

Attitude

Dr. Frank's attitude toward the social worker was cooperative and respectful.

Motor Status

Dr. Frank's movements showed motor retardation. He hardly gesticulated and remained in a stooped sitting position. These movements were congruent with his mood. He showed no evidence of ecopraxia, and there was no detection of catatonic features.

Speech Quality

Dr. Frank spoke in a low monotone and his speech was slow, lacking any inflection. His speech appeared congruent to his mood. He showed no evidence of echolalia.

Thought Process

Dr. Frank's thought processes were within normal limits with the exception of derailment, which occurred four times during the interview. He reported losing his ability to pay attention to the interview, causing his thinking "to stop."

Mood/Affect

Dr. Frank reported feeling "very depressed and apathetic about my life." He described feeling little motivation for anything and did not want to read because he cannot concentrate despite the fact that reading normally made him feel better. He felt that his depressed mood prevented him from engaging in any type of interpersonal communication, be it on the telephone or talking to a neighbor he might come across in his apartment building.

Dr. Frank's affect was blunted and congruent with his mood. He sat in a slouched position, rarely looking at this therapist, and sighed often.

Sleep/Appetite Status

Dr. Frank reported having difficulty falling asleep and, once asleep, difficulty staying asleep. He indicated that he probably slept 4 to 5 hours during the 8 hours he stayed in bed. He indicated that on awakening he felt tired, as though "I didn't sleep at all."

Dr. Frank reported a diminished appetite. He indicated that during the past 3 weeks he had lost interest in eating, "forcing myself to eat so that I wouldn't get sick." He reported that during this past 3-week period he had had a weight loss of 12 pounds. He said, "This is a lousy way for anyone to diet. Just kidding, I wasn't trying to lose weight."

Suicide Assessment

Ideation

Dr. Frank indicated that for the past 4 months he has had recurring thoughts "that I'd rather be dead; then I wouldn't have to feel that pain I feel every day, day in, and day out."

Plan

Dr. Frank indicated that being a physician, he knew how to end his life with medication, but denied any specific plan.

Intent

Dr. Frank denied any intent to kill himself. He said, "I've been here before and things tend to work out. Besides, I don't think I have the courage to do it. Or maybe, because I'm a physician, I find it hypocritical to do the opposite of what I would do for a patient."

Means

Dr. Frank denied having a firearm, collecting medications, or any other means. He said, "It's sort of a silly question because getting access to medications would be easy for me."

History

Dr. Frank indicated that when he was in hiding during the Holocaust he experienced suicidal ideation but never had a plan or intent. "If anything, it would have been a selfish act. If I was going to kill anyone, it would be a Nazi, not myself." He indicated that when he was 51 and was diagnosed with major depression, he once again experienced suicidal ideation, but had no plan or intent.

Homicidal Assessment

Ideation

Dr. Frank denied homicidal ideation.

Plan

Dr. Frank denied having a homicidal plan.

Intent

Dr. Frank denied having a homicidal intent.

Means

Dr. Frank remarked that "as a physician I have the knowledge to kill someone but, of course, I would never use such knowledge."

History

Dr. Frank denied any history of homicidal ideation, plan, or intent.

Mental Status Exam

Orientation

Dr. Frank was oriented to person, place, and time. He was able to identify who he is, who the social worker is, where the interview was taking place, and the correct time of day and date.

Memory

Dr. Frank was able to recall three objects in forward and reverse orders that were presented to him. However, he experienced difficulty counting forward by 7 after the fifth reiteration of 7. He experienced a greater frequency of errors when subtracting 7 from 100 after the third reiteration of 7.

General knowledge

Dr. Frank demonstrated an accurate knowledge of general questions about state capitals, current and past politicians, and putting a list of items into discrete categories.

Abstractions

When asked to interpret the phrase *A rolling stone gathers no moss*, he said "that if one stays productive in life, he will continue to grow and not become stuck." This interpretation was within a normal range.

Sensorium

Dr. Frank reported that food did not seem to "taste like it used to." He indicated that he adds spices and salt to his meals to "boost up" the taste. He was unable to determine whether there was any change in his ability to smell. He reported that he could not see without glasses, having been nearsighted for the majority of his life. He indicated that he has some difficulty hearing people speak if he is in a noisy restaurant or meeting hall. If the room is quiet, he indicated that this difficulty does not occur, except for periods when he experiences tinnitus.

Spirituality/Religion

Dr. Frank indicated that he is "Jewish, but not practicing." He said that because of the Holocaust he does not believe in God. He does have a spiritual sense with strong moral and ethical values. He indicated that he accepts that he will eventually die and looks at the process of death and dying as a matter of "what happens in life." He feels that this pragmatic view of death and dying comes from his medical training and years of dealing with the death and dying of his patients.

Older Adult Abuse

Dr. Frank denied any abuse. He did not present with any signs of abuse; he seemed well nourished, not isolated, and in charge of his finances. He denied being a victim of sexual abuse.

Collateral Interviews

Mr. Bern, who brought Dr. Frank to the emergency room, was interviewed after securing permission from Dr. Frank. He confirmed that Dr. Frank attends to all his needs, seems to eat regularly, and is not isolated. Mr. Bern indicated that he is Dr. Frank's chess partner. Mr. Bern reported that Dr. Frank seemed to become increasingly depressed over the past 3 weeks and that this concerned him. This was the reason why he brought Dr. Frank to the emergency room for evaluation. Mr. Bern said that he did not hear Dr. Frank expressing any thoughts about suicide.

DSM-5 Diagnosis

Major depressive disorder, recurrent

Goals for Change

Dr. Frank came to a consensus with the social worker that he would like to stabilize and then eliminate his depression, experience a return of interest in sex, and eventually find another partner. He and the social worker agreed that treatment might last for 6 to 9 months, being seen for individual psychotherapy once per week. Dr. Frank agreed to be evaluated by a psychiatrist to determine whether medication might be helpful on a short-term basis if psychotherapy did not bring relief within the next few weeks. It was explained that his psychotherapy would have an existential and solution-focused orientation (see Chapter 3, Intervention Theories Informing the Clinician Treating Older Adults). This eclectic mix of orientations was explained to Dr. Frank in detail, and he indicated that he understood the theoretical approaches that would guide his therapy.

SUMMARY

Many mental health agencies use a checklist assessment form that enables the therapist to gather demographic information, mental status information, and psychiatric and substance-use history. These forms end with a *DSM-5* diagnosis, treatment plan, or disposition to another agency. Though efficient for a rapid collection of information, these forms do a disservice to the older client. Little or no engagement occurs between social worker and older client, and developmental history is rarely explored during the assessment session. In addition, in many agencies an intake worker performs the assessment, then refers the older client to another social worker for treatment. Because of time constraints, many social workers rely on the diagnosis and treatment plan established during the assessment session by the intake worker. In addition, making a *DSM-5* diagnosis thrusts the social worker into the theoretical dissonance of viewing the older client from a person-in-environment perspective while simultaneously using the medical model perspective of diagnosing a psychiatric disease (see Chapter 1, Theories to Inform the Clinician Practicing With Older Adults).

As can be seen by the assessment of Dr. Frank, an opportunity was created by a thorough discussion of Dr. Frank's demographic history, along with the information covered by typical mental health agencies. The difference in Dr. Frank's assessment was the structure of the assessment. A thorough exploration of all aspects of a mental health and biopsychological assessment were explored in detail, rather than rushing through a checklist assessment.

This gives the social worker a unique opportunity to engage with the client and to learn who the client is, what he or she feels, and what the older adult client experienced in his or her lifetime. It is suggested that social workers should advocate eliminating the intake worker from mental health agency settings. The social worker who will be continuing with the older client's counseling should also assess the older client.

DISCUSSION TOPICS

If in a classroom setting, form several small groups. Each group creates an assessment of an older adult in the old-old age range (see Chapter 1, Theories to Inform the Clinician Practicing With Older Adults). Include information in all the assessment categories relevant for the older person being created. When finished, using the assessment just created, produce a new assessment for the same older adult as he or she would have presented in the following prior developmental periods:

1. Middle adulthood
2. Young adulthood
3. Adolescence
4. Childhood
5. Birth

By examining biopsychosocial factors that occur developmentally through a retrospective lens, this exercise helps develop an understanding of older adults. This will help sharpen your assessment lens with a greater comprehensive understanding of the contributions of prior developmental stages.

If done in small groups, share your findings and insights into the dynamic complexities of an older adult who presents for assessment. This may also be done as an individual exercise to help sharpen assessment skills.

CHAPTER 3

Intervention Theories Informing the Clinician Treating Older Adults

The optimal therapeutic relationship is not what is often called positive trans-ference. *Rather, it is one in which there is a state of* rapport *between therapist and patient.*

—Sidney Rosen, *My Voice Will Go With You: The Teaching Tales of Milton H. Erickson, M.D.*

An ideal therapist is a social worker. Any social worker is a gestalt of his or her history, training, and current life situation. The therapeutic alliance works based on the idea that the social worker is a willing participant whose primary concern is to provide support to an older client's effort for desired change. Knight (2004) finds that interpersonal psychotherapy is an effective method to help older adults adjust to the many health and social challenges that they confront. The relationship between the social worker and older adult client is a reciprocal process that entails the social worker understanding the older adult client and the older adult feeling a positive sense of recognition (Eriksen, Sundfor, Karlsson, Raholm, & Arman, 2012). This reciprocal relationship allows a shared experience in which the older adult has a greater degree of understanding of subsequent treatment and the social worker has the ability to comprehensively share his or her exper-tise (Clark, 2010; Hain & Sandy, 2013).

Unfortunately, today's mental health agencies that service older adults are influenced by managed care companies and Medicaid and Medicare policies that pressure a social worker to provide short-term psychotherapy that often spans just a few weeks. Miller (1996) feels that this effort by these agencies and government programs is in effect the rationing of mental health care. Many older adults are forced to accept limited short-term intervention when a long-term course of psycho-therapy would be appropriate, which defeats the underlying premise of the social worker being a willing and unconstrained participant in the therapeutic process.

In addition, this creates an ethical dilemma for the social worker. Van Heugten (2002) found that many social workers practicing in New Zealand enter private practice because they find that agency work demands that are not part of clinical practice cause ethical and philosophical dilemmas for them. By being free to apply systems-oriented theories to their work in private practice they are able to counter what they feel are negative influences often found in mental health agencies that embrace the medical model of a disease etiology: short-term psychotherapeutic intervention, pharmacotherapy, and, occasionally, electroconvulsive treatment (ECT).

When considering theoretical orientations to treating an older adult that are consistent with the short-term constraints found in most mental health agencies, one is faced with a multitude of theories, some extended for older adults, most created for younger adults. Cognitive behavioral therapy (CBT) and various interpersonal psychotherapies are effective for older adults, though an older adult's response to these therapies may have a different temporal course and require modifications in technique (Duffy, 1999; Galagher-Thompson & Thompson, 1996; Pinquart & Soerensen, 2001). Because of the chronic nature of psychological problems in older adults, the focus for the clinician shifts from resolution to support, repair of resiliency, and symptom management (Knight, Teri, Wohford, & Santos, 1995).

Bengston, Rice, and Johnson (1999) state that theories are sets of lenses that are used to understand what is observed in research. This metaphor can be extended to how a social worker can view an older adult from a multitude of theoretical viewpoints. Metaphorically, in Figure 3.1 a person would have three possible choices of what the picture is: that it is a picture of a cube with a dot on the front surface, or a cube with a dot on the rear inside surface, or a dot floating in the middle of the cube. Staring at the cube will cause the dot to appear on each of the choices, depending on what one is looking for. This author views this phenomenon as *believing is seeing*.

This optical illusion cannot be explained based on the retinal image because it is perceived as three dimensional even though retinal images are two dimensional. One's visualization of one's world is in three dimensions despite the two-dimensional limitation of retinas. This same illusion cannot be explained by knowledge because it defies knowledge. One knows that Figure 3.1 is not a three-dimensional cube and the dot occupies its own space on the paper. Seeing a cube in one's mind with various locations of

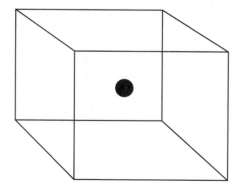

FIGURE 3.1 What do you believe? Is the dot on the back of the cube? Is the dot on the front wall? Or is the dot floating in the middle?

the dot suggest that past experience plays a role in what is seen. One readily agrees with suggestions of where the dot is. Past experience can include touching a three-dimensional cube and being taught that when lines are made consistent with Figure 3.1 a cube is represented.

ARE THEORIES AN UNCONTAMINATED VIEW OF AN OLDER ADULT?

A social worker uses a process analogous to the cube metaphor when assessing or treating older adults. Knowledge of a theoretical orientation is analogous to where the dot seems to exist. Knowledge of many theoretical orientations gives the clinician the accurate advantage of seeing an older adult from multiple perspectives, or as Bengston et al. (1999) stated, from multiple lenses. This clinical flexibility is advantageous to the older client, who can only benefit from a social worker's willingness and competence to assess and treat from a perspective that is client centered, addressing the unique needs, problems, and strengths that each older client brings to the practice arena. However, false information and stereotypes (see Chapter 4, Stigma and Older Adults) held by the social worker are views of older adults that more often than not cloud the clinician's lens, skewing his or her ability to view an older adult correctly.

SOURCES OF CONTAMINATION

Sorry, No Theory Available

The classic opaque lens is the orientation postulated by Sigmund Freud (1953). Freud indicated that adults age 50 or older are not candidates for psychoanalysis because learning stops at age 50. Obviously, if one followed this model, there would be no treatment for older adults. Consistent with Freud's attitude toward older adults, many contemporary psychotherapy theories are oriented to younger and middle-aged adults, or children, and then extrapolated to older adults by social workers seeking some guideline for treating an older adult.

Ageism

In a classic study, Butler (1969) describes a phenomena called *ageism* that is indicated by one having negative attitudes and stereotypes of older adults. These negative attitudes and stereotypes fuel a general tendency in some social workers to base their opinions about older persons on prior false information about the elderly. The false information accumulates, creating a history of biased impressions of older people that carries through to future interactions with older adults. This discrimination occurs simply because a person is viewed as being *old* (Schaie, 1993). Butler (1969) states that mental health professionals often perceive older clients as not being able to be helped by psychotherapeutic techniques. Discriminatory behaviors toward older adults are seen more often in men and younger people (Rupp, Vodanovich, & Crede, 2005).

Many social workers in training are unmotivated to engage in a psychotherapeutic relationship with an older adult. Lee, Volans, and Gregory (2003) feel that this phenomena is derived from a conception that an older adult is rigid in his or her ways and unable to change. In addition, Lee et al. feel that a younger social worker's reluctance to work with an older adult arises from his or her own anxiety about death and illness.

The New Ageism

In another classic study, Kalish (1979) describes a phenomenon in older professionals who, although being advocates for older adults, were found to have an age bias toward the clients they served. Kalish calls this phenomenon *new ageism.* Bodner and Lazar (2009) feel that this discriminatory behavior of older adults to older adults is a reflection of an aging process in which the discriminating actor had ageist views as a younger person and brought these views along a developmental process to old age. These authors call this phenomenon *self-ageism.*

Kalish (1979) suggests that older health professionals operating in the new ageism orientation stereotype their older clients as *less capable, less healthy, and less alert* in comparison to themselves. Kalish feels that the ageist older health professional viewing an older client as helpless and dependent will tend to recommend dispositions that will reduce the client's freedom and consequently restrict the older client from making decisions about his or her own life. Kalish suggests that this forced transformation from independent to dependent and helpless creates a *failure model* biasing an older health care professional's view of an older client. This model postulates that the older person is in a state of failure or is going to fail, if not on assessment then sometime thereafter. This orientation then gives rise to two additional failure models—the *incompetence model* and the *geriactivist model.*

The Incompetence Model

The incompetence model (Kalish, 1979) is an artifact of advocates of older people who, in a sincere attempt to advocate for funding of programs for older adults, make a case for the incompetence of older adults, thus creating a need for funding of specialized programs. These programs in turn facilitate the notion of incompetence in social and psychological functioning of the very older adults they intended to help. In effect, older clients are caught in a social paradox—to be made dependent and helpless by the very programs established to help them not be dependent or helpless.

The Geriactivist Model

The geriactivist model (Kalish, 1979) describes how older persons who become advocates for older adult clients identify with younger mental health professionals and, as a consequence, bias treatment decisions for the older people they are trying to help. By viewing older clients as helpless and dependent simply because they are seeking help and are not helpers like themselves, the older clients are viewed as failures because the only way they seem to be able to deal with their own problems is by seeking professional help.

THEORETICAL ORIENTATIONS FOR TREATING OLDER ADULTS

Most older adults who precede the baby boom generation have a reluctance to present for psychotherapy because of social learning that discouraged this cohort from expressing emotion throughout their development (Knight & Satre, 1999). In addition, Knight and Satre feel that members of this cohort are unaware of the availability of psychotherapy and do not understand the process of psychotherapy. In order to overcome these barriers, effective psychoeducational programs are needed to educate this cohort. This is extremely important because it is estimated that by the year 2030 there will be 14.4 million older adults suffering from psychological problems (Battels & Naslund, 2013). Many older adults in the current cohorts, like most adults, have a conception of psychotherapy as being the stereotypical psychoanalytic psychotherapy. The older adult will anticipate a limited response from the social worker, a pressure to free associate, lying on a couch rather than with face-to-face contact, and, of course, blaming his or her mother for everything that has happened in his or her life. Thus it is important for the social worker to be clear and assertive to the older adult regarding the social worker's theoretical orientation and how it differs from the stereotypes held by the client. This explanation should be free of jargon, using simple, easy-to-understand language to demystify complex theoretical orientations.

The following theoretical orientations are the lenses that this author uses when assessing (see Chapter 2, Assessing an Older Adult), formulating treatment plans, treating an older adult, making dispositions when treating older adults, and evaluating research conclusions. These models are easily adapted to the managed care, short-term environment of most agency settings and government-mandated restrictions on treatment length, as well as to a private practice setting.

FOUNDATIONS UNDERLYING EXISTENTIAL, BRIEF SOLUTION, COGNITIVE BEHAVIORAL, AND NARRATIVE THERAPIES

Empowerment Theory and the Strength Perspective

A social worker treating an older adult client must be aware of a phenomena described by Zarit (1980) whereby a therapist must be open to helping an older client rediscover dormant problem-solving skills rather than focusing on teaching an older client new skills. Paradoxically, this process of an older adult client rediscovering old problem-solving skills offers an opportunity to the social worker to discover in himself or herself new skills not yet learned, a phenomenon not often recognized by a social worker or described in the literature. Identifying an older adult's strengths is an essential aspect to all the therapies discussed here.

The concept of strength identification is consistent with Saleeby's (2009) concept that views a person presenting for therapy as having difficulty with systemic problems interfacing with environmental stressors rather than psychopathology represented by the medical model. Older adults are a minority experiencing oppression similar to the oppression that people of color experience. The social worker helps the older adult realize that achieving old age represents the ability to overcome numerous environmental stressors experienced over a lifetime. This recognition leads to a state of empowerment by an older adult understanding that one has a repertoire of positive, strength-based choices when interfacing with environmental stressors (Wachtel & Messer, 1997).

Constructivist Theory

Constructivist theory is a conceptual framework that is foundational to existential therapy, cognitive behavioral therapy, and narrative therapy. Each of these therapeutic orientations is discussed in subsequent sections. Constructivism stresses the concept that reality is a product of the perception of the perceiver and that there are as many realities as there are perceivers of reality (DiGiuseppe & Linscott, 1993; Neimeyer, 1993). Therefore, an older person has spent his or her lifetime as an active creator of his or her reality with cognitive constructs that are intimately related to internal feelings, affect, and behavior. When an older person needs to make a psychological change, a change must be made in his or her internal cognitive constructs or, more simply, his or her reality story. The role of a social worker practicing in any therapeutic orientation with a constructivist foundation is that of a facilitator and coauthor with the older client of new, strength-based, empowering cognitive constructs, or reality stories.

Existential Theory

Although there is a dearth of research on clinical applications of existential theory, existential psychotherapy has emerged as an effective and useful clinical tool despite its lack of quantification. Cooper (2003) feels that quantitative research on existential psychology is difficult because of the heterogeneity of techniques and orientations under the existential theoretical umbrella. Burston (1996) explains that existential thought, which is based on choice, self-consciousness, and the awareness of death, lends itself to qualitative analysis and rules out research applications from the scientific, quantitative world. Yalom (1980) argues that existential psychotherapy is seen as a marginal branch of mental health by more conventional psychotherapists.

Paradoxically, society is becoming more existential and more existential methods for successful coping are needed. Existential psychotherapy is extremely beneficial for the older adult client because it enables the client to feel his or her pain in the moment and have the social worker witness the older client's moment. This mutual experience of the older adult client's pain facilitates engagement and reinforces the element of safety that a social worker's office lends because the social worker sits as a nonjudgmental witness and an interactive participant (Knox & Hill, 2003). This sharing of the older client's pain changes the client's perspective of his or her pain to something less toxic and less dangerous and opens an opportunity for the client to view his or her pain as a response choice to one or many biopsychosocial stressors. This paves the way for therapeutic growth culminating in the client's realization that his or her choice of response to a biopsychosocial stressor may be changed to a more adaptive choice that in turn heightens his or her resilience to the biopsychosocial stressor.

Existential-phenomenological theory

Burston (1996) describes existential-phenomenological theory as a branch of existential theory. This theory focuses on primary life experience coupled with one or more themes. Burston describes how universal existential psychotherapy searches for meaning, authenticity, and transcendence, which are found in most writings of existential theorists. This search for meaning provides an older adult with positive psychological benefits, which include feelings of happiness and self-fulfillment (King, Hicks, Krull, & Del Gaiso, 2006; Steger & Kashdan, 2007). People experiencing happiness with a strong sense of meaning show reduced levels of health anxiety because of a strong sense of meaning acting as a stress moderator (Steger, Mann, Michels, & Cooper, 2009). Meaning serves as a catalyst for achieving positive psychological health (Ho, Cheung, & Cheung, 2010; Kleftaras & Psarra, 2012). Paradoxically, negative associations in meaning are associated with depression, anxiety, and substance abuse (Melton & Schulunberg, 2008; Schulunberg, Hutzell, Nassif, & Rogina, 2008) (see Chapter 5, Psychopathological Problems in Older Adults, and Chapter 8, Older Adult Substance Abusers).

The etiological assumption of these searches for meaning is found in the person-in-environment model, not as an outgrowth of biological disease as reflected in the medical model (see Chapter 1, Theories to Inform the Clinician Practicing With Older Adults). The medical model focuses on a brain disease, chemical imbalances, synaptic abnormalities, and damaged receptor sites. Existential phenomenological theory states that a person's process is derived from interpersonal experiences in the environment, the context of these experiences as set by the individual's cognitive constructs, and a person's ability to foresee a future. Burston (1996) equates a person's ability to shape his or her life as equality between one's choice and intentions with one's heredity and environment.

In a classic study, Estes (1979) postulated that choice for older adults is not based on what they can or cannot do but on lack of opportunity controlled by the political industrial economy. Estes feels that the dilemma of being older must be understood in the context of the labor economy and the inability of older people to participate in production. Laing (1960) feels that existential phenomenology is a process of a client trying to improve his or her life as an authentic self through the experience of achieving authenticity in the course of the therapeutic relationship, which is the phenomenon of the relationship (Rosen & Erickson, 1991).

The therapeutic relationship lends an opportunity for the social worker to expand his or her theoretical perception of the older adult by gaining experiential knowledge of the client's feelings and sharing this knowledge with the older adult client. In order to acknowledge the uniqueness of each client, Lawner (1981) suggests that the social worker approach each client from a position of *not knowing*, freeing the social worker to view the older client without contamination by expectations, preconceived ideas, stereotypes, and stigma in the existential moment. This approach to an older adult will increase the client's sense of well-being, which Fava and Ruini (2003) feel is the cornerstone for any successful psychotherapeutic relationship.

Frankl (1992) discusses the need for a person to have a purpose in order to move forward with his or her life. Without such purpose, a situation of being stuck is constructed, which is considered an existential vacuum. Keshen (2006) feels that a defensive reaction to an existential vacuum is the use of a purpose substitute in lieu of purpose—in other words, negative sideways movement rather than a positive forward movement with one's life (Figure 3.2). An existential vacuum is considered a symptom of the reduction of resilience to biopsychosocial stressors rather than psychopathology emanating from a disease process or synaptic failure within the brain.

Keshen suggests five types of purpose substitutions: *addictive, social, morally good, social status seeking,* and *unfulfilling engagement* (2006). The *addictive type* will show an older adult substituting repetitive compulsive activities such as substance abuse, pathological gambling, eating-disorder behaviors, excessive spending, and so on. The *social type* will engage in superficial relationships, produce drama as an attention-getting device, or join an organization for social acceptance without necessarily being interested in the organization. The *morally good* type will demonstrate altruistic behaviors and advocate for causes in an inauthentic manner. The *social status seeking* type will externalize self with symbols of money such as material goods or organizational positions (jobs, community organizations, political offices, country club memberships, etc.) that lend prestige

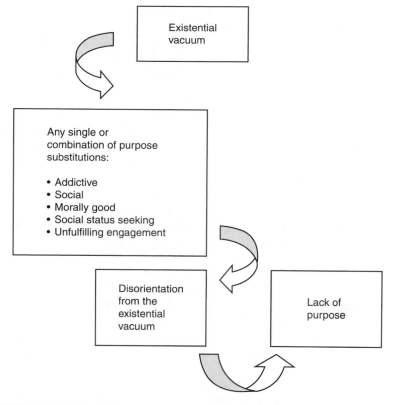

FIGURE 3.2 Existential vacuum, purpose substitutions, and lack of purpose.

and power. The *unfulfilling engagement* type will substitute with excessive activities such as long working hours, devotion to excessive television viewing, compulsive Internet use, overly rigid schedules, or other unfulfilling noninterpersonal activities.

An older adult employing purpose substitution creates an existential permanency of lack of purpose (see Figure 3.2). The goal of existential psychotherapy is to have the older adult choose to eliminate these substitutions and replace them with positive coping skills based on the older adult's strengths and problem-solving abilities. This will lead to an enhanced resilience to biopsychosocial stressors and a sense of empowerment and forward movement. By engaging in forward movement, an older adult can achieve self-actualization (Fava & Ruini, 2003; Lent, 2004; Maslow, 1968). Forward movement is facilitated by problem-solving techniques taught by the social worker to the older client (Luszczynska, Guttierrez-Dona, & Scgwarzer, 2005).

Cognitive Behavioral Theory

According to Beck (1979), the major mechanism that produces psychopathological states is the tendency in a client to distort reality by producing inaccurate, negative mind-sets. In cognitive behavioral therapy (CBT; Cuijpers et al., 2013) a social worker targets maladaptive thinking in the client and teaches the client to modify or replace inaccurate, negative mind-sets, or *cognitions*, with positive mind-sets grounded in reality. This change is created through different homework assignments agreed on by the social worker and the older client. Successful completion and application of the homework assignments facilitates a change in the way an older client feels, which in turn changes the client's behavior. Cuijpers et al. (2013) performed a meta-analysis of cognitive therapy research from 1966 to 2011. Cuijpers et al. indicate that cognitive restructuring is the core element of cognitive behavioral treatment. In addition, relaxation techniques and social skills education are essential subcomponents of cognitive restructuring. Neukrug (2011) feels that empathy is an important component in the success of cognitive behavioral therapy despite the fact that cognitive behavioral theorists have historically not embraced empathy as important.

The success of this therapeutic approach relies on the level of engagement the social worker creates with the older client and the older client's motivation to cooperate with the therapeutic process. Figure 3.3 illustrates that the linear presentation proposed by Beck is not all encompassing. A client may modify thoughts to change feelings, as proposed by Beck, or may modify behaviors that will in turn change feelings and thinking. It is also possible for a client to have a change in feelings that results in subsequent changes in thinking and behavior. Wilkinson (1997) feels that pathological thoughts, feelings, and behaviors created by an older adult arise from the older adult's tendency to exaggerate thoughts about losses caused by retirement and/or disability, fears of death, exaggerations of unpleasant events, and a negative view of the aging process.

Cognitive behavioral theory presents a technical challenge to an older adult's social worker. Knight (1999) suggests that a social worker's style of communication with an older adult must shift to a slower pace to accommodate slower information processing in older clients. As part of

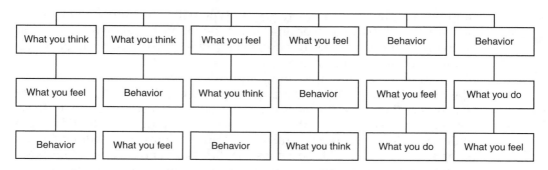

FIGURE 3.3 The process of cognitive theory.

this slowing-down process, Gallagher and Thompson (1996) feel that repeating new concepts and instructions throughout the therapy session helps the older adult incorporate homework instructions, which are a significant part of the cognitive behavioral process. Along with slowing down speech and repeating instructions, a social worker must keep an older client's focus in the here and now because older clients have a tendency for reminiscence (Butler, 1963), which interferes with the cognitive therapy process. A strategy for successful client learning is suggested by Zeiss and Steffen (1996), who indicate that repeating and summarizing material and assignments periodically throughout the cognitive behavioral psychotherapy session is more effective with an older adult than summarizing material and assignments at the conclusion of the session. It may be helpful to include a spouse, partner, roommate, or caregiver when giving homework instructions to the older client to provide support at home for doing the homework assignments. In addition to facilitating the homework process, the client shifts the emphasis of improvement from the social worker to his or her own efforts, which leads the older adult client to a feeling of empowerment.

Despite these difficulties, CBT is an evidence-based psychotherapy and an effective therapeutic orientation (see Chapter 5, Psychopathological Problems in Older Adults) for the treatment of depressive mood disorders (Arean, 2004). Stanley et al. (2003) find that CBT is effective for treating anxiety disorders, which are commonly seen in clinical practice with older adults. Because CBT is short term, Samuels (2004) suggests that referrals can be facilitated by primary care physicians, who explain the referral to a social worker as a way to improve the psychological condition the older adult is experiencing in a relatively short period. This is in contrast to explaining a referral in pathological terms suggesting that the older adult is ill and needs to be cured. However, Alvidrez and Arean (2002) indicate that most primary care physicians are unwilling to refer an older adult for psychotherapy and provide little education about psychotherapy to an older adult (Gask, 2013).

Narrative Theory

Koch (2000) makes an interesting point by emphasizing that most gerontological research is composed of outside observations of older adults. Koch proposes that the emphasis must be on getting to know an older person as a person rather than relying on external observations. Hence, narratives are an ideal way to have a personal encounter with an older adult. This is accomplished by the social worker listening to the telling of the older person's story and sharing the social worker's common experiences (Quillman, 2012) and by the older person reporting his or her observation of self and informing the social worker of his or her experience while telling the story (Korte, Bohlmeijer, Cappeliez, Smit, & Westerhof, 2012).

Because narrative therapy has a constructivist foundation, the meeting place for the social worker and the older adult is in the constructions, or reality stories, that the older client has created and modified over his or her lifetime. These stories are an ever-evolving definition of an older client's identity (Kenyon, Clark, & de Vries, 2001) and occur in the present. These constructed stories provide meaning for the older adult, which is created in the space between the client's observation (story) and the client's experience. Because this story is ever changing, it can keep the older client in a homeostatic position or skew the client into a meaning crisis. Patton (2002, p. 21) instructs that "to understand fully the complexities of many situations, direct participation in and observation of the phenomenon of interest may be the best research method." This technique of participant observation is analogous to an older client's process of communicating his or her experiences through narrative. The older client is able to enrich the presentation of his or her story with knowledge of events antecedent to the story and during the story and consequences from the story.

By joining the older client in his or her narrative, the social worker, in effect, becomes a participant observer of the client's narrative. The social worker, through a lens of *empathic neutrality* (Patton, 2002), joins the client in reformulating the client's narrative to facilitate the client in constructing a strength-based narrative reinforced by the social worker's empathic response to the older adult client (Carkhuff, 2009; Egan, 2010). By modifying his or her narrative, the older adult achieves an empowered state that causes a reduction of psychological conflict or resolution of one or more life problems. Kenyon (1996) termed this joining *biographical encounters*. This joining enables the social worker to help the client observe his or her story from many different diverse foci. These include gender, race, sociopolitical contexts, economic scenarios, or any other autobiographical emphasis that holds importance for the older client.

Luborsky (1993) cautions social workers to be aware that the biopsychosocial status of an older person determines the flexibility of the narrative of the older adult client (see Chapter 2, Assessing an Older Adult). So-called *normal* older adults tend to have narratives that follow the life stages and are open to various interpretations and representations. In contrast, a depressed older adult will tend to have narratives that are problem focused and are less flexible for alternative interpretations and representations. Rather than viewing this difference as fixed by psychopathology, the social worker can see a truncated narrative as a starting point to help the older client to achieve flexibility for alternative interpretations and representations.

Externalizing the reality story

White and Epston (1990) describe the power of a client to externalize his or her story, making it psychologically visual and public. This enables the older client to view his or her story objectively and to share the story with the social worker, allowing the older adult to collaborate with the social worker rather than to be stuck in an internal, isolated dialogue. This externalization of the older adult's narrative allows reality checking by the social worker and a greater understanding by the social worker of the older adult's experiences and associated feelings by creating an empathic bond (Carkhuff, 2009; Wampold, 2010).

This phenomenon of *externalizing the reality* story can be extended to family therapy, conjoint therapy with kin or substitute kin, or any conflicted interpersonal relationship the client may be experiencing. Multiple persons in conflict with the older adult simultaneously experience an externalized objective examination of the conflicts with each other and create an opportunity for the social worker to join with them in collaborative healing. This enables the social worker to experience comprehensive understanding of the client's experiences and associated feelings. This technique is called *collateral joining* (White & Epston, 1990).

Reauthoring: recognizing the power of choice

Reauthoring (Figure 3.4) an older adult's narrative enables the client to explore alternative stories and story outcomes for his or her narrative. The social worker uses reauthoring as an opportunity for the older client to draw on dormant problem-solving skills and the stories around them. Once dormant problem-solving skills are identified, the social worker helps the older adult client tell the story around each dormant problem-solving skill. Through this understanding of the relationship of a dormant problem-solving skill and a story, the client is then asked which of the dormant problem-solving skills can be applied to his or her current narrative. By the social worker joining the older adult in his or her authored story, the social worker, using supportive suggestions, becomes a coauthor of the narrative with the client. Eventually a sense of empowerment arises within the client, who begins to appreciate the power of authoring and reauthoring his or her narrative (Westerhof, Bohlmeijer, & Webster, 2010).

Reminiscence Therapy

Reminiscence is not unique to old age; people across the developmental scale reminisce. However, for older adults, reminiscence is a strength-based strategy often employed to validate a sense of intimacy with the past, to integrate the many transitions of life, and as a preparatory method for death (Webster, 1995). Butler (1963) cautions that although reminiscence is a useful therapeutic technique that older adults readily embrace, it can interfere with cognitive behavioral interventions by shifting the focus from the present to the past. However, coupling reminiscence with narrative therapy techniques can reverse this shift. Reminiscence may be used as a therapy unto itself (Haight & Webster, 1995) or may be used as an adjuvant to other therapies (Bohlmeijer, Westerhof, & Emmerik-De Jong, 2008; Peake, 1998).

Feminist Theory

Friedan (1963, 1993) makes an interesting association between the struggles of women and the struggles of aging adults. Friedan feels that the negative depiction of women through stereotype and false information is equivalent

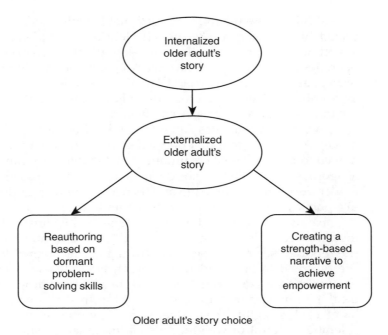

FIGURE 3.4 Reauthoring, recognizing the power of choice.

to the negative depiction of older adults through stereotype and false information (see Chapter 4, Stigma and Older Adults). Greene (2003) indicates
that age is a critical analytical category, along with ethnicity, nationality,
class, and sexuality, to avoid generalizations about women; understanding the complexity of these categories identifies women's uniqueness and
repertoire of strengths. For older women, the key to overcoming the limitations set upon them by outside forces is to break the mystification of aging
through education and advocacy, creating a positive experience of older
life. Simultaneously, women need to overcome the limitations caused by a
male-dominated society. This is important because the majority of older adults
are women who must confront the problems of widowhood, multiple chronic
illnesses, dementia, and economic hardships, as well as gender discrimination.

THE CASE OF HENRIQUA

Henriqua* is a 79-year-old Latina widow living alone in a suburban retirement community. For most of her adult life, Henriqua was a hard worker,
preferring work to other pleasures in life. She began her career when she
was 19 years old as an administrative assistant in a law firm. After working
in this position for 10 years, Henriqua decided to attend college at night
while retaining her position at the law firm. After 9 years of hard work and
study, she completed her undergraduate degree in English literature. At
age 38, Henriqua applied to law school, was accepted, and entered a part-
time, evening program. She continued working at her day job at the law
firm, which led to a promotion to a paralegal position.

---

*Names and other identifying information have been changed to preserve confidentiality.

While at law school, Henriqua met her husband, who had just completed his law degree. At age 41, Henriqua completed law school and joined her husband's small general-law practice. Henriqua and her husband devoted their lives to law, working long hours, sometimes 7 days per week. Early on in her marriage, Henriqua and her husband decided not to have children, feeling that their devotion to their legal work did not allow the time needed to be proper parents.

When Henriqua was 70 years old, her husband died from pancreatic cancer. At age 71 Henriqua decided to retire from law, sold her firm, and moved to the retirement community in which she currently resides. Used to a vigorous work schedule, she devoted her time to gardening, first in a small garden surrounding her patio and then a community garden she sponsored in a public park near her retirement community.

Faced with extraordinary problems of loneliness, Henriqua found herself working longer and longer hours in the community garden, which she reported seemed to block or distract her feelings of loneliness. When she returned to her residence at night, Henriqua was fatigued and had enough energy to just watch her favorite television program and eat a light meal. Not having time to cook, she got in the habit of bringing fast food home for her nightly meal. Over several months, Henriqua gained a considerable amount of weight. This alarmed her geriatrician who felt that her weight gain posed a significant health risk. This is the major reason Henriqua presented for therapy.

On assessment, it was discovered that Henriqua was severely depressed. She complained of crying nearly every day for the past month or so. She indicated that she is rapidly losing interest in her gardening and nothing else seems to give her pleasure. Henriqua is very angry that her husband died and feels nothing goes right for her. She lost her ability to concentrate, so she no longer reads or watches television, both activities that in the past helped her relax after a long day of gardening. Henriqua indicates that she has frequent thoughts of committing suicide, feeling that is would be better if she never woke again. When asked if she had a plan to kill herself, Henriqua indicated that she bought some sturdy rope from a nautical supply store and often visualizes hanging herself from her favorite tree in the neighborhood garden. Henriqua denied that she intends to do this; she just feels relief thinking about killing herself.

SUMMARY AND APPLICATIONS OF THEORETICAL ORIENTATIONS TO HENRIQUA'S CASE

This chapter introduced many theoretical orientations that inform the clinician when developing a treatment plan. The following is a view of Henriqua seen through the different theoretical lenses.

Henriqua Through the Optic of Existential–Phenomenological Theory

Henriqua's counseling began with constructing an understanding of her depressed symptoms as a reaction to the death of her husband and finding herself living alone in an existential vacuum (Figure 3.5). During this initial phase, the focus is on how these events caused feelings of loss for

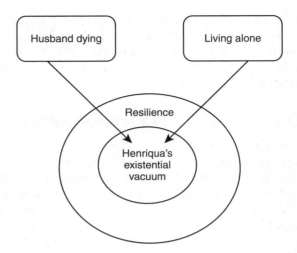

FIGURE 3.5 Biopsychosocial stressors converging on Henriqua, breaking through her resilience, and producing an existential vacuum.

Henriqua and dramatic changes in her life circumstances. Henriqua's symptoms were discussed in the context of the way in which she chose to react to her biopsychosocial stressors. Exploring Henriqua's role in choosing her reactions was done in the context that she has a responsibility for how she responds to a given stressor. Rather than seeing herself as a victim of circumstance, Henriqua gradually understood that her depressive symptoms were a manifestation of choosing a negative strategy for coping with the loss of her husband.

The next phase of Henriqua's counseling consisted of exploring the change in meaning in her life. Henriqua discussed in detail the amount of fusion that occurred with her husband and how when he died she felt that part of her also died. She described her fear of her own death, especially dying alone. Henriqua began to recognize that she lost her ability to foresee a future. After reaching a comprehensive understanding of the etiology of her depressive symptoms and her loss of meaning for forward movement in her life, Henriqua began to identify the purpose substitutions she embraced as maladaptive defenses to the existential vacuum she subsequently created. She was able to identify and accept that she chose an addictive type of purpose substitution (overeating) and an unfulfilling engagement type of purpose substitution (excessive gardening).

The final stage of Henriqua's counseling focused on responsibility and choice. Henriqua now recognized that any choice she made had a subsequent consequence. Being able to view this with acceptance rather than defensiveness enabled Henriqua to make new choices that would restore balance and meaning to her life. These choices included removing the purpose substitutions of overeating and excessive gardening. By initiating a weight-loss program with a nutritionist, she developed a sense of empowerment over her situation and felt that her life was starting to move forward. Henriqua cut back on her gardening to a time allocation that allowed her to enjoy gardening while enabling more free time for socialization with neighbors and friends from who she isolated herself. By rediscovering her strengths, she felt a returning purpose and forward movement in her life. She indicated that she still feels sad about her husband but now recognizes that part of her did not die with her husband, that she is a whole person, and eagerly looks forward to discovering new ways to define and express herself.

Henriqua Through the Optic of Cognitive Behavioral Theory

The beginning phase of Henriqua's counseling was spent defining her thoughts, feelings, and behaviors (Figure 3.6). Once identified, the social worker explored the relationships among her thoughts, feelings, and behaviors. Henriqua started keeping a thoughts–feelings–behaviors journal in which she would identify each thought, feeling, or behavior as it occurred, causing Henriqua to achieve an increased awareness of herself. Each week for the first 3 weeks she would review her journal with the social worker to reinforce her learning about the relationships in this triad of thoughts, feelings, and behaviors.

The next phase of counseling was an intervention phase, in which Henriqua developed new thoughts, or *cognitions,* that reframed her negative thoughts into positive ones. For example, when Henriqua thought that she was *fat and ugly,* she reframed it into *I'm a beautiful person who*

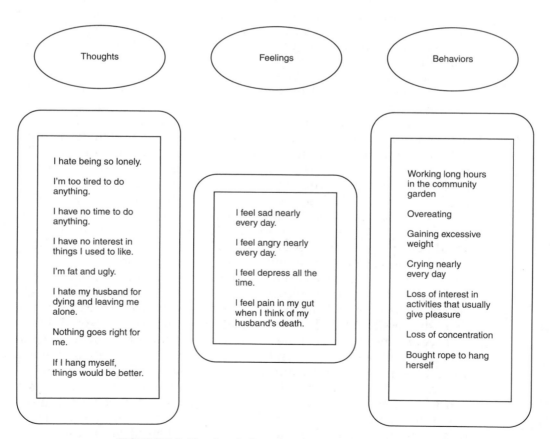

FIGURE 3.6 Henriqua's thoughts, feelings, and behaviors.

is going to start taking care of my body to feel better about myself. The social worker stressed to Henriqua the importance of developing her own positive thoughts rather than the social worker giving her a positive thought to use for the reframing process. This enabled her to feel a sense of control over her interventions and an ownership of her therapy produced a sense of empowerment.

Henriqua's behaviors were examined and she was able to suggest changes in her behaviors that she was willing to accomplish. These included consulting a nutritionist for dietary advice and returning the rope she bought to the hardware store to symbolically let go of her plan to hang herself. Henriqua continued to keep her thoughts–feelings–behaviors journal each day.

After 15 weeks of treatment Henriqua noticed changes in herself resulting from her efforts that become obvious and that were reflected in her thoughts–feelings–behaviors journal. She was able to initiate a weight loss; by 15 weeks, she'd lost 12 pounds since seeing the nutritionist at the fourth week. Henriqua no longer ate fast food and enjoyed spending time cooking meals planned with the help of her nutritionist. Her time spent in the community garden returned to the amount of time that was normal for her before her depression. Henriqua reported no longer feeling anger at her husband for dying, although she still missed his companionship. She began to watch her favorite television programs again. On follow-up at 6 months, Henriqua continued to maintain her thoughts–feelings–behaviors journal, which she now calls her *friend*. She reported that she no longer experiences the symptoms of depression that she reported at the initiation of her counseling. In addition, Henriqua reported that she has increased her socialization with her neighbors and has made many new friends.

Henriqua Through the Optic of Narrative and Reminiscence Theory

Henriqua's therapy began by Henriqua telling the social worker her story, reporting her observations of her past, and benefiting from the social worker being a witness to her story. Thus, Henriqua and the social worker were meeting in the stories of her lifetime and consequently achieved engagement. As her stories evolved, Henriqua was able to create a workable space between her present perceptions and her past experiences of her story. In addition, this gave the social worker an opportunity to participate in the story through editorial suggestions and active listening to and observation of Henriqua.

By joining with Henriqua, the social worker was able to help her reformulate her story into a strength-based narrative. This construction of a strength-based narrative enabled Henriqua to achieve an empowered state that caused her to relieve her feelings surrounding her husband's death. The immediate impact of externalizing her narrative allowed the social worker to help Henriqua lose her suicidal ideation and deal with her depression by substituting other choices based on prior strengths. Henriqua recognized the satisfaction she felt in the past when she studied English literature before going to law school. She decided to volunteer at a local high school to mentor students in writing and literature studies. This enabled Henriqua to break her isolation, rediscover the joys she experienced in the past through interpersonal contact, and develop new friends among the school's faculty and administration. Because Henriqua did not have a history of obesity, she felt that she "returned to myself" with her subsequent weight loss as her depression diminished.

Henriqua Through the Optic of Feminist Theory

The social worker, being sensitive and conversant with feminist theory, was able to be emphasize to Henriqua the atypical strengths she had as a younger woman who did not allow herself to be limited by the prejudice and negative stereotypes of women common to her cohort and oppressive to most women during Henriqua's development. The therapist pointed this out by having Henriqua acknowledge her accomplishment of becoming an attorney. In addition, Henriqua was encouraged to acknowledge her abilities to overcome the limitations and barriers derived from patriarchal social forces that were identified by her interactions with her social worker. This enabled Henriqua to realize that she was fully capable of coping with widowhood and loneliness.

DISCUSSION TOPICS

1. Using three different theoretical perspectives, discuss an older client with whom you are working. Note how your perception of the older client's problems differs from theoretical perspective to theoretical perspective.
2. Discuss an eclectic view of your older adult client by combining all three theoretical perspectives into one perspective. How does this eclectic viewpoint change your perception of your older client?

CHAPTER 4

Stigma and Older Adults

The fear of death haunts humans. . . . It is the main spring of human activity.
—Ernest Becker, *The Denial of Death*

Goffman, a pioneer in stigma studies (1963), indicates that the process of stigmatization reduces vulnerable people to a status of "less than" persons having *spoiled identities*. This status of spoiled identities aggregates individuals into minority groups based on labeling—too old, Black, transgender, poor, ill, gay male, lesbian, and so on. Meyer (1995) feels that stigma arises from interpersonal interaction. The stigmatized people internalize views of self based on the views of others who view stigmatized people as "less than," and based on a value system held by the majority (Cavelti, Kvrgic, Beck, Rusch, & Vauth, 2012). This phenomenon occurs when a majority group's worldview discriminates against a minority group not representing their worldview (Burke, Martens, & Fauchner, 2010).

With respect to older adults, unfortunately, they symbolically represent people nearing mortality. Therefore, a dual process occurs: Older people are stigmatized by others and also self-stigmatize. By identifying with the stigma propagandized in the public arena, older adults will convert a stigmatizing concept into an internalized *self-stigma*, or a process of endorsement of the propagandized stigma (Cavelti et al., 2012).

Dovidio, Major, and Fan (2000) indicate that stigma occurs when individuals are devalued by society because of physical deformities, psychological problems, or medical illnesses. This devaluing subjects individuals to prejudice, discrimination, and stereotyping. Link and Phelan (2001) feel that stigma is a reciprocal process in which social institutions that stigmatize and exclude target groups act in synergy with individuals who are represented in the excluded category. In addition, according to Goffman (1963), the stigmatized individuals are not the only ones to be tainted by stigma; their relatives, friends, and loved ones are stigmatized as well. Goffman calls this phenomena *courtesy stigma*. This phenomenon is also reported by Corrigan, Watson, and Miller (2006) and Ostman and Kjellin (2002).

Stigma is the foundation that distorts the many social constructs affecting how social workers view older adults. According to Crowther and Zeiss (2003), the heterogeneity seen in older cohorts is more diverse than in younger age groups. This diversity has profound influences on how social workers who are biased about certain ethnic and cultural subgroups view older clients (Jackson & Samuels, 2011; Williams & Mohaemd, 2009). For example, when looking at ethnicity in older American adults, the Office on Aging, Department of Health and Human Services (2010) indicates the following statistics on the diversified subgroups of older adult Americans: 45,942,504 Whites in 2010, reaching 64,360,470 in 2050; 4,274,333 Hispanics in 2010, reaching 22,642,470 in 2050; 4,942,504 Blacks in 2010, reaching 13,020,151 in 2050; 309,189 American Indians and Native Alaskans in 2010, reaching 837,328 in 2050; 2,014,022 Asians in 2010, reaching 9,488,038 in 2050; 51,338 Native Hawaiians and Pacific Islanders in 2010, reaching 216,295 in 2050. Another complication in working with diverse populations in that by the year 2050 it is estimated that 20% of Americans (one in five) will be from a multiracial background (Jackson & Samuels, 2011). The Office on Aging reports 382,474 multiracial older American in 2010, reaching 1,472,535 in 2050. Therefore, social work diversity education needs to recognize multiracial populations as an additional subgroup because of the complex aspects of their identities and cultures.

EXAMPLES OF OPTICS AFFECTED BY STIGMA AND THEIR SUBSEQUENT EFFECTS ON OLDER ADULTS

Many socially constructed optics produced by stigma can bias social workers' views of older people (Figure 4.1). Whether by a single optic or a combination of optics, social workers are at risk of becoming biased

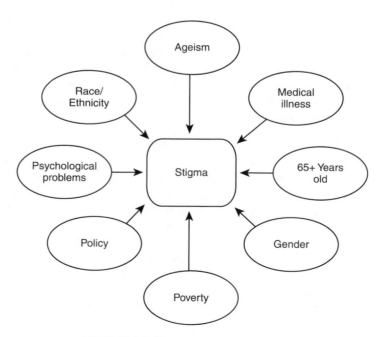

FIGURE 4.1 The many lenses of stigma.

toward older adult clients. These biases affect client care by producing underservice of stigmatized older adults or no service at all. Older adult clients in turn internalize perceived stigma from others, causing them to engage in self-stigma, which exacerbates the consequences of biased treatment from social workers. Throughout the world, stigma is recognized as the major socially constructed barrier for people in need of mental health or psychological services (Satorius et al., 2010). Given this international phenomenon of stigma-created barriers for essential medical and psychiatric services, an effort must be made for more evidence-based studies to develop strategies to ameliorate stigma-created barriers (Satorius et al., 2010; Weiss & Ramakrishna, 2006).

Ageism

This author feels that the etiology for ageism resides in *terror management theory*. Terror management theory is based on the *theory of generative death anxiety* first discussed by Becker (1973), which describes the anxiety experienced by people knowing that their death is inevitable. Greenberg, Pyszczynski, and Solomon (1986) extend the theory of generative death anxiety by explaining that people unconsciously engage in behaviors to avoid the knowledge of their ultimate mortality. This extension forms the foundation of *terror management theory*.

Greenberg and Arndt (2011) feel that death anxiety is the most intense form of anxiety chronically experienced by people. Death anxiety is an existential anxiety, which, unlike more acute anxiety that is experienced with conscious awareness, is experienced unconsciously (Windielman & Berridge, 2004). One defense against this existential anxiety is *in-group bias/ out-group prejudice* (Greenberg et al., 1990). Therefore, younger children and young and middle-aged adults may form prejudices against older adults, who are the ultimate symbolic representation of upcoming death, as a maladaptive way to alleviate their unconscious existential anxiety about their own mortality. This attitude of younger children, young adults, and middle-aged adults toward older adults is called ageism.

A comprehensive discussion of the classic ageism theories of Butler (1969) and Kalish (1979) (*new ageism, incompetence model*, and *geriactivist model*) are found in Chapter 3, Intervention Theories Informing the Clinician Treating Older Adults.

There are four types of ageism: institutional, personal, intentional, and unintentional (Anti-Ageism Task Force, 2006). *Institutional ageism* occurs when institutions create rules and practices that discriminate against older people. *Personal ageism* occurs when other people view older people as incompetent or incapable. *Intentional ageism* occurs when attitudes and rules that discriminate against older people are maintained even though they are recognized as age biased. *Unintentional ageism* occurs when there is no recognition that attitudes and rules are discriminatory against older people.

Barrett, Street, and Whiteford (2004) studied university undergraduates' drawings of older people. They found that their drawings reflected the stigmas of older people being ugly, in some state of dementia, asexual, and paradoxically predominantly male given that the older population is primarily female. Barrett et al. postulate that this inaccurate representation of men being the majority in old age is a phenomenon of gender bias reflecting predominant views of women as necessary caretakers of older men. Therefore, in reality, the focus is on men who are in the minority, not on women, who are the majority. These findings are consistent with analysis of adolescent drawings at Michigan's Gender and Achievement Research Program (Siegal, 2005).

Knight and Satre (1999) indicate the importance of recognizing age cohorts as a diverse category. They feel that learning the folkways and worldviews of the different age cohorts of older adults is equivalent to a social worker's responsibility to be aware of multicultural differences in older adults. In addition, cohort attitudinal differences produce ageism between the different older adult cohorts mirroring the phenomena found in the geriactivist model (see Chapter 3, Intervention Theories Informing the Clinician Treating Older Adults).

Race/Ethnicity/Sexual Orientation

It is important for a social worker to understand that race, ethnicity, and sexual orientation are social constructs that bias clinical care. In addition, stigma associated with race, ethnicity, and sexual orientation produce psychosocial stressors that converge on older clients, which exacerbate their physical and psychological health statuses (T. N. Brown, Sellers, Brown, & Jackson, 1999; D. R. Williams & Mohaemd, 2009).

For example, being in a partnered or marital relationship is a critical form of emotional and financial support for older people. Unfortunately, most research is oriented to heterosexual coupling. There is a dearth of information about gay male and lesbian couples (see Chapter 11, Gay Male, Lesbian, Bisexual, and Transgender Older Adults). However, there is a current initiative to establish programs to combat homophobia as a stigmatizing force (D. Altman et al., 2012). Whether married or partnered, coupling provides a defense against loneliness, access to a confidant, mutual economic support, and an opportunity for sexual intimacy. The stigma of race/ethnic/sexual orientation categories has a discriminating effect on partnerships and marriage.

Even though older men are more likely to be married than older women, Asians/Pacific Islanders and Whites are more likely to be married than Hispanics, Native Americans, and Blacks (American Community Survey 2005 Questionnaire, 2005). Black people who are married report lower satisfaction with marriage than married White people, which suggests additional stigmatized socioeconomic–political intersections that discriminates Whites from Blacks (Connidis, 2001). However, African American older married people show greater adaptability in sharing domestic chores than their White counterparts (Stoller & Gibson, 2000). This greater adaptability in roles is thought to be a paradoxical strength that arose from enslavement, when African families were forced by circumstance to be flexible in roles such as caretaking, having extended family and friends substituting caretaking responsibilities for family members forcibly separated during the period of enslavement. Unfortunately, this aspect of African American history receives little attention in gerontology research (McKinney, Harel, & Williams, 1990).

Lack of health care information is seen in older people from inner-city minority populations (M. V. Williams, Davis, Parker, & Weiss, 2002). Even though it is suggested that older African Americans be given Internet training to expand their access to health care information (Detlefsen, 2004), this population is affected by the intersection of poverty and race. Poverty limits their ability to have Internet access. Consequently, when older African Americans do not have Internet access, they have limited access to diversified health information. A predictor for higher rates of Internet access for health care information is found in older cohorts who have higher education levels and are not impoverished (Wagner & Wagner, 2003).

Underutilization of service by Latinas and African American women and men appears to be determined by a lower socioeconomic status and social value constraints (Ojeda & McGuire, 2006). Miranda et al. (2005) find that in order to provide mental health services to minority groups, cultural and language competence is required by the providing social workers, who must be flexible and willing to modify existing therapeutic modalities that are relevant to and historically developed for the White majority. This is critical because minorities are less likely than Whites to seek mental health services (Alegria et al., 2002; Husaini et al., 2002; Miranda & Cooper, 2004; Swartz et al., 1998).

African Americans show lower levels of life satisfaction when compared with Whites (Hughes & Thomas, 1998) and have higher levels of psychological problems when compared with Whites (Gray-Little & Hafdahl, 2000). However, when studying self-esteem levels, no difference is found between African Americans and Whites. Most likely, the higher levels of psychological problems in African Americans are related to greater amounts of psychosocial and economic stressors and an environment fraught with discrimination. Williams and Harris-Reid (1999) find that, like African Americans, Mexican Americans and Asian Americans exhibit psychological distress that is linked to perceptions of discrimination.

Gender

According to Calasanti and Kiecolt, gender relations are "inequalities of wealth, authority, labor, and esteem between the sexes that are supported by ideologies that justify men's greater privilege in most settings" (2007, p. 10). This is most important when considering the effects of gender inequality and how they are exacerbated when intersecting with other optics of stigma affecting older women. Gender discrimination is linked to deleterious effects on psychological health (Ferrie et al., 2006).

Women represent a greater percentage of older people than men, yet older men have a greater likelihood of being married than older women (Connidis, 2001). Older men appear to be more satisfied with marriage than older women unless the marital dyad reports equality in decision making; then older women report greater satisfaction than older men (Kulik, 2002). This phenomenon is biased by a heterosexual optic of marriage that does not illuminate the special problems of older lesbian, gay male, bisexual, and transgendered people whose abilities to marry are hampered by social policies, norms, and laws (Connidis, 2006; see Chapter 11, Gay Male, Lesbian,

Bisexual, and Transgender Older Adults). Although there is a dearth of studies on gay male, lesbian, bisexual, and transgender relationships, nevertheless, findings show that lesbians tend to favor monogamous relationships throughout generational life stages, whereas gay men tend to favor monogamous relationships as older people (Connidis, 2006; Huston & Schwartz, 1995). Older people who live together as an alternative to marriage tend to not own their homes, to not have adequate health insurance, and to have limited social networks. Older people living together tend to consume alcohol at a higher rate than married older people (S. L. Brown, Lee, & Bulanda, 2006) (see Chapter 8, Older Substance Abusers). Another trend in heterosexual couples is *living apart together* relationships in which monogamy, love, and commitment are embraced while living in separate residences. This trend in older relationships lessens conflict about inheritances to children from prior marriages, not being subjected to blending issues from prior marriages, and enables each partner to maintain his or her familiar routine (Borell & Ghazanfareeon Karlsson, 2003; Connidis, 2006; Ghazanfareeon Karlsson & Borell, 2005).

When examining men and women who struggle with depression (see Chapter 5, Psychopathological Problems in Older Adults), women have an incidence of depression that is 1.5 to 3 times that of men (Kessler et al., 2003). This is critical because many studies have shown that women use mental health services at a greater rate than men, which may cause an underservice to men, who are not as visible to the mental health system as women (Mojtabai, Olfson, & Mechanic, 2002; Narrow et al., 2000; Olfson et al., 2002). Ryff, Keyes, and Hughes (2003) found that women feeling high levels of discrimination in their lives have a lower eudemonic well-being. This is reflected in diminished feelings of growth, mastery, autonomy, and self-acceptance.

Poverty

Youdin and Cleaveland (2006) found that social work students' attitudes toward impoverished older people are determined by religious affiliation, which may have a consequence of some social workers not servicing or underservicing older poor clients. Students with a secular orientation had the most positive attitude toward old poor people, with Jewish orientation having the second most sympathetic attitude, followed by Christian/Catholic, and Christian/Protestant having the most negative attitude toward older impoverished people. Ojeda and McGuire (2006) report that mental health services use by minorities is determined by financial and social barriers. McGuire et al. (2002) feel that availability of psychotherapy services and pharmacotherapy is essential to minimizing the severe financial consequences depressive disorders have on minority populations. Severe financial consequences of depressive disorders cause economic pressure that, combined with other debt-service payments, causes considerable jeopardy for older minority people. Because most poor or middle-class people approaching or recently passing 65 years of age have high levels of debt service, these obligations are prompting an increase in bankruptcy filings. This is a critical problem for older adults because it delays or prevents retirement and adds jeopardy to an already vulnerable population. Sullivan, Warren, and Westbrook (2006) offer competing theories of stigma to explain the increase in bankruptcy filings. The *reduced stigma hypothesis* states that there is less stigma associated with bankruptcy than in the past, causing people to have recurrent debt problems that are reflected in repeated bankruptcy filings. An opposite theory is the *increased stigma hypothesis*, which states that economic forces propel more people into bankruptcy, while increasing stigma prevents more families from filing bankruptcies. The increase in filings is thought to be the result of increased economic pressure from banks, mortgage brokers, and credit card institutions that cause greater debt services in the population. However, these numbers of filings do not reflect the number of families that withhold bankruptcy filings because of social stigma. It is thought that these families feel that bankruptcy is less private, with Internet records and disclosure to potential employers, neighbors, and family members.

Policy

Older Americans are being demonized and blamed for inadequate service provision to younger Americans. Callahan (1987) warns of an upcoming bankruptcy of the health care system because of the high utilization by older people. Preston (1994) indicates that advocates for children blame older Americans who receive government funding and benefits for causing inadequate funding for food, housing, and education for children. Altman and Shactman (2002) identify a trend in the media of blaming the aging baby boom generation for creating funding problems for Social Security and Medicare that place the burden to pay for these services on younger Americans. This fear and prejudice toward older people is palpable in the concern that organized older people may consolidate political power worldwide, creating a *political titan* that may instigate intergenerational war in developed countries (Peterson, 1999). Campbell believes that the root of this bias toward older Americans is paradoxical. By being successful beneficiaries of governmental policies, older adults in turn are demonized for their success by younger policy makers (Campbell, 2003).

Currently, the National Council on Aging (2012) reports that there are several policy issues that have a negative impact on older adults. These issues include senior program funding cuts, with major reductions in housing, energy, and employment assistance for low-income seniors; and long-term care insurance under the Affordable Care Act, called Community Living Assistance Services and Supports Program (CLASS), which would facilitate older adults aging in place rather than spending down assets and savings to qualify for Medicaid or entering a nursing home for care. Unfortunately, a Republican-led initiative in Congress has suspended this program because many members feel it should be repealed. In addition, Congress is trying to reduce access to *Meals on Wheels* programs as part of the Republican-led deficit-reduction initiative.

Ageism has a continued presence in the workplace. McCann finds that even though the *Age Discrimination and Employment Act* has been in place for more than 35 years, age discrimination continues to deny employment opportunities to older people (McCann, 2003). A classic example of employment discrimination against older people is described by Bendick,

Brown, and Wall (1999). Their study had a younger worker (32 years old) and an older worker (57 years old), both male, apply for the same entry-level job, with the same credentials, to 102 companies. The younger worker received 58.8% more offers than the older worker, which clearly illustrates the barriers for people over the age of 50 in need of employment. Consistent with the international phenomenon of discrimination against older adults, Jopling (2007) indicates that even though legislation was passed in 2006 banning age discrimination in the workplace and work training in the United Kingdom, this legislation does not protect people past the age of 65.

Psychological Problems

The stigma of mental illness (see Chapter 5, Psychopathological Problems in Older Adults) serves to increase the suffering of older people struggling with psychological problems while also increasing the suffering of family members, loved ones, and caregivers who experience *courtesy stigma* (Corrigan, Watson & Miller, 2006; Goffman, 1963; Ostman & Kjellin, 2002; Shrivastava, Bureau, Rewari, & Johnston, 2013). The stigma of having mental illness constructs a barrier to the older adult suffering with mental illness, which in turn hinders the older adult to return to a healthy mental state (Shrivastava et al., 2013). In the United States, *institutional stigma* constructs a delay barrier for initial treatment after onset of symptoms for those suffering from depression (delay of 8 years) or drug and alcohol problems (delay of 5 years; Wang et al., 2005).

Mak and Wu (2006) feel that when clients experience psychotic disorders they blame themselves for causing their disorders and consequently experience an intense amount of self-stigma (Sarisoy, et al., 2013). When these clients are taught to reframe the etiology of their disorders to psychosocial, environmental, and biological sources, self-stigma is reduced or eliminated. If not intervened upon quickly and effectively, self-blame can lead some individuals to commit suicide as a maladaptive strategy to escape such stigma (Gomez, Miranda, & Polanco, 2011; Pompili, Mancinelli, & Tararelli, 2003).

The *Diagnostic and Statistical Manual of Mental Disorders,* third edition (*DSM-III*; American Psychiatric Association [APA], 1980a) set the stage for current labeling of people struggling with psychological problems and associating these psychological problems with treatment, primarily with psychiatric medications. Wilson (1993) feels that the *DSM-III* conveniently served the interests of the pharmaceutical industry, regulatory agencies, and insurance companies by having a diagnostic labeling system that could be tied to types of treatment, duration of treatment, and a system for assigning medications for treatment of psychiatric diagnoses. The transition from the *DSM-I* (APA, 1952) and *DSM-II* (APA, 1968), both of which are anchored to psychoanalytic treatment, to the *DSM-III*, laid the foundation for making older people's psychological problems the province of psychiatry and pharmacy. The *DSM-IV-TR* (APA, 2000) and the next (current) version, the *DSM-5* (APA, 2013a), in part categorize psychological problems that many older people struggle with and facilitate the convenience and utility of psychopharmacological agents as a treatment of choice for most agencies and hospital-based programs treating older people. According to Healy (2002), "The 1980s and 1990s handed over to pharmaceutical companies the power to decide when and for what diagnoses should drugs be prescribed through aggressive advertising, promotion perks from pharmaceutical reps, and from demands by consumers influenced by radio and television advertising" (p. 314).

Corrigan (2007) indicates that clinical social workers facilitate stigmatization of their clients as a consequence of using diagnostic categories that reinforce public perceptions that people with psychological problems belong to groups that are considered less than or different from the majority. Corrigan indicates that stigmatizing people with psychological problems can lead to noncompliance with treatment or no treatment because clients needing help wish to avoid the negative effects of the stigma resulting from the diagnostic label. This is especially of concern to social workers treating older people, who are vulnerable by age, and this vulnerability is exacerbated when stigmatized by a psychiatric label. Courtesy stigma occurs when, for example, family members who are in the position of facilitating assessment and treatment of a person suffering from schizophrenia distance themselves from the suffering relative, preventing subsequent referral for mental health services (S. Lee, Lee, Chiu, & Kleinman, 2005). These authors found that stigma toward mental illness is greater than stigma toward a person suffering from diabetes, a much more socially acceptable illness.

When family members experience courtesy stigma (Goffman, 1963), the result is often family dysfunction and social isolation (Corrigan, Edwards, Greene, Diwan, & Penn, 2001; Feldman & Crandall, 2007). This psychiatric labeling effect extends to older people who, because they are considered mentally ill, are underserviced by general medical care providers (Druss, Bradford, Rosenheck, Radford, & Krumholz, 2000). Older people have greater difficulty obtaining safe housing and employment when viewed as psychiatric patients (Feldman & Crandall, 2007). Older people seeking psychological services often face clinicians with negative views of older adults, leading to misdiagnosis of psychological problems or lack of enthusiasm for treating older people because of assumed inaccurate, limiting prognoses (Goodstein, 1985). Diagnostic errors include older people reporting symptoms of depression that are attributed by the social worker as normal to old age (Zarit, 1980), or anxious symptoms that are attributed to irritability or senility (Goodstein, 1985). James and Haley (1995) attribute this bias to stigma constructs of physical aspects of aging. Crystal, Sambarmoorthi, Wallup, and Akincigil (2003) attribute misdiagnosis to lack of knowledge about older people by mental health clinicians. Bentancourt (2004) suggests that because older Americans are becoming more diverse, if health care providers increase their knowledge of diverse groups, they will increase the probability of their communication to diverse older clients, which will subsequently improve treatment compliance and outcomes and lessen the impact of stigma.

Butler and Lewis (1983) state that mental health professionals often perceive older clients as not able to be helped by psychotherapeutic techniques. This is reflective of the shift from psychoanalytic treatment to psychopharmacologically oriented treatment with the introduction of the *DSM-III* and is consistent with a longitudinal trend started by Freud (1953), who indicated that adults age 50 or older are not candidates for psychoanalysis because learning stops at age 50. These attitudes are based on false information and stereotypes that facilitate stigmatization of older people. Older clients are often viewed as childlike or nice grandparents, and therefore clinicians tend to take a paternalistic stance with them that compromises assessment, treatment plans, and disposition (Edelstein & Kalish, 1999; Hovath & Bedu, 2002; Newton & Jacobowitz, 1999). In the United Kingdom, government assistance for mental services is limited or in some cases arbitrarily cut off to people older than age 65 (Jopling, 2007). Weiner (1995) claims that the biological theory of mental illness reduces stigma attributed to clients suffering from mental illness. This finding is disputed by Read and Harre (2001), who find that stigma increases as a result of viewing people suffering from psychological problems as being ill or having a biological illness.

The stigma of suffering from mental illness may also prevent an older person from seeking treatment for his or her psychological problems (Bayer & Peay, 1997; Bucholz & Robins, 1987). This limitation on seeking mental health services becomes critical in rural areas where there is a dearth of social workers, leaving most mental health intervention to primary care physicians (Komiti, Judd, & Jackson, 2006). It is felt that this hesitation to seek help for mental health problems is magnified because of the social enmeshment in rural communities and the lack of personal anonymity (Barney, Grifiths, Jorm, & Christensen, 2006 January)

Compton, Esterberg, McGee, Kotwicki, and Oliva (2006) report that police officers, another type of service provider to older people, have negative views of people suffering from schizophrenic spectrum disorder. Police officers view these people as having the potential for violence. It is found that crisis intervention training can reduce these negative attitudes. Pre- test and post-test attitudinal scores improved because of crisis intervention training focusing on providing accurate information on schizophrenic spectrum disorder. This is consistent with findings by Phelan and Link (1998), who indicate that in the United States people perceived as suffering from mental illness are viewed as being violent, causing more people to discriminate against them (Corrigan, Greene, Lundin, Kubiak, & Penn, 2001). This discrimination by police officers responding to psychiatric emergencies may be exacerbated by a lack of knowledge and understanding of older people. Sever and Youdin found that police officers' knowledge and understanding of older people can be increased by education and training (2006).

Compounding the problems faced by being placed in a stigmatized group by psychiatric labels, clients will engage in self-stigmatizing by internalizing the devaluation by others and engaging in dialogue that is self-depreciating and, in turn, self-stigmatizing (Link & Phelan, 2001; Meyer, 1995; Ritsher, Otilingam, & Grajales, 2003). Corrigan, Watson, and Barr (2006) describe three states of self-stigma: *stereotype agreement, self-concurrence, and self-esteem decrement.* Self-esteem decrement is described by Schmeichel et al. (2009) as a key indicator of a person's reaction to stigma. If there is a strong sense of self-esteem, the effects of stigma are attenuated. Corrigan, Watson, and Barr (2006) indicate that there is a difference between public stigma and self-stigma. In order for self-stigmatizing to occur, the older person has to believe the stigmatizing of older people by the public. This is consistent with Link (1987), who feels that in order for an older person to experience self-stigma, he or she must embrace and internalize lay stereotypes of mental illness in early childhood and carry these perceptions and stereotypes throughout adulthood. In the case of psychological problems, self-stigmatizing exacerbates the stigma of suffering from psychological problems, causing greater debilitation in older people, even though the self-stigma did not emanate from depression. In addition, the self-stigma becomes a risk factor for suicide in a depressed older adult (Pompili et al., 2003).

An art exhibit in England featured a bust of Sir Winston Churchill in a straightjacket. This exhibit was titled Black Dog, the name given by Churchill for his depression (Storr, 1988). Rather than an insult to Churchill, the artist used it as an antistigma metaphor demonstrating the need to remove stigma from people suffering from psychological problems. Churchill struggled with depression, as did Teddy Roosevelt, Abraham Lincoln, and Ronald Reagan; composers Chopin and Handel; astronaut Buzz Aldrin; and many other accomplished people (London, Scriven, & Lalani, 2006). Stigma is an unnecessary burden that serves to exacerbate the pain of depression by superimposing shame for experiencing depression.

Medical Illness

The stigma of medical illness (see Chapter 7, Medical Problems in Older Adults) affects all levels of society, including all age groups. Some American presidents were deeply affected by the stigma of medical illness. "George Washington nearly died of pneumonia in 1790," concealing his illness from the American public as admitted by Thomas Jefferson to a friend (Malone, 1951, p. 267). "Grover Cleveland underwent a life-threatening operation in 1883 to remove a huge cancerous lesion from his jaw: the White House described it as a minor dental problem involving an infected tooth" (Nevins, 1932, p. 530). "When Woodrow Wilson suffered a major stroke in 1919, nothing remotely truthful was revealed about his condition until after he had left office the following year" (Weinstein, 1981, p. 348). The same can be said of Franklin D. Roosevelt who hid most of his polio symptoms from the public (Oshinsky, 2005), continuing the precedent for secrecy surrounding a president's health that started with George Washington and is followed to this day.

Callahan (1987, p. 20) warns that older people represent a "demographic, economic, and medical avalanche" that has the potential to bankrupt health care resources for younger adults and children. Rather than reassessing why the health care system in the United States is failing to serve all age groups, stigmatizing older people as potential victimizers of younger people's health care causes a phenomenon of underservice of the medical needs of older people and further increases prejudice toward older people. Paradoxically, stigmatized older adults are at greater risk for health problems, which in turn creates a greater burden on the health care system (Williams & Mohaemd, 2009). Lee, Hatzenbuehler, Phelan, and Link (2013) feel that it is unfair to blame stigmatized older adults for the inadequacies in the health delivery system. Lee et al. contend that older people are unfortunately caught in the intersection of social, economic, and health stressors.

Underservice as a result of stigma is also seen in the approximately 1 million people in the United States who have HIV/AIDS (Schneider, Glynn, Kajese, & McKenna, 2006). Underservice is evidenced by delays in or refusal for HIV testing (Chesney & Smith, 1999), with a consequence of increased high-risk sexual behaviors (see Chapter 9, Older Adult Sexuality) (D. B. Preston, D'Augelli, Kassab, & Starks, 2007) and underservice by HIV agencies (Schuster et al., 2005). Even though older people with HIV/AIDS suffer from the double stigma of being old and having HIV/AIDS, Emlet (2006) finds these older people report experiencing ageism and HIV/AIDS stigma separately, rather than as a combined force. Carr and Friedman (2005) find that severely obese people report being denied health care or receiving inferior health care because of their obese status. This finding occurred throughout the lifecycle in their sample, which studied adults 25 to 74 years of age. Many older adults suffering from neurological diseases that cause them to have tremors, difficulty walking, visual ticks, awkward postures, and speech impairments suffer from *neurological stigma* (Friedman, 2013).

Impoverished African Americans and older poor African Americans prefer to get medical information from their health care providers or established sources (Detlefsen, 2004), which makes them vulnerable to information biased by health care providers or institutions influenced by stigma. Weinick, Jacobs, and Stone (2004) find that older Latino Americans are not homogenous but rather vary by culture and socioeconomic class determined by country of origin, and this variance of diversity is evidenced by differences in health care needs. Similar results are found in Native Americans and Asian and Pacific Islanders (Kagawa-Singer, Wellisch, & Durvasula, 1997; D. Williams & Wilson, 2001). Certain medical conditions tend to carry their stigma from generation to generation despite advances in medical care and medical knowledge. For example, in Japan, despite a 1996 law banning forced institutionalization for Hansen's disease (leprosy), older Japanese adults who were recently deinstitutionalized by this law still experience stigma by being banned from hotels and spas and experience fear of being rejected by neighbors if they return to their homes (McCurry, 2004). This follows a history of forced sterilizations, abortions, and imposed physical and social isolation (2004).

Older adults suffering from dementia also suffer from the negative reactions to them because of their diagnosis (Milne, 2010). When stigma associated with the diagnosis of dementia intersects with the stigma of old age, it causes a phenomenon called *double jeopardy* (Benbow & Reynolds, 2000). Further compounding the situation for the older adult suffering from dementia, the relatives or caregiver for the older adult in turn suffer from courtesy stigma (Goffman, 1963; Werner & Heinik, 2008). Further negative impacts on older adults suffering from dementia include less aggressive referral and treatment because of the poor prognosis for the older adult with dementia (Vernooij-Dassen et al., 2005) and lack of parity of health care compared with patients with other diagnoses (Beecham, Knapp, & Fernandez, 2008).

THE INTERNET: A TOOL FOR FIGHTING STIGMA

The Internet is a tool for older people to use to access information and communicate with others. This use is seen internationally. For example, Burns, Jones, Iverson, and Caputi (2012) report that 85% of 55- to 59-year-olds and

50% of adults 75 years and older in Australia report having some online experience. It is projected that baby boomers will show an increased and consistent use of the Internet as this cohort continues aging (Abbey & Hyde, 2009; Alpay et al., 2004; Gilleard & Higgs, 2008). Because impoverished African Americans and older poor African Americans prefer to get medical information from their health care providers or established sources, Detlefsen (2004) suggests that impoverished African Americans be given availability to Internet training resources in order to have alternative medical information, which would lessen the probability of receiving biased, stigmatized information. Correspondingly, the Internet is a valuable resource for the social worker to use to obtain accurate information about diverse populations in order to purge stereotypes and inaccurate information (Figure 4.2) that would in turn bias clinical decision making.

THE CASE OF MICHAEL

Michael* is an 82-year-old African American male who resides in a retirement community that has a majority White population of older adults and some African American and Latino older adults. Since moving to this community 9 years ago, Michael has enjoyed many sexual relationships with women in the community. This community reflects consistent population statistics for older adults found in the general population—there are more women than men. Consequently, this reduces pressure on the older heterosexual adult males to participate in monogamous relationships, enabling

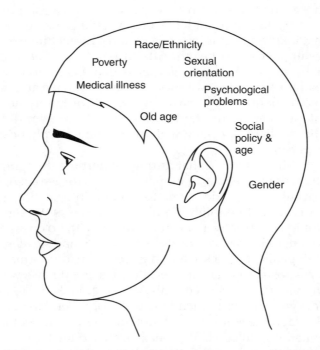

FIGURE 4.2 Filling a social worker's brain with accurate, antistigma information about diversity and older adults from Internet resources.

*Names and other identifying information have been changed to preserve confidentiality.

them to experience a sexual freedom not experienced as younger adults. Therefore, Michael had been enjoying having multiple sexual partners without the constraints of cheating on a partner or spouse. In addition, because his sexual partners were all older adult women, there was no need for birth control, so the use of a condom was never considered.

One evening, Michael noticed what looked like a small collection of sores, about eight shiny sores clustered together near the head of his penis. He panicked when he saw this. Michael wondered if this was a sexually transmitted disease. "Was it AIDS? Herpes? The clap? Do I dare go to a doctor who may expose me to the community as having a disease? What about my partners?" Michael worried that this would make trouble for him because he is Black and having sex with White women as well as African American women. Even though his community seemed liberal and tolerant to the African Americans residing there, he felt this would awaken latent racism in the White community members.

Fortunately, for Michael, his community hired a social worker to help organize the community and assist in case management of health-related problems and to make referrals for those members needing psychotherapeutic help. A significant aspect of the social worker's community organization work was to set up a computer center within the community's clubhouse. The purpose of this center is to help the older adults become familiar with how to communicate with others using e-mail, have video chats with others, use a basic word-processing program to write letters, and learn how to use search engines to find information about any topic on the Internet. The social worker organized classes for beginners and for those who had some prior experience with a computer.

Michael did not have any experience using a computer but thought that taking a beginning class would distract him from the anxieties he was feeling about his health. After a few weeks, he was able to turn on the computer and use an Internet search engine to find information, download music, and view videos. He did not have an interest in learning how to e-mail; he did not have any friends or family he wanted to communicate with via computer because they themselves did not own computers. Michael liked speaking with them on the telephone or meeting with them in person.

Michael found that during dinnertime the computer center was usually without people, or at most only one or two people were there. He felt that this was an ideal time to look up information about the sores on his penis so that he might figure out what was wrong with him because he would be virtually alone in the room, with no one looking at his computer screen. Using search words *herpes, AIDS,* and *syphilis,* and combining them with penis, he quickly found good and bad information by looking at pictures posted on various websites. The good news was that he did not find any pictures associated with AIDS that looked like the sores on his penis. This gave him a tremendous sense of relief. However, he did notice that although the sores did not look like herpes or syphilis, they did look like something called HPV. He next searched the term *HPV* and learned it was a sexually transmitted disease that is often passed by unprotected vaginal intercourse. Though it seemed more serious for a woman, he still felt a significant degree of concern for himself and concern that he might pass it to a lover.

Michael next looked for a local urologist who would accept Medicare. During this search, he was able to view the doctors in various group practices who had posted their pictures. He was pleased to find an African American urologist who practiced near his community. This relieved Michael, who felt that an African American doctor would treat him without the prejudice he experienced in the past from many White physicians. Michael was especially concerned about prejudice because his problem entailed a sexually transmitted disease that may have been transmitted from a White woman or that he may have transmitted to a White woman.

SUMMARY

Stigma is a psychosocial construct that is multidimensional, containing many different elements that oppress individuals. Stigma causes *spoiled identities* that in turn become a chronic oppression of an individual or a group of people. People are stigmatized by others or, paradoxically, stigmatize themselves. This is called self-stigma. Many dimensions of a person may be a focus for stigma, such as physical deformities, psychological problems, medical illnesses, race, religion, gender, poverty, sexual orientation, and age. In most cases, an individual is found in the intersection of two or more stigmas. People who tend to stigmatize others are those from majority populations, those in health care professions or governmental policy organizations, law enforcement personnel, and journalists—in other words, anyone who has power over others. Efforts are being made to combat stigma emanating from these sources by the establishment of global antistigma campaigns (Evans-Lacko, Brohan, Mojtabai, & Thornicroft, 2012; Thornicroft, Brohan, Kassam, & Lewis-Holmes, 2008).

DISCUSSION TOPICS

1. Discuss your own history experiencing stigma. Give experiential references for:
   a. Self-stigma
   b. Courtesy stigma
2. Discuss experiences your older adult clients have with ageism. Cite specific examples for:
   a. Intentional ageism
   b. Unintentional ageism
   c. Institutional ageism
   d. Intentional ageism

SPECIALIZED PROBLEMS AND ORIENTATIONS IN GERONTOLOGICAL SOCIAL WORK PRACTICE

CHAPTER 5

Psychopathological Problems in Older Adults

Madness need not be all breakdown, it may also be break-through.
—R. D. Laing, *The Wings of Madness: The Life and Works of R.D. Laing*

THE MEDICAL MODEL OF PSYCHOPATHOLOGY

Healy (2002) states, "In recent history a disease has been thought of as an entity established by an underlying biological lesion." The medical model in psychiatry assumes medical intervention is the treatment of choice for the constellations of diagnosed symptoms that comprise various mental disorders. These treatments may include pharmacotherapy, electroconvulsive treatment, brain stimulation, and psychosurgery. Psychosurgery did not disappear after the demise of frontal lobotomy. Today, capsulotomy is used for the treatment of obsessive-compulsive disorder (Ruck et al., 2008). Sadock and Sadock depart from the medical model of treating a brain disease by indicating that "the major goals of the pharmacological treatment of older persons are to improve the quality of life, maintain persons in the community, and delay or avoid their placement in nursing homes" (2008, p. 697). Therefore, psychopharmacology for older adults can be considered palliative rather than a cure for a brain disease causing psychopathology. In addition, the risk/benefit ratio for psychopharmacological therapy is skewed toward risk. Azermai, Bourgeois, Somers, and Petrovic (2013) indicate that the limited effectiveness of psychopharmacological therapy for older adults does not justify subjecting these older adults to the high risk of side effects from psychiatric medicines and interaction with other pharmaceuticals older adults are taking for medical conditions.

When the *Diagnostic and Statistical Manual of Mental Disorders*, third edition (*DSM-III*; American Psychiatric Association [APA], 1980a) and the *Diagnostic Criteria for the* DSM-III (APA, 1980b), was published in 1980, Bayer and Spitzer (1985) hailed it as a major advance for psychiatry and as an indication of the emergence of a broad professional consensus on diagnostic issues. Inclusive in this statement is the assumption that the myriad psychiatric disorders described have a biological etiology, despite the fact that most people with psychiatric disorders have no demonstrable underlying lesions. Figure 5.1 illustrates the many limitations of medical-model thinking. However, using the person-in-environment model (Figure 5.2), the constellations of symptoms categorizing different psychopathological problems are seen as a reduction of resilience and a consequent set

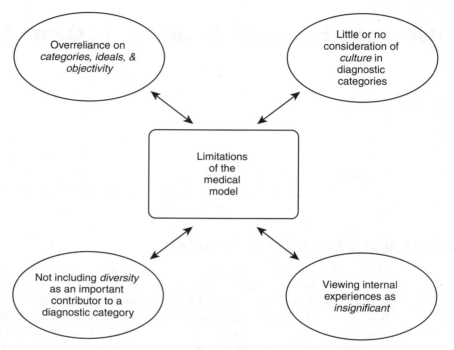

FIGURE 5.1 Limitations of the medical model.

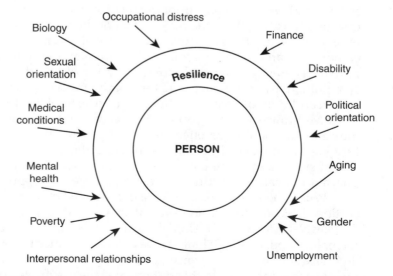

FIGURE 5.2 The protective role of resilience in the person-in-environment model. When there is a reduction in resilience, psychological symptoms are produced.

of maladaptive responses to psychosocial–biological stressors. In addition, the person-in-environment model takes into consideration an older adult's culture and differences arising from diversity and inner processes. As discussed in Chapter 3, Intervention Theories Informing the Clinician Treating Older Adults, an older adult struggling to cope with distress in his or her life can consider these maladaptive responses inappropriate choices. Therefore, the importance for the clinician is not the label of psychopathology but rather the etiology of the symptomatology. Are the symptoms emanating from a disease in the brain? Alternatively, are they a reflection of a reduction of resilience (see Figure 5.1)?

Goffman (Manning, 1980, p. 267) felt that psychiatry was composed of *tinkers* inventing psychiatric syndromes to justify medical interventions under the guise of scientific identification of diseases. Wilson (1993) indicates that for the first time in psychiatric history a method of diagnosis (the *Diagnostic and Statistical Manual of Mental Disorders; DSM-IV;* APA, 1994) was created to meet the needs of pharmaceutical companies; insurance companies; psychiatrists shifting their method of practice from psychoanalysis to pharmacotherapy (Mojabai & Olfson, 2008); and regulatory agencies that oversee hospitals, mental health centers, pharmacies, and, to a lesser extent, private practice. This is further complicated by direct-to-consumer advertising that causes older adults to pressure their primary care physicians for antidepressant medications that in turn reduce the need for primary care physicians to make referrals for psychotherapy (Kravitz et al., 2005). This is consistent with a national trend that indicates psychotherapy is a less prominent choice of intervention when compared with the increasing trend of outpatients receiving psychotropic medication without psychotherapy (Olfson & Marcus, 2010). This phenomenon seems to be a consequence of the dominant position of the medical provider in relationship to the older client, causing the older clients to have a greater exposure to psychotropic medications (Vilhelmsson, Svensson, & Meeuwisse, 2013).

This is not the only argument against the medical model. There are many examples of outdated medical psychiatric practices—such as in 1793 when Philippe Pinel took the chains off inmates in asylums (Roback & Kiernan, 1969); Walter Freeman's controversial lobotomy treatment of people diagnosed with chronic schizophrenia, depression, and manic-depressive illness from the late 1930s to the mid-1950s (El-Hai, 2005); or, in the early 20th century, when Harry Cotton, medical director of Trenton State Hospital (New Jersey), believed that mental illness arose from bacteria in one's body (Scull, 2005). This theory led to involuntary extraction of patients' teeth, resection of stomachs and intestines, and forced hysterectomies, all in the name of curing mental illness. The current criticism of the continuance of the *DSM* as the definitive guide to diagnosis is that it is a convenient method of categorizing mental illnesses and assigning as treatment various psychoactive compounds (Azermai et al., 2013), electroconvulsive therapy, or electrical brain stimulation.

PSYCHOPATHOLOGICAL PROBLEMS IN OLDER ADULTS

Older adults experience many psychopathological problems, including anorexia tardive, anxiety disorders, delusional disorders, mood disorders, personality disorders, schizophrenia (low amount of symptoms), and co-occurring disorders with substance abuse/dependence disorders. Dementias are discussed in Chapter 6, Alzheimer's Disease and Other Dementias, and substance abuse/dependence disorders are discussed in Chapter 8, Older Adult Substance Abusers. Older adults have a prevalence rate of 25% when including all psychopathological categories (Gatz & Smyer, 2001). Sadock and Sadock (2008, p. 695) indicate that older adults are at risk for psychological disorders when faced with "loss of long-term social roles, loss of autonomy, financial pressures, death of close friends and relatives, cognitive problems, and isolation." Evans, Singleton, Meltzer, Stewart, and Prince (2003) indicate that poverty, isolation, medical disorders, and poor living conditions are associated with high levels of mental health issues in older adults. These risk factors are consistent with the person-in-environment model. Therefore, it is critical for the social worker to understand the various manifestations of psychological problems in older adults from the perspective of an older adult, rather than extrapolating information commonly taught in social work programs that neglect to focus on older adults and restrict teaching to psychopathological problems in younger and middle-aged adults (Lewis, Hems, Bosanquet, & Overend, 2013).

Anorexia Tardive

Although a rare occurrence in later life, the social worker should be aware that an older adult may experience anorexia nervosa, which is indicated in the literature as *anorexia tardive*, or late-onset anorexia nervosa (Nicholson, 1998). The clinical presentation appears the same as the more common anorexia nervosa of childhood, late adolescence, or early adulthood (Inagaki et al., 2002). The psychosocial stressors instigating anorexia tardive are complicated bereavement, late divorce, and anxiety about the future. Late-onset anorexia nervosa does not have the characteristic psychosocial stressors of sexuality, attractiveness, thinness, parental relationship dysfunctions, or early sexual abuse as seen in the classical presentation of anorexia nervosa (Sadock & Sadock, 2008). Late-onset anorexia nervosa must be carefully differentiated from unintentional weight loss that occurs in older adults who are depressed; from medical conditions (see Chapter 7, Medical Problems in Older Adults) such as cancer, cardiovascular disease, gastrointestinal disease, and poor nutrition; or that may occur as a side effect of a medication or polypharmacy (Huffman, 2002).

Anxiety Disorders

The anxiety disorders seen in older adults are panic disorder without agoraphobia, panic disorder with agoraphobia, agoraphobia without a history of panic disorder, specific phobia, social phobia, obsessive-compulsive disorder, acute stress disorder, posttraumatic stress disorder, and generalized anxiety disorder.

Sadock and Sadock indicate that there is a prevalence rate of 5.5% for older adults experiencing anxiety disorders. Specific and social phobias occur in 4% to 8% of older adults, and panic disorder occurs in 1% of the older adult population (2008). Anxiety disorders in older adults cause reduced quality of life, poor health outcomes, increased presentation for mental health services, decreased activity, and coexistent diagnoses (Beekman et al., 2000). Older Asian and Latino adults have a higher incidence of anxiety disorders when compared with African Americans and Whites (Arean & Alvidrez, 2001).

Sadock and Sadock (2008) feel that specific phobia is the most common anxiety disorder seen in older adults. Diefenbach et al. (2003) find that generalized anxiety disorder may have a subdiagnosis of *sub-syndrome generalized anxiety*. Sub-syndrome generalized anxiety is defined as symptoms not meeting the full criteria for generalized anxiety disorder. In the study, older adult patients reported significant distress when diagnosed with generalized anxiety disorder and significantly less distress when diagnosed with sub-syndrome generalized anxiety disorder, when compared with older adult patients not showing clinical anxiety symptoms.

Stanley et al. (2003) find that cognitive behavioral therapy is an effective treatment for anxiety disorders, particularly with generalized anxiety disorder, which is the most common anxiety diagnosis seen by primary care physicians. The social worker counseling an older adult suffering from anxiety must consider paring cognitive behavioral therapy techniques with self-hypnotic relaxation techniques. Self-hypnotic relaxation techniques enable the older adult to experience a feeling of empowerment from the learned ability to relax his or her body at will, to simultaneously stop anxiety thoughts by using visualization techniques to compete with verbalizations, and to intimately learn to shut down verbalizations while simultaneously relaxing. An interesting finding by Stratford, Lal, and Meara (2012) is that heart rate and anxiety decrease in both the client and therapist after a therapeutic session using these techniques. This author recommends that social workers working with older adults seek training in Ericksonian hypnosis (Rosen & Erickson, 1991).

Co-Occurring Psychological Disorders and Substance Abuse/Dependence Disorders

Although substance abuse/dependence disorders are discussed in Chapter 8, Older Substance Abusers, it is worth noting the phenomena of co-occurring psychological and substance abuse/dependence disorders. Older adults experiencing these co-occurring disorders present for help at a greater frequency when compared with those seeking help for either a psychological disorder or a substance abuse/dependence disorder. This phenomenon is found internationally (Andrews, Henderson, & Hall, 2001; Bijl & Ravelli, 2000; Jacobi, Wittchen, & Holting, 2004; Scott, McGee, & Oakley Browne, 2006; Wang, Lane, & Olfson, 2005). However, it is reported that approximately one third to one half of older adults with co-occurring disorders do not seek mental health services (Andrews et al., 2001; Harris & Edlund, 2005). This may be due to financial barriers to receiving care, the stigma (see Chapter 4, Stigma and Older Adults) of being diagnosed with a psychological or substance abuse/dependence disorder (Evans-Lacko, Brohan, Mojtabai, & Thornicroft, 2012), or lack of knowledge of mental health services among older adults (Meadows, Burgess, & Bobevski, 2002;

Mojtabai, 2007). Mechanic (2003) feels that the prevalence of these disorders does not prove to be a good predictor for use of mental health services because this older population is underserved.

Delusional Disorder

Delusional disorder may occur at any time during late adulthood (Sadock & Sadock, 2008). Many older adults who experience delusional disorder have a history of premorbid personality disorders. These include schizoid personality disorder, paranoid personality disorder, or other symptoms of personality disorders (Zweig & Hillman, 1999).

Mood Disorders

Mood disorders seen in older adults are major depressive disorder (single or recurrent), persistent depressive disorder (dysthymia), bipolar I disorder, bipolar II disorder, and cyclothymic disorder. Mood disorder caused by a medical condition is discussed in Chapter 7, Medical Problems in Older Adults, and substance-induced mood disorder is discussed in Chapter 8, Older Adult Substance Abusers.

Depressive disorders experienced by older adults are major depressive disorder (single or recurrent); persistent depressive disorder (dysthymia); bipolar I disorder, most recent episode depressed; bipolar II disorder (depressed); and depressive disorder not otherwise specified (NOS). Depressive symptoms have a prevalence rate of 15% among older adults (Sadock & Sadock, 2008). In older adults the prevalence rate for depression differs in communities where people are considered relatively equal (Minicuci, Maggi, Pavan, Enzi, & Crepaldi, 2002; Takkinen et al., 2004) compared with those who have clear socioeconomic class bias that creates inequality (Romero, Ortiz, Finley, Wayne, & Lindeman, 2005). Where this is a sense of equality among people in a community, the prevalence rate for depression is 1.6 to 1 (women to men). Miech, Eaton, and Brennan found that the higher prevalence rates in women are a result of lower incomes compared with men, widowhood, lower levels of education compared with men, and poor vocational skills (2005). In contrast, in communities where people are treated unequally the prevalence rate is 2 to 1. Older adults who experience chronic stressors and poor social relationships, accompanied by a lower socioeconomic status, throughout their development explain the differentiation in prevalence of depression between communities where stratification is a confounding variable (Grundy & Sloggett, 2003; Rieker & Bird, 2005). These findings were confirmed by Zunzunegui et al. (2007) in an international comparative study of older adults in Europe and Israel. Hybels, Blazer, and Pieper (2001) find that the prevalence rate combined for men and women in the community is 9.9%. Conn, Clark, and van Reekum (2000) find that Jewish Holocaust survivors are often diagnosed with major depressive disorder that is co-occurring with posttraumatic stress disorder.

Alexopoulos et al. (2002) find that depression in an older adult is usually co-occurring with medical conditions (see Chapter 7, Medical

Problems in Older Adults). This comorbidity is described by Chi et al. (2005) in older Chinese adults in Hong Kong and by Bisschop, Kriegsman, Deeg, Beekman, and van Tilburg (2004) in older adults in Holland. These medical conditions include cardiovascular disease, viral infections, endocrine disorders, cancer, cerebrovascular disease, dementia, hearing impairments, and metabolic disorders. An interesting finding shows that the relationship between depression and physical illness is related to the disability that arises from the depression rather than the illness itself (Hays et al., 1998). However, Bora, Harrison, Yucel, and Pantelis (2013) suggest that cognitive impairment is often seen with older adults experiencing major depression. This impairment may indicate co-occurring vascular or neurodegenerative disease processes.

Lopez and Mermelstein (1995) suggest that cognitive behavioral intervention with older adults suffering from medical illness and a comorbid depression is successful, with 30-minute sessions, three to four times per week, using cognitive restructuring techniques. In a meta-analysis, Braun, Gregor, and Tran (2013) found that cognitive therapy and behavioral interventions are more successful with older adults than the supportive therapy used by many social workers. Cognitive behavioral therapy alone or combined with psychopharmacological treatment is found to be more effective than treating an older adult solely with psychiatric medication (Cuijpers et al., 2013).

Leszcz (2002) indicates that chronic depression is shown to cause considerable psychosocial distress in older adults and consequent psychosocial distress in family members. As discussed in Chapter 6, Alzheimer's Disease and Other Dementias, depression is often a predictor of dementia occurring within approximately 10 years after the onset of an older adult's depression. Johnson, Weissman, and Klerman (1992) attribute increased expenditure in the provision of psychiatric services to older adults diagnosed with minor depression (depression NOS). Minor depression is found to be a significant diagnosis in minorities presenting for primary medical care. Unfortunately, older African Americans are less likely to be referred for outpatient psychotherapy when compared with older White adults (Joo, Morales, de Vries, & Gallo, 2010). Arean and Alvidrez (2001) find that on presentation, 10% of African Americans, 12 % of Asian Americans, and 15% of Latinos experience minor depression. In addition, minor depression increases mortality risk in men.

Judd et al. (2002) find that the majority of older adults diagnosed with bipolar I disorder presented with chronic major depression, which is a depression that lasts 2 years or more. Older adults experiencing mania or hypomania account for approximately 10% of older bipolar patients. Although older adults suffering from mania or hypomania are often treated with pharmacological interventions similar to younger adults, older adults experiencing chronic depression do not find relief from pharmacotherapy (Ghaemi, Lenox, & Baldessarini, 2001). Havens (2004) recommends that the phenomena of the therapeutic relationship is a dynamic way to alter mood in a manic or hypomanic older adult and is more effective in the older adult than pharmacotherapy. This is a basic principle of existential-phenomenological psychotherapy discussed in Chapter 3, Intervention Theories Informing the Clinician Treating Older Adults. This is consistent with the findings of Sadock and Sadock (2008), who indicate that pharmacotherapy is palliative rather than a cure and is useful to prevent or delay the placement of an older adult experiencing psychological problems in a nursing home. Singh, Clements, and Fiatarone Singh (2001) find that weight training has a significant effect in diminishing the symptoms of major depression but is less effective for minor depression. Steffens (2013) indicates that studies show mixed results on the efficacy of exercise in the treatment of depression. This may explain the differential results of weight training for major and minor depression treatment.

Williams et al. (2000) find that when older adults are treated for minor depression with paroxetine hydrochloride (Paxil) or problem-solving psychotherapy, both independently showed clinical improvement when compared with a placebo. This is a significant finding because it indicates that problem-solving psychotherapy eliminates the need for pharmacotherapy when treating minor depression. This is consistent with the person-in-environment model. In addition, psychotherapeutic intervention eliminates the risk of psychiatric medication interaction with other medicines an older adult may be taking for medical conditions.

Suicide is discussed in a separate section later in this chapter because its cause is not restricted to mood disorders.

Personality Disorders

Personality disorders commonly seen in older adults are schizoid, schizotypal, antisocial (dissocial), borderline, histrionic, narcissistic, avoidant, dependent, paranoid, and obsessive-compulsive personality disorders.

Personality disorders in older adults are often underdiagnosed by clinicians during assessment (Abrams, Alexopoulos, Spielman, Klausner, & Kakuma, 2001). Devanand, Turret, and Moody (2000) argue that diagnosis of personality disorders in older adults is indeed less common than in younger adults or middle-aged adults, but there is not a great disparity. One possible explanation for this phenomenon is that what are considered as classical signs of a personality disorder in a young or middle-aged adult may present in a different form in an older adult. Personality disorders are considered an ongoing psychopathological process throughout adulthood. However, many clinicians are uninformed of the evolutionary changes that occur in these disorders. Sadavoy and Fogel (1992) feel that these changes include attenuation of symptomatology in older adults. This attenuation of symptomatology in older adults is not clearly articulated in psychiatric texts and diagnostic manuals, which mistakenly suggests a consistent presentation of symptomatology from early adulthood through old age.

There is a dearth of literature on the comorbidity of personality disorders with other psychopathological disorders in older adults. However, Devanand et al. (2000) indicate that there is a high co-occurrence with personality disorders and mood disorders, especially major depressive disorder (single or recurrent) and persistent depressive disorder (dysthymia). In addition, Zweig and Hillman (1999) find that older adults diagnosed with paranoid personality disorder or schizoid personality disorder in early adulthood tend to have a co-occurrence with psychotic disorders in late adulthood.

There is little evidence for specific therapies for older adults with personality disorders. Complicating the clinical picture is the fact that personality disorders are ego-syntonic to the older adult. Being ego-syntonic, the older adult does not perceive his or her behavior as problematic. In contrast, an older adult presenting with other disorders presents in an ego-dystonic state. He or she perceives these psychopathological problems as painful. Consequently, the older adult wants therapeutic change. Several therapeutic modalities may be effective when treating an older adult with a personality disorder if a positive therapeutic alliance can be established. This positive therapeutic alliance, which has shown to be effective in other psychopathologies of older adults, can be achieved using cognitive behavioral therapy, narrative therapy to address internal issues, supportive psychotherapy, and group therapy oriented to group problem solving (Alexopoulos, Raue, & Arean, 2003; Clark, 2011; Kenyon, Clark, & de Vries, 2001; Klasuner et al., 1998; Krishna et al., 2011). Markovitz suggests that psychopharmacological treatment for personality disorders is relatively ineffective because medications are used primarily to relieve specific symptoms without resolution of the personality disorder (2004).

Schizophrenia

Sadock and Sadock (2008) indicate that a primary episode of schizophrenia in older adults is rare. However, they indicate that late-onset schizophrenia (occurring after 45 years of age) does occur, more often in women than in men. Many older adults who experience late-onset schizophrenia have a history of premorbid personality disorders. These include schizoid personality disorder, paranoid personality disorder, and other symptoms of nonspecified personality disorders (Zweig & Hillman, 1999). Schizophrenia in older adults presents with diminished symptoms, unlike its presentation in children and younger adults.

Suicide

Suicide ranks eighteenth among the most common causes of death among adults 65 years of ages and older ("Web-based Injury Statistics Query and Reporting System [WISQARS]," 2006). According to the National Institute of Mental Health (2007) older adults comprise only 12% of the population in the United States yet account for 16% of death by suicide. Non-Hispanic Whites have the highest rate of suicide (15.8 per 100,000) compared with African Americans (5.0 per 100,000), who have the lowest. Asian and Pacific Islanders (10.6/100,000) and Hispanics (7.9 per 100,000) fall in the middle. This report indicates that 75% of older adults who commit suicide visited a physician 1 month before their death. This statistic underlies the importance of physicians and mental health professionals increasing their skill base in assessing an older adult (see Chapter 2, Assessing an Older Adult) for possible risk of suicide. This risk for suicide increases in old age as ability to function decreases, chronic illness increases, and rate of depression increases, including an increased incidence of sub-syndromal and major depressive disorders (Fassberg et al., 2012). In addition, older adults who are socially isolated are at a high risk for suicidal ideation, nonfatal suicidal behavior, and subsequent successful suicide later in the aging process (2012).

McNeil (2001) feels that the aging cohort of baby boomers stand a greater chance for mental health intervention because of their assertiveness concerning health care needs. Hinshaw and Cicchetti (2000) feel that this cohort is more likely to seek mental health services because of the continuing trend of destigmatization of mental health diagnoses and treatments. Unfortunately, there is a dearth of research on older people in this cohort or in previous cohorts. This causes a lack of informational resources to health and mental health providers that ultimately affects older adults served by health care providers. McKenzie, Serfaty, and Crawford (2003) feel that this problem is further exacerbated by the lack of research on culturally sensitive clinical assessments and culturally specific psychotherapy interventions. Chiu et al. (2004) find that substance use (see Chapter 8, Older Adult Substance Abusers) is a significant facilitator of suicide in older adults. In addition, the authors find that older adults with a diagnosis of schizophrenia are at significant risk for suicide.

During a psychosocial–biological assessment, older adults are less likely, when compared with younger adults, to report suicidal ideation (Barnow & Linden, 2000; Kuo, Gallo, & Tien, 2001). Older adults experiencing psychological problems are at risk for self-harm behaviors (see Chapter 10, Older Adult Abuse; Chiu et al., 2004), have a high probability of these self-harm behaviors resulting in lethal self-harm behaviors within 1 year after nonlethal self-harm behaviors, and have a continued risk of suicide within 15 years (Hawton, Zahl, & Weatherall, 2003). Therefore, the clinician, during an assessment (see Chapter 2, Assessing an Older Adult), must be very direct in asking the older adult client about suicidal ideation, plan, intent, means, and history as routine questions. Kaplan, Adamel, and Rhoades (1998) find that primary care physicians do not ask their older patients about their access to firearms (means). This is significant because men, more often than woman, use firearms to kill themselves. Women prefer to use poison. This should not suggest that firearms and poison are the exclusive means for older adults ending their lives, just that firearms and poison are high-risk means for suicide. In addition, older adults are more likely to express suicidal ideation to family members or friends (Waern, Beskow, & Skoog, 1999).

Many studies indicate that diagnosable psychopathologies often co-occur with suicide attempts and suicide completion (Beautrais, 2002; Harwood, Hawton, Hope, & Jacoby, 2001; Waern et al., 2002). Harwood et al. (2001) find that in the United States there is a prevalence rate of 78% of psychological problems in older adults who died because of suicide. Waern et al. (2002) find from retrospective analysis that there is a 97% prevalence rate of psychological problems in older people who have died because of suicide and that having a diagnosable psychological disorder puts an older adult at extreme risk for suicide. The most prevalent psychological disorders associated with suicide are mood disorders (Beautrais, 2002; Harwood et al., 2001; Waern et al., 2002), schizophrenia, and substance use (Chiu et al., 2004).

THE CASE OF ANTHONY

Anthony* is an 87-year-old Italian Catholic man whose home health companion contacted a local social service agency in the Boston metropolitan area seeking the help of a social worker. On assessment, the social worker learned that for the past 5 weeks Anthony has refused to get on the elevator and his movements have been restricted to his floor and his apartment. Anthony uses a walker, is unable to use the staircase, and when having to walk for an extended distance, he resorts to the aid of a wheelchair.

The home health companion indicated that she called the agency because Anthony had appointments with his family physician, his oncologist, and his dentist, all of which he was unable to attend because of his refusal to use the elevator. Anthony told the social worker that when he thought of going in the elevator he felt very fearful. When asked what he meant by fearful Anthony said that someone put "the evil eye" on him. He felt that a neighbor that he did not get along with cursed him by putting the "evil eye" on him. The social worker, recognizing that this might be a cultural interpretation of anxiety by Anthony because he was an immigrant from Italy, asked Anthony what it felt like to have an "evil eye" on him. Anthony indicated that he was not afraid of anything and that his problem was just the "evil eye."

On further probing after deepening her engagement with Anthony, the social worker was able to determine from Anthony that the "evil eye" caused his heart to suddenly beat faster, making him feel as though he was about to have a heart attack. In addition, he indicated that his legs would start shaking and sometimes he would lose his balance, almost falling. He denied ever falling. Anthony said that when he was feeling he was having a heart attack he feared that he would lose control over his bladder and embarrass himself in front of a neighbor or his home health companion. Anthony also indicated that when this happened he felt like he "entered another world."

Anthony said that he recognized that his reaction to anticipating getting on an elevator was excessive and did not make sense to him. However, he indicated that returning to his apartment, where he was unable to see the elevator, made him feel better and the fear went away.

Anthony's social worker determined that he was experiencing a specific phobia, situational type. His anxiety reaction was specific to an elevator and occurred when thinking about getting on an elevator or when attempting to get on an elevator. Anthony's anxiety reaction was so intense that it prevented him from being able to enter the elevator and ride it to the ground floor. Anthony lives on the tenth floor of his apartment building. His specific phobia prevented him from attending health appointments and being able to leave his apartment house and restricted visits with friends to friends who were able to travel to his apartment. All his other needs, like obtaining prescriptions from his local pharmacy, getting food from the local supermarket, and getting his favorite newspaper from the local newsstand were done by his home health companion.

---

*Names and other identifying information have been changed to preserve confidentiality.

Anthony's social worker developed the following treatment strategies to help him resolve his specific phobia:

1. The social worker taught Anthony how to induce a relaxation response using self-hypnotic Ericksonian (Rosen & Erickson, 1991) techniques.
2. The social worker helped Anthony recognize that he could change the way he feels by using the techniques he learned.
3. The social worker decided to employ the behavioral technique of systematic desensitization to help Anthony be able to use the elevator.
4. The social worker had Anthony develop a scale with his different experiences of an elevator in terms of how severe of an anxiety response he experienced when exposed to each of them. These experiences were ordered from a mild reaction to the most severe reaction. The order was as follows: the thought of getting on an elevator, a picture of his elevator, looking at his elevator from his apartment door, looking at the elevator by standing in front of it, entering the elevator without it moving, and entering the elevator to travel to the lobby.
5. The social worker started with the mildest experience, the thought of getting on the elevator, and had Anthony use his relaxation technique to relieve the anxiety reaction he experienced to thinking about getting on an elevator. This was repeated until Anthony was able to think about going on an elevator without experiencing the horrific anxiety he would normally experience. Each subsequent experience in his list followed that same protocol until he was no longer experiencing his specific phobia and was able to use his elevator and resume his normal activities.

SUMMARY

When viewing an older adult who is suffering from psychological problems, a social worker must decide between two basic orientations—the medical model or the person-in-environment model. This is a critical choice, because each model leads the older adult down a different treatment path. The medical model invariably subjects the older adult to pharmacotherapy, electroconvulsive treatment, or brain stimulation, and in some cases concurrent psychotherapy. In contrast, the person-in-environment model subjects the older adult to various psychotherapy methods geared to drawing on the older adult's strengths and oriented to increasing an older adult's feelings of empowerment. A strength-based psychotherapy intervention helps the older client understand and appreciate that he or she has successfully survived many difficult situations and hardships during his or her lifetime by using existing strengths and problem-solving skills (Saleeby, 2009). By enlisting these strengths and skills, solutions to current problems can be successfully executed, consequently giving the older client a greater sense of empowerment.

The medical model, which considers the etiology of psychological problems as a disease or biological aberration in the older adult's brain, concludes that medical intervention is the treatment of choice for the constellations of diagnosed symptoms that comprise various mental disorders. The person-in-environment model attributes psychological problems as a constellation of symptoms indicating a reduction of resilience in the older adult to converging pressures emanating from culture, finance, medical problems, stigma, diversity, and inner psychological processes. An older adult struggling to cope with distress in his or her life can consider these maladaptive responses to environmental stimuli inappropriate choices. Therefore, the importance for the clinician is not the label of psychopathology but rather the etiology of the symptomatology; the clinician must guide the older adult to positive coping choices, which in turn will reestablish resiliency, a greater sense of empowerment, and the elimination of the symptomatology.

DISCUSSION TOPICS

1. Discuss a case of an older adult you are working with from a medical model orientation.
   a. What is the diagnosis?
   b. What treatment modalities are you using?
   c. What medications are being used?
2. Discuss the same case from a person-in-environment perspective.
   a. How does your treatment plan differ from the medical model perspective?
   b. Describe how the older adult client participates with you compared with the medical model. What are the differences?

CHAPTER 6

Alzheimer's Disease and Other Dementias

Death is not the greatest loss in life. The greatest loss in life is what dies inside us while we live.

—Norman Cousins, BrainyQuote

Rowe and Kahn (1998) suggest that loss of mental functioning is a threat to independent functioning that older adults most fear. These fears are often associated with Alzheimer's disease, causing most older adults to be hypervigilant about their memory functioning (Lachman, 2000; McDougall, 2000). Lachman finds that 39% of people between the ages of 25 and 75 report noticing memory problems at least one time per week. Although Alzheimer's disease is the most feared of the dementia disorders, there are more than 100 different types of dementia. All types of dementia are progressive, causing permanent changes in the anatomy and physiology of an older adult's brain. Of the many types of dementia, five of the most prevalent dementia disorders in older adults found in social work practice are discussed here.

MILD COGNITIVE IMPAIRMENT

Many older adults are diagnosed with mild cognitive impairment (MCI), a condition that does not meet the criteria for dementia (Bennett, 2004). Although showing some memory impairment, the older adult with MCI does not evidence any functional impairments or personality change. MCI is considered a risk factor for Alzheimer's disease–related disorders (ADRD). ADRD includes vascular dementia and mixed dementias. An older adult diagnosed with ADRD experiences memory loss, personality changes, behavioral impulsivity, and functional disturbances throughout the course of his or her dementia (Lyketsos & Olin, 2002). The importance of early recognition of MCI is that it creates an opportunity for pharmacological intervention that may slow the dementia process, giving an older adult a longer period of high functioning.

Although there is an argument that early diagnosis leads to recommendation for early intervention with medicines, self-help groups (Yale & Snyder, 2002), or other forms of advocacy (Kuhn, 2003), there is a counterargument. Brierley et al. (2003) feel that an early MCI diagnosis may lead to distress in the older adult, who may focus on progressing to ADRD or to Alzheimer's disease. Increased sensitivity is required by the social worker because Chan, Kasper, Black, and Rabins (2003) find that older adults with an MCI diagnosis have a higher rate of co-occurring psychological diagnoses (see Chapter 5, Psychopathological Problems in Older Adults) than older adults without an MCI diagnosis or other related dementias. The most prevalent psychological diagnosis is depression (Spira, Rebok, Stone, Kramer, & Yaffe, 2012). A depression diagnosis often precedes a diagnosis of mild cognitive impairment. This diagnosis should prompt a social worker assessing an older adult to screen for cognitive impairment (Tung, Chen, & Takahashi, 2013).

VASCULAR DEMENTIA

Vascular dementia occurs when the oxygen supply to an area of the brain is reduced, causing brain cells to die. Vascular dementia is a consequence of the brain damage that occurs after a stroke, or a series of mini-strokes. A stroke is a sudden, acute vascular lesion of the brain caused by hemorrhage, thrombosis, or embolism. Unlike other dementias that increase in incidence with age, the incidence of vascular dementia decreases after age 80 (Jellinger, 2013).

In vascular dementia, the consequences of a stroke or mini-strokes are disorientation to one or more spheres (person, place, or time), confusion, difficulty walking, increased risk of falling, and behavioral problems often stemming from premorbid psychological difficulties. In addition, vascular disease is thought to be an etiological factor for depression in many older adults (Krishnan, Hays, & Blazer, 1997). Fuher, Dufouil, and Dartigues (2003) find that men who are hypertensive and develop cerebrovascular disease are at a high risk to become depressed and then progress to dementia. Therefore, when diagnosing an older adult with depression, the social worker must be alert that the depression may be a prodromal sign signaling a subsequent dementia. These changes are not reversible or curable. Vascular dementia often necessitates the hiring of an in-home companion to assist with activities of daily living (ADLs) such as bathroom activities, supervised walking, medication dispensing, food shopping, bathing, and cooking.

DEMENTIA WITH LEWY BODIES

Lewy body dementia is a condition in which Lewy bodies develop inside neurons in the brain. These spherical structures cause multiple symptoms in older adults. These include fainting, falling, or turning with bizarre movements, visual hallucinations, and sleep disturbance (Grace, Walker, & McKeith, 2000). Often, older adults will have no trouble sleeping during daylight hours but will experience disturbed sleep with intermittent hallucinations and nightmares. There is no cure for this condition and, as in vascular dementia, in-home help is needed to assist with ADLs.

FRONTAL LOBE DEMENTIA (INCLUDING PICK'S DISEASE)

Frontal lobe dementia (FLD) occurs primarily in the frontal lobe of the brain. Initially, psychological symptoms are seen, but later states include memory deficits. Older adults experiencing FLD exhibit a lack of empathy toward others, often appearing narcissistic, self-centered, or selfish to friends, relatives, and caretakers (Beers, Porter, Jones, Kaplan, & Berkwits, 2011). An interesting personality phenomenon occurs whereby an older adult who was an extrovert prior to the FLD diagnosis becomes introverted. Likewise, an older adult who was an introvert premorbidly becomes extroverted. As FLD progresses, the older adult will exhibit a loss of impulse control, often becoming aggressive and violent and acting out sexual behaviors in public places (e.g., public masturbation, exhibitionism). In addition, the older adult may develop an affinity for sweet foods that can cause a consequent weight gain.

Communication becomes a problem. At times, the older adult will have difficulty choosing the right word to say, will struggle with spontaneity of conversation, and will evidence circumlocution in his or her speech (using many words with little content); speech becomes markedly reduced or, in the extreme disappears entirely. During these episodes, the older adult is easily distracted and lacks insight into his or her behavior. There is no cure for this disorder.

KORSAKOFF SYNDROME

Korsakoff syndrome (Beers et al., 2011) is a direct consequence of alcohol dependence. An older adult experiencing later stages of alcohol dependency will show disturbances in orientation (person, place, or time), distractibility from external stimulation, falsification of memory (confabulation), and hallucinations (primarily visual hallucinations). Korsakoff syndrome is also called chronic alcoholic delirium. There is no cure for this disorder.

PARKINSON'S DISEASE

Parkinson's disease is a slowly progressive, degenerative central nervous system disorder. Primary symptoms are decreased movement, muscular rigidity, resting tremor, postural instability, and sleep disturbance (Bilwise, Rye, & Dihenia, 2002). It affects about 1% of older adults (Beers et al., 2011). A common error is the assumption that part of the constellation of symptoms of Parkinson's disease is dementia. This is not so. Older adults experiencing Parkinson's disease have the same rate of dementia as older adults not experiencing Parkinson's disease. Therefore, dementia is co-occurring with Parkinson's disease, not part of Parkinson's disease.

ALZHEIMER'S DISEASE

Early detection of Alzheimer's disease is a difficult problem for social workers and family members. Ideally, there is a reliable observer who can detect and document early changes in functioning over time (Carr, Gray, Baty, & Morris, 2000). Unfortunately, older adults in beginning stages of dementia are not reliable sources for information on functional changes because of deficits that need to be observed by others, or because of denial of such changes. Another complicating factor in early detection of Alzheimer's disease is that many older adults with early-stage Alzheimer's disease appear normal to health care professionals and family members. Morris, Price, McKeel, Higdon, and Buckles (2004) find that older adults who appear normal 1 year before death show an incidence of Alzheimer's disease between 39% and 47% at autopsy. Most dementias are retrospectively diagnosed at autopsy (Jellinger, 2013). Depression in older adults is thought to be a high-probability prodromal symptom of Alzheimer's disease (Wilson, Arnold, Beck, Bienias, & Bennett, 2008). Nevertheless, personality changes seem to appear before the cognitive changes associated with Alzheimer's disease.

Seven stages mark the progression of Alzheimer's disease (Beers et al., 2011). It is important to know these stages so that an older adult in a particular stage can be identified during a social work assessment (see Chapter 2, Assessing an Older Adult).

Stage 1

At this stage, no discernible memory problems are observable on assessment. However, on a neuronal level, structural changes may develop for as long as 20 years before recognition by a health care professional or social worker, which usually occurs in stage 3.

Stage 2

During this stage, an older adult may begin experiencing forgetfulness with names of acquaintances and lose personal objects such as car or house keys, a wallet, eyeglasses, or other items regularly used by the older adult. This type of forgetfulness is recognized by the older adult but is not obvious to others who are in frequent contact with the older adult or to the older adult's social worker.

Stage 3

At this stage people who are in frequent contact with the older adult notice problems in memory that occur in a home setting or workplace. Errors in naming people close to the older adult become obvious. The struggle of the older adult to remember new names of acquaintances or fellow workers becomes more common and obvious to others. Concentration difficulties occur that begin to impair social or occupational functioning. Disorganization in the older adult increases, demonstrated as a greater frequency of losing objects and problems in the older adult's ability to organize daily activities at home or in a vocational setting. Concentration difficulties begin to be evidenced in an older adult's ability to read, often having difficulty following a story or passage because of an increasing inability to retain information from passages read.

Stage 4

An older adult has increasing difficulty remembering recent events or recently learned information. During a mental status exam, there is a marked inability to perform calculations or remember digit spans. An older adult will have difficulty in abstract thinking, which is manifested in difficulties managing finances, forgetting to pay bills, having difficulty planning social events with others, and marked impairment in vocational settings. On examination, an older adult will have difficulty remembering aspects of his or her personal history. These reduced cognitive abilities often cause an older adult to socially withdraw, which is often misdiagnosed as depression or social anxiety.

Stage 5

At this stage, memory impairment is marked, showing severe deficits in daily functioning. This stage often triggers family members to assist in daily living activities of the older adult or to retain outside help for this assistance. Assistance with daily living activities includes dressing (choosing proper combinations of clothing), house cleaning, meal preparation, and financial organization. On assessment, the older adult will often have disturbances in person, time, or place. The older adult will make errors or be unable to respond to questions of general knowledge. Greater deficits are seen in calculations, remembering three objects, and remembering digit spans. Impairment in knowledge of personal details becomes more extensive, generalizing from recalling his or her name to errors and omissions of personal historical events.

Stage 6

Most, if not all, recent events are difficult to remember at this stage. However, distant events may still be recalled. Help with ADLs is needed. These include eating, bathing, and bathroom activities. At this stage, in many older adults delusional thinking is evidenced along with paranoid thought processes. These pathological thought processes might lead to violent behavior. In addition, it is not uncommon for the older adult to be disoriented in two or more spheres (person, place, or time).

Stage 7

This final stage finds the older adult bedridden, unable to feed himself or herself, and incontinent. In addition, the older adult is unable to communicate except in very primitive ways, such as hand signaling or verbal grunts rather than clear verbal commands.

A BASIC GUIDE TO MEDICINES FOR ALZHEIMER'S DISEASE

It is important that a social worker counseling patients with Alzheimer's disease and their families have a basic understanding of how the medications work. This is imperative because a social worker must be the bridge between patients with Alzheimer's disease and their families and the various medical professionals in the patient's treatment team. This will enable the patient, family members, and caretakers to better understand the importance of medication compliance. In addition, the social worker will be more comfortable interacting with medical professionals and more fluent in the recognition of side effects.

To understand how medications help the older adult suffering from Alzheimer's disease, the social worker must understand the role the synapse (the site in the brain where neurons communicate) plays in the pharmacological treatment of Alzheimer's disease. The *synapse* (Figure 6.1) is the anatomical location where communication between *neurons* (nerve cells) occurs. The synapse has three primary parts: the neuron, which releases *neurotransmitters* from *storage vesicles* located in its ending; the space in between the two neurons where chemical communication takes place; and the receptor site of the next neuron, which receives the chemical transmission.

Neurotransmitters

Neurotransmitters are compounds synthesized (manufactured) in the neuron (the first part) and released by the storage vesicles (the second part) into the synaptic cleft (the space between two neurons) to communicate chemically with another neuron. The third part is the beginning of the neuron being communicated to, which contains receptor sites.

Pharmacological interventions in Alzheimer's disease attempt to change the communication between neurons by increasing the levels of a neurotransmitter called *acetylcholine*, or by partially blocking the ability of high levels of the neurotransmitter called *glutamate* from overstimulating the receptor sites in the neurons receiving chemical communications. Acetylcholine is a neurotransmitter involved in memory storage and memory retrieval. Autopsies of people who have died of Alzheimer's disease find that acetylcholine receptors in the cerebral cortex (the thinking part of the brain) are largely absent (Jellinger, 2013). Therefore, acetylcholine levels in the brain of an older client with Alzheimer's disease must be raised to increase the stimulation compromised by the reduced amount of receptor sites. Glutamate at low levels is vital to the processes of learning and memory. High levels of glutamate overstimulate receptor sites called NMDA (N-methyl-D-aspartate) receptors. These high levels disrupt

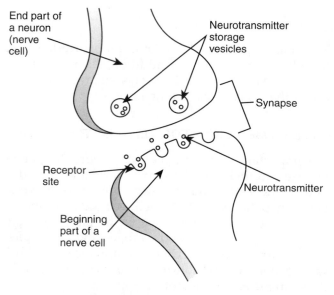

FIGURE 6.1 The synapse.

learning and memory and may lead to the destruction of the NMDA receptor sites. It is postulated that some older adults with Alzheimer's disease have increased excitatory activity from high glutamate levels (Makino & Porsteinson, 2011).

Cholinesterase inhibitors

Medications called cholinesterase inhibitors increase the available levels of acetylcholine by inhibiting the ability of cholinesterase, an enzyme that binds with acetylcholine and breaks down acetylcholine after the excitation of a nerve, reducing the availability of acetylcholine. Cholinesterase inhibitors, specifically acetylcholinesterase inhibitors, block the ability of cholinesterase to break down acetylcholine and keep its availability for further neural stimulation. Currently available medications in this class are donepezil (brand name: Aricept), galantamine (Razadyne), and rivastigmine (Exelon). Another cholinesterase inhibitor, tacrine (Cognex), was the first cholinesterase inhibitor approved for the treatment of Alzheimer's disease but is rarely used as a treatment today because of its toxic effects on the liver.

Figure 6.2 shows how acetylcholine is released from the storage vesicles at the end of a neuron into the synaptic cleft. The end part of this neuron communicates with the beginning of the next neuron using the acetylcholine released in the synaptic cleft; the acetylcholine works its way to the receptor site at the beginning to the next neuron. Once this communication is accomplished, acetylcholine esterase is released to break down the leftover acetylcholine and clear the synaptic cleft for the next neural communication. The cholinesterase inhibitors reduce the amount of acetylcholinesterase in the synaptic cleft, making more acetylcholine available for the next neuronal communication. This facilitates neuronal communication in the brain of a client suffering from Alzheimer's disease, where there is a reduction of receptor sites.

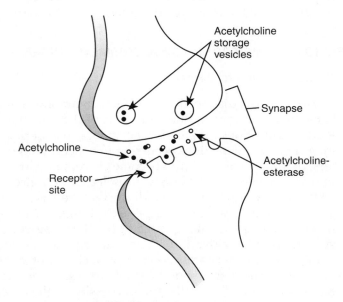

FIGURE 6.2 Acetylcholine synapse.

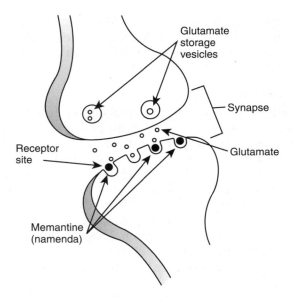

FIGURE 6.3 Glutamate NDMA receptor antagonist.

NMDA receptor antagonist

The NMDA receptor antagonist in current use is memantine (Namenda). Figure 6.3 shows how an NMDA receptor antagonist partially blocks the receptor sites in the neuron receiving communication from another neuron. The NMDA antagonist takes the place of glutamate, which would normally stimulate the receptor site. By partially blocking the NMDA receptor sites, there is less glutamate stimulation. This is thought to be helpful for some clients suffering from Alzheimer's disease whose glutamate level is excessively high, consequently overstimulating the client and over time destroying the glutamate receptor sites. Therefore, overstimulation and destruction of the receptor sites interferes with learning and memory.

THERAPEUTIC INTERVENTIONS FOR ALZHEIMER'S DISEASE PATIENTS

Agitation States Common to Dementias

Sundowning is a diagnostic description commonly associated with agitated behaviors that occur in the latter part of the day; these behaviors include loud vocalizations, aggressive behaviors, wandering, and inappropriate interpersonal interactions occurring in concert with other negative behaviors, or alone, that appear to become exacerbated in the late afternoon into the early evening (Kim, Louis, & Muralee, 2005; Volicer, Harper, & Manning, 2001). Bilwise and Lee (1993) indicate that there is a parallel process in caregivers in which caregivers experience fatigue at the end of the day that makes evening caretaking difficult for the caregiver and may exacerbate symptoms in the older adult Alzheimer's patient. Consequently, it is more appropriate to refer to sundowning as a cluster of symptoms rather than a syndrome. The presence of the sundowning phenomenon tends to exacerbate cognitive decline, falls, and depression in the older adult Alzheimer's disease patient (Scarmeas et al., 2007).

Either way, this phenomenon must be addressed clinically by the social worker coordinating the care of the older adult with dementia by managing the care interventions performed by the older adult's caregivers. An innovative approach, called *overnight camps,* is now being instituted in many care facilities for dementia patients who do not sleep at night, wake up early in the evening and stay awake, or become frightened, agitated, or disruptive at nightfall (Fitzgerald, 2012). These overnight camps allow caregivers respite while giving the dementia patients much needed physical activity and positive social experiences. In addition, it is suggested that activities, especially music therapy, that engage the older adult with sundowning symptoms may reduce the severity of these symptoms (Yevchak, Steis, & Evans, 2012).

Caregiver Support Groups

Greene, Aranda, Tieman, Fezekas, and Currow (2012) indicate that caregiver support groups are extremely important. They suggest that a social worker facilitate the formation of a support group within the home geographic environment. The exasperation of distress felt by an older adult's caregivers is of great concern. An earlier study by Gallagher-Thompson, Brooks, and Bilwise (1992) showed that without intervention by a social worker, an older adult may be transitioned to institutionalized care prematurely (Pollak, Perlick, & Linsner, 1991). This necessitates psychoeducational interventions with caregivers in order to allow the older adult to age in place as long as possible. In addition, Woodruff (2012) emphasizes that many adult caregivers suffer from the slow loss of the person they knew over the course of a dementia process. This grief over the loss of the person they once knew needs to be addressed with psychoeducational intervention and psychological support services.

Psychotherapeutic Interventions in Early-Stage Dementias

Kasl-Godley and Gatz (2000) find that older adults in beginning stages of dementia respond well to reminiscence therapy (RT), psychoeducational support groups, and cognitive behavioral therapy (CBT). In addition, CBT is found to be helpful in encouraging older adults with dementia to exercise (Anshel, 2013). Woods (2003) indicates that RT is an effective psychological intervention with mild impaired older adults suffering from dementia.

Psychoeducational Support Groups for Alzheimer's Disease Patients

Psychoeducational support groups allow the merging of learning about dementia with concomitant psychological support. Yale and Snyder (2002) found that this type of group support enables older adults suffering from early-stage Alzheimer's disease to break their denial about their disease, to become less secretive and more open to others knowing about their condition, which in turn facilitates increased interpersonal functioning. This is accomplished by including family members in the psychoeducational group. The breaking of denial enables older adults in these support groups to make better sense of their disease, increasing their abilities to comply with treatments and caretakers. Similar findings by Zarit, Famia, Watson, Rice-Oeschger, and Kakos (2004) indicate that *memory groups* consisting of older adults with early dementia and their partners are effective in improving understanding of the dementia process and subsequent improvement in the psychological statuses of participating older adults with dementia.

Cheston (1996) cautions that psychoeducational group support is not a generic intervention for all older people with dementia. Cheston indicates that only those who are motivated and open to such intervention will be successful. Pratt, Clare, and Aggarwal (2005) find that older adults experiencing dementia are willing to join a therapeutic group that is not focused on the diagnosis of dementia but rather on talking about social interactions and increasing interpersonal satisfaction. These groups include participation by older adults and their care partners. This is consistent with McKinnes-Dittrich (2005), who finds that reminiscent group intervention with or without older adults experiencing dementia is a positive intervention to help older adults resolve past conflicts, losses, and trauma while identifying positive achievements and life events.

Egdell (2012) suggests three types of support networks, *organic*, *guided*, and *chance*. Organic networks are created by the direction of a physician or social worker. Guided support networks differ from organic support networks because guided support networks are created by the caregiver through his or her own contacts or social networks. Chance support networks have a random quality because they are created when a caregiver is in a crisis and happens to encounter a health professional or a knowledgeable lay individual.

Another aspect of support is the need for medication education groups for families and caretakers (Lavretsky, 2012). These groups have a specific emphasis on the many over-the-counter medications that are often taken by the dementia patient. These medications can have adverse or catastrophic results when interacting with prescribed medications or taken improperly. Again, social workers must be familiar with medicines in order for there to be a quick recognition of dangerous side effects or dangerous combinations of medications.

Leisure Activities and Therapeutic Recreation

Leisure activities, whether community based or solitary, are shown to be protective against dementia or, at the least, stall the onset of dementia. Seidler, Bernhardt, Nienhasu, and Frolich (2003) find that social engagement with or without intimate social relationships is protective against dementia. Social activities that have the most protective effect, whether done in group settings or as solitary older adults communicating by telephone or computer social networks, must require cognitive effort (Flatt & Hughes, 2013). These activities may include gardening, board games, traveling, knitting, or topical discussions (Richards, Hardy, & Wadsworth, 2003; Verghese et al., 2003; Wang, Karp, Winblad, & Fratiglioni, 2002). Group music therapy is shown to be effective in engaging older adults suffering from dementia in singing and playing musical instruments once a week on a long-term basis (Raglio & Gianelli, 2013). These activities increase socialization and may decrease the incidence of further cardiovascular and cerebrovascular disease (Takahashi & Matsushita, 2006).

With the progression of dementia, an older adult tends to be deprived of meaningful activity and therapeutic recreation, which leads to an increase of disruptive behaviors (Aubert, Beck, Kowanowski, Whall, & Richardes, 2001; Bennett, 2000). Recreation therapy is shown to be effective intervention for this lack of meaningful activity (Buettner & Martin, 1995). Buettner, Fitzsimmons, and Atav (2006) find that 79% to 91% of inactive older adults suffering from dementia were significantly altered, reducing passive and agitated behaviors when intervention that increases meaningful activity occurs.

Cognitive Training Intervention Programs

Many authors (Ball et al., 2002; Cavallini, Pagnin, & Vecchi, 2003; McDougall, 2000; Singer, Lindenberger, & Baltes, 2003) feel that age-related cognitive decline can be reversed to varying degrees with cognitive training. Ball et al. (2002) suggest cognitive training for speed of processing, reasoning, and mnemonic strategies. Willis and Schaie (1999) suggest cognitive training for spatial orientation and inductive reasoning. Stanley et al. (2013) encourage *peaceful mind* therapy, which is a combination of cognitive and behavioral interventions that are geared to reduce anxiety symptoms and sleep disturbances. Older adults learn deep-breathing techniques, coping self-statements, behavioral activation, and sleep-management techniques. In concert with the older adult patients, caregivers and family members learn coaching techniques to facilitate and reinforce the techniques taught to the older adult clients. Stark and Budson (2012) suggest that in addition to medications used for improving memory, social activities, exercise, and visual stimulation (pictures, artwork, etc.) are effective in delaying memory deficits.

DRIVING RETIREMENT

Although physicians in most states are mandated to determine the suspension of driving privileges of impaired adults, there are no clear criteria for determining when to retire an older adult from driving. Seiler et al. (2012) find that caregivers, not physicians, tend to determine the risk of an older adult needing to cease driving. In addition, the authors found that being female and experiencing disturbances of ADLs increase the probability of an older adult having driving privileges suspended. Unfortunately, many older adults with functional disorders (Dubinsky, Stein, & Lyons, 2000; Perkinson et al., 2005) or dementia (Foley, Heimovitz, Guralnik, & Brock, 2002) outlive their abilities to drive.

Fain (2003) indicates that licensed drivers over the age of 65 number more than 20 million, with an expected exponential increase with the aging of the baby boom generation. Fain indicates that a system must be developed that would determine when an older adult's driving privileges should be revoked. Carr, Meuser, and Morris (2006) feel that hallucinations experienced by an older adult diagnosed with dementia with Lewy bodies and apathy and memory loss experienced by older adults with frontal lobe dementia (including Pick's disease) are ideal criteria for driving retirement, though this is theoretical and not prescribed by law. Screening for driving cessation is often neglected by medical practitioners treating older adults (Tung et al., 2013).

FALL RISK WITH DEMENTIA

Persons suffering from Alzheimer's disease have a fall incidence that is twice that of non–Alzheimer's patients (Taylor, Delbaere, Close, & Lord, 2012). These falls cause medical complications that often require hospitalization and in some cases cause death. To date, there is no explanation for this higher rate of falls.

INAPPROPRIATE SEXUAL BEHAVIORS

Tsatali, Tsolaki, Christodoulou, and Papaliagkas (2011) find that patients with dementia often have decreased sexual activity with respect to their age cohort. However, because of the disinhibition that occurs with dementia, the dementia patient often exhibits aberrant sexual behaviors. These include touching inappropriately; unwanted fondling; in residential settings, entering the bed of a fellow resident without being invited; exposing genitals; publically masturbating; removing one's clothes in a public place; or displaying pornographic material in a public setting.

DEMENTIA IN IMPRISONED OLDER ADULTS

The proportion of older imprisoned adults compared with younger inmates has been consistently rising on an international level. This trend is observed in England, Wales, Canada, and the United States (Walmsley, 2000). There is a dearth of literature about this underserved, oppressed population. Fazel, McMillan, and O'Donell (2002) suggest that incarceration is an inappropriate intervention for older adults experiencing dementia. These older adults are unable to rehabilitate their thinking because of severe cognitive impairments, and they are unable to participate in retraining activities. These authors feel that it would be more appropriate to transfer older adults suffering from dementia to specialized nursing homes that may provide care that is ethical and humane while still segregating these adults from the outside population.

LONG-TERM CARE FOR DEMENTIA

Long-term care for dementia is discussed in Chapter 12, Care and Residential Settings for Older Adults.

THE CASE OF DAIKI

Daiki* is an 86-year-old Asian woman who lives alone in a small one-bedroom apartment in the suburbs of New York. Daiki's husband died 15 years ago after a long battle with prostate and lung cancers. Up until 6 months ago, Daiki was in remarkably good health for her age. Her cognition was intact and Daiki kept herself busy volunteering as a tutor for sixth-grade children in a local grammar school. Daiki is an avid reader whose intelligence belies her formal education. Being a female child, her

---

*Names and other identifying information have been changed to preserve confidentiality.

parents insisted that her brothers attend college and forbade Daiki from entering college. Instead, she attended a business school to learn secretarial skills. For most of her adult life, Daiki worked as an administrative assistant for numerous corporations.

Approximately 6 months ago, Daiki began experiencing fainting spells in her apartment that caused her to fall and remain unconscious for brief periods, which Daiki estimated as a minute or so. The amount of time she was unconscious was not verifiable by neighbors who responded to her telephone calls for help or by her personal physician. After each fainting and falling episode, Daiki was rushed to the emergency room but no definitive diagnosis was made. It was felt that Daiki might have experienced cardiac arrhythmias that caused a temporary loss of consciousness. At her last presentation to the emergency room, after being screened with magnetic resonance imaging it was discovered that Daiki had suffered multiple small, punctate strokes in the cortical areas of her brain that control speech and memory. A diagnosis of vascular dementia was made.

Daiki had no family members who lived near her. Her two sons and one daughter lived in different states and were unable to participate as caregivers for Daiki. Because Daiki was in danger of falling again, the family arranged for 24-hour coverage with registered home companions through a local social service agency. As part of her assessment, Daiki met with a social worker, who determined that she was experiencing multiple cognitive deficits. Daiki was unable to provide a comprehensive history because she showed marked impairment in short-term memory, had difficulty retrieving the correct words when speaking, often showed confabulation, and occasionally had her thoughts derailed.

Daiki was able to be stabilized with the help of 24-hour home companions, medications from her primary care physician, and counseling from the agency's social worker. Daiki regained the weight she lost during the initial phase of her illness, before any interventions. Because the home companions were administering her medications, she became compliant and was able to control a tendency she initially experienced of wandering out of her apartment in the evening. It was reported that approximately 4 months before having home companions, Daiki was found wandering in the lobby of her apartment in various states of undress. The doorman reported that he would escort her back to her apartment, and during these episodes of wandering Daiki appeared to be confused and unaware of where she was or the time of day. Retrospectively, it appears that Daiki sustained brain damage from her strokes before the emergency room physician diagnosed her.

Daiki's physician was concerned that she might be in an early stage of Alzheimer's disease. He prescribed Cognex. Daiki became sedated from this medication, and there was no improvement to her mental status. Her physician withdrew the medication and concluded that she was not experiencing an early stage of Alzheimer's disease and reconfirmed the diagnosis of vascular dementia.

Daiki's children, although satisfied with the care from the home companions, became worried about Daiki's wanting to drive her car. Even though each home companion had a car and would transport Daiki to shopping excursions, movies, and visits to friends, Daiki felt that she was still able to drive. Her physician was reluctant to notify the motor vehicle bureau to have her license revoked. The social worker suggested to Daiki's older son that he come to Daiki's home and discuss with her the possibility of obtaining a general power of attorney so that he would be able to handle her financial affairs and make legal decisions if her condition continued to deteriorate. After some negotiation, Daiki agreed to give her son a general power of attorney. Her son was a successful business owner and Daiki saw him as her husband's successor in taking leadership of the family. Daiki's son then took possession of Daiki's car, sold it, and gave Daiki the proceeds. Through counseling with the social worker, Daiki was able to accept the loss of her car and understand the limitations on her life imposed by her vascular dementia.

Over the course of Daiki's vascular dementia, Daiki and her social worker developed different strategies to facilitate Daiki's positive adjustment to her disease:

1. The social worker coordinated through her social service agency the placement of registered home companions on a 24-hour basis.
2. The social worker used psychoeducational interventions to help Daiki understand and adjust to her vascular dementia.
3. The social worker coordinated and facilitated Daiki's son obtaining a general power of attorney, which enabled her son to sell Daiki's car and remove the danger of Daiki attempting to drive with her impairments. This strategy bypassed Daiki's physician's reluctance to authorize the revocation of Daiki's driver's license.

Daiki responded to cognitive therapy and reminiscence therapy interventions and was able to learn to reframe her thoughts about her diagnosis, enabling her to develop a positive attitude about her disease and to reestablish a sense of purpose and meaning in her life.

We learn from the case of Daiki that misdiagnosis plays a significant role in an older adult experiencing cognitive difficulties as evidenced by her physician's first diagnostic instinct to assume that she is suffering from Alzheimer's disease, which prompted him to prescribe Cognex. It must be understood that many forms of dementia share symptoms in common with Alzheimer's disease. However, rigorous medical and psychological assessments are needed to correctly differentiate which condition an older adult is experiencing. Fortunately, Daiki was covered for these services by Medicare, a supplemental health policy, and a long-term care policy.

SUMMARY

One of the most feared aspects of aging for an older adult is the possibility of dementia. This fear is partially based in the contemporary public awareness of Alzheimer's disease, which causes most people to be vigilant about putative memory problems. It is reported that 39% of people between the ages of 25 and 75 report noticing memory problems at least once per week. The bottom line is that most people, young and old, fear Alzheimer's disease.

Although Alzheimer's disease is a serious problem, this chapter focuses on the five types of dementia commonly seen in practice. These include vascular dementia, dementia with Lewy bodies, Korsakoff syndrome, frontal lobe dementia (including Pick's disease), and Alzheimer's disease. Parkinson's disease is often misunderstood as producing a dementia unique to Parkinson's disease. In fact, Parkinson's disease includes a subgroup of older adults who experience dementia, but contemporary thought is that the rate of dementia is equal to the older population at large, therefore occurring independent from the Parkinson's disease process. Mild cognitive impairment is not dementia but is a significant risk factor for a subsequent dementia diagnosis.

The complicated issue of driving cessation is a co-occurring problem with any type of dementia. Making a decision regarding driving cessation requires a team effort that includes the older adult's physician, social worker, as well as the caretakers and the older adult. A clear policy mandate is needed that would facilitate decision making when an older adult's driving privilege must be taken away. This policy mandate should arise from evidence-based research, which would in turn facilitate psychoeducational interventions by the older adult's health care providers.

Finally, this chapter introduces the problem of incarcerated older adults experiencing dementia. This underserved population raises many ethical and human rights issues. Should older adults suffering from dementia be forced into the rehabilitative process claimed by prison authorities when they are unable to understand retraining programs designed to rehabilitate their thinking? Is it humane to have these older adults in a prison setting? Would it be better to develop specialized nursing facilities that would provide the necessary care for dementia? These, among many other questions, have not been adequately answered in the clinical literature. This international problem of dementia exists in all cultures and desperately needs addressing by social work professionals.

DISCUSSION TOPICS

1. Discuss the different types of dementia you have seen in your fieldwork or practice.
2. Discuss the social work interventions you have used when working with clients with dementia.
3. Discuss which interventions seemed to work best with each type of dementia you have encountered in practice.

CHAPTER 7

Medical Problems in Older Adults

All parts of the body which have a function if used in moderation and exercised in labors in which each is accustomed, become thereby healthy, well developed and age more slowly; but if unused and left idle they become liable to disease, defective in growth and age quickly.
— Hippocrates, *Physical Activity and Health: The Evidence Explained*

Medical problems challenge older adults' abilities to cope with illness, and at times they experience co-occurring psychological disorders (Yohannes, 2012). Therefore, social workers must provide services to assist older adults who are experiencing acute or chronic medical conditions. Significant health disparities exist among minority populations and the poor compared with White, socioeconomically advantaged Americans (Conway, May, & Blot, 2012; Louie & Ward, 2011). Alvarez-Galvez and Salvador-Carulla (2013) suggest that health policies need to be enacted to reduce the impact of discrimination against any oppressed population.

As one ages, the incidence of medical illness, and at times co-occurring psychological disorders, increases. Social workers underserve older adults experiencing medical illness, especially minority groups and socioeconomically disadvantaged populations (Conway, May, & Blot, 2012). The older adult prisoner population is also neglected by social workers. This cohort has significantly more health problems than a nonprisoner older adult population (Fazel, Hope, O'Donnell, Piper, & Jacoby, 2001). In addition, social workers' knowledge of specialized counseling for particular medical illnesses is limited as a result of the dearth of medical information incorporated into training programs for social workers.

COMMONLY OCCURRING MEDICAL PROBLEMS EXPERIENCED BY OLDER ADULTS

Arthritis

Nearly one in three older adult Americans has some form of arthritis or musculoskeletal disease (Altman, Hochberg, Moskowitz, & Schnitzer, 2000). Osteoarthritis is the most prevalent form of arthritis among older adults

(Zhang et al., 2002). All forms of arthritis cause significant impairment in older adults' function. Impairments include a decreased ability for self-care, significant joint restriction, and associated muscle weakness.

Although joint replacement surgery has been promoted as a second chance for older adults with significant joint restriction, joint replacement surgery is associated with significant postoperative pain (Laskin, 1999). Poor pain management is a common complaint made by older adults with arthritis and musculoskeletal disorders (Watt-Watson, Garfinkel, Gallop, Stevens, & Streiner, 2000). In addition, Appelt, Burant, Siminoff, Kwoh, and Ibrahim (2007) found that men age 70 years and older felt that arthritis was a normal aspect of aging as compared with men 50 to 59 years old. This aspect of misinformation in men older than 70 years often prevents them from seeking available medical information and treatment.

Most arthritis patients experience pain. Older adults experiencing arthritic pain often experience a co-occurring depression (Hill, Dziedzic, & Ong, 2010). Social workers are uniquely qualified to provide psychotherapy and teach these older adults pain control using guided imagery techniques (Devine et al., 1999). This enables an older adult to achieve a sense of empowerment (Deisch, Soukup, Adams, & Wild, 2000) by learning how to self-employ guided imagery techniques, which help reduce the need for opioid and synthetic opioid medications. Ivers, Dhalla, and Allan (2012) find that opioid medications and synthetic opioid medications only provide a minimal benefit compared with nonopioid medication and consequently increase the risk for abuse. In addition, guided imagery pain control techniques help reduce the probability of an older adult developing a co-occurring opioid or synthetic opioid dependency disorder (see Chapter 8, Older Adult Substance Abusers). Nonmedication pain control reduces the incidence of falls, sedation, confusion, and urinary incontinence in an older adult patient. Because some older adults suffering from arthritis will experience a hip fracture from a fall, treatment with opioid and synthetic opioid medications before a hip fracture increases the probability of death within 1 year from the fracture (Agusi et al., 2012).

Cardiovascular Diseases

Cardiovascular diseases include high blood pressure, coronary heart disease, heart failure, stroke, and congenital heart defects. The average rate of cardiovascular disease in men ages 35 to 44 years is 3 per 1,000. The rate increases to 74 per 1,000 in men ages 85 to 94. The increased incidence in women occurs about 10 years later than in men. However, these statistics belie the disparity in the prevalence of cardiovascular disease among Whites, Mexican Americans, and Blacks. White males have a prevalence rate of 37.8%, Mexican American males 26.1%, and Black males 45.9%. In addition, this disparity of prevalence rates is seen in White females, who have a prevalence of 33.3%, Mexican American females 32.5%, and Black females 45.9% (AHA, 2009).

Dietary problems and obesity are significant contributors to cardiovascular disease in older adults. Differences of Whites compared with Blacks can be explained by several lifestyle variables. White males have a 32.3% prevalence rate of obesity (BMI 30.0 or higher) compared with Blacks, who have a prevalence rate of 36.8%. White females have a prevalence rate of

32.7%, and Black females have a prevalence rate of 52.9%. Related to obesity, White males have a prevalence rate of diabetes of 5.8% compared with Black males, who have a prevalence rate of 14.9%. White females have a prevalence rate of diabetes of 6.1% and Black females a prevalence rate of 13.1%. Consistent with these differences, White males have a prevalence rate of high blood pressure of 34.1% compared with Black males, whose prevalence rate is 44.4%. White females' prevalence rate is 30.3% compared with Black females, whose prevalence rate is 43.9% (AHA, 2009). This is an obvious phenomenon seen clearly in poor neighborhoods. The major sources of nutrition in these neighborhoods are fast food restaurants, bodegas that sell junk food, and high-priced vegetables and fruits; of course, organic foods are either not available or are too expensive.

Research indicates that older adult patients who do not comply with medical treatment have an increased morbidity and mortality (Hain & Sandy, 2013). This circumstance presents an ideal opportunity for social workers to join the treatment team and intervene with group therapy. Partners/spouses or caregivers join the groups so that they may act as coaches to the older adult patient to increase compliance with treatment. In addition, social workers can institute individual therapy for those older adults who have co-occurring depression or anxiety that is interfering with their compliance to medical treatment (see Chapter 5, Psychopathological Problems in Older Adults).

Depression is a psychological problem that often co-occurs with cardiovascular illness and is a significant precursor of stroke (Wouts et al., 2008). This phenomenon is exacerbated in minority groups and lower socioeconomic groups (Krantz, Sheps, Carney, & Natelson, 2000). Krantz et al. find an older adult suffering from depression has a significant co-occurrence of coronary heart disease, and Burg and Abrams (2001) find depression significantly co-occurring in coronary artery disease. Lane, Carrol, and Lip (2003) find a high prevalence of depression in older patients after myocardial infarction. In addition, older adults suffering from depression and cardiovascular disease have a higher incidence of mortality (Barth, Schumacher, & Herrmann-Lingen, 2004; Severus, Littman, & Stoll, 2001). Further, cardiac disease and obesity are highly correlated with cognitive decline as one ages (Bakalar, 2011; Belluck, 2011).

Lane et al. (2003) reports a significant association between anxiety and cardiovascular disease. Strik, Denollet, Lousberg, and Honig (2003) and Grace, Abbey, Irvine, Shnek, and Stewart (2004) indicate an association among anxiety, unstable angina, and myocardial infarction. The anxiety the older adult experiences increases the frequency of medical treatment after a cardiac event.

The phenomenon of co-occurring cardiovascular disease and psychological problems demands an increase in the amount of information on cardiovascular disease that is offered in training programs for social workers (Anderson et al., 2001; Proctor, Morrow-Howel, Li, & Dore, 2000). Not only do social workers have to be aware of the psychological needs of cardiovascular patients, but they must use psychoeducational techniques to teach caregivers, who often present for family therapy sessions (Lim & Zebrack, 2004).

A social worker must be sensitive to gender differences in co-occurring cardiovascular disease and psychological disorders. Because most cardiac research is oriented to men, social workers in training are not exposed to comprehensive information about women with cardiovascular disease. In addition, Sabbadini, Travan, and Toigo find that older women experiencing heart failure are underdiagnosed (2012). Older women have a greater level of anxiety after experiencing a cardiovascular event (Brezinka, Dusseldorp, & Maes, 1998). Older women also show increased depression after experiencing myocardial infarction (Mendes de Leon et al., 2001). These authors feel that the greater degree of depression is attributed to lower socioeconomic status and lack of a strong support system (Sabbadini et al., 2012). If an older woman is Black, she has a poor post–myocardial infarction prognosis when compared with an older White woman (Vaccarino, Krumholz, Yarzebski, Gore, & Goldberg, 2001).

Schneiderman et al. (2004) find that cognitive behavioral therapy (CBT) combined with social support is the best clinical approach for co-occurring cardiovascular disease and depression. Rejeski, Brawley, Amrosius, Brubaker, and Fox (2003) find that men who are involved in a structured group therapy program to keep them physically active as a lifestyle change have a better prognosis with co-occurring depression and cardiovascular disease. Ai, Tice, Petersen, and Huang (2005) stress that a social worker should carefully evaluate an older adult's spiritual support system and combine spiritual interventions with psychotherapeutic interventions. This is extrapolated from findings of psychotherapeutic and spiritual interventions with surviving victims and relatives of victims who experienced the 9/11 crisis in New York City.

Cancers

The major cancers experienced by older adults are breast cancer; chronic lymphocytic leukemia; lymphocytic lymphoma; colorectal cancer; lung cancer; mouth, head, and neck cancers; multiple myeloma; prostate cancer; skin cancers; and vulvae cancer (Beers & Jones, 2004).

Cancer is a major challenge to an older adult's sense of self and can lead to loss of functional abilities and family or vocational roles, a chronic interface with pain, and concerns over his or her future and, of course, mortality. Kissane and Clarke (2001) describe a psychological *demoralization syndrome*. This has symptomatology similar to major depression but does not meet the criteria for a major depressive episode. Demoralization syndrome causes an older adult to feel hopeless and helpless about his or her future, being thrust into an existential crisis in which there is no foreseeable future, a loss of motivation to employ historically successful coping mechanisms and personal strengths, and a consequent social isolation. Kissane and Clarke indicated that the major differential diagnostic feature between demoralization syndrome and major depressive disorder (single or recurrent) is the lack of anhedonia in the present and for the future. The demoralization syndrome shows only a lack of positive sense of the future.

Mitchell, Ferguson, Gill, Paul, and Symonds (2013) feel that anxiety, not depression, is the primary concern with long-term cancer survivors and their spouses/partners and other family members. For this reason, social workers need to improve recognition of anxiety during assessments of older adult clients (see Chapter 2, Assessing an Older Adult), as well as their partners/spouses. In addition, there is a need for more research to create evidence-based therapies for cancer patients that target anxiety.

Existential crisis should be considered when an older adult oncology patient evidences a lowering of self-esteem and increased sense of hopelessness, with a consequent loss of autonomy (Yedidia & MacGregor, 2001). Feelings of hopelessness often manifest in an older adult as a desire to hasten death (Breitbart et al., 2000). Midtgaard et al. (2012) find that combining existential humanistic therapy with cognitive behavioral therapy techniques increases the probability of restoring resilience and meaning to the older adult's life when experiencing cancer. In addition to psychotherapeutic intervention and family/caregiver education and support for this existential crisis in the older adult patient, the social worker should simultaneously evaluate the older adult's spiritual or religious orientation, which is shown to be an essential component for recovery in many cancer patients (Schnoll, Harlow, & Brower, 2000). When necessary, the social worker assessing the older adult should help him or her connect with a spiritual or religious advisor. In a classic study, Weisman and Worden (1976–1977) found that the existential crisis in an older adult oncology patient starts with the diagnosis and continues for 2 or 3 months. This finding heightens the importance of a social worker identifying the existential crisis on assessment (see Chapter 2, Assessing an Older Adult) and providing a rapid short-term intervention using cognitive behavioral techniques (see Chapter 3, Intervention Theories Informing the Clinician Treating Older Adults).

Chronic Obstructive Pulmonary Disease

A study in Belgium indicated that by the year 2030, chronic obstructive pulmonary disease (COPD) is expected to be the fourth leading cause of death and disability (Boeckxstaens et al., 2012). In addition, Boeckxstaens et al. recognize that there is a high degree of co-occurrence with other chronic diseases. Ability to have a positive adjustment to COPD is shown to be correlated to a knowledge of the disease and positive coping skills (Scharloo, Kaplan, Weinman, Wilens, & Rooijmans, 2000). With this in mind, an opportunity exists for social workers in a hospital setting, or those working in an agency that provides in-home counseling, to initiate a psychoeducational program that integrates medical information with the teaching of positive coping skills. This is important because patients have a significantly better outcome coping with their disease when they have social support from a spouse/partner, family member, or friends, compared with patients engaged in self-blame and self-stigma (see Chapter 4, Stigma and Older Adults; Halding, Heggdal, & Wahl, 2011; Halding, Wahl, & Heggdal, 2010; Mars, Kempen, Mesters, Proot, & Van Eijk, 2008; O'Neill, 2002; Wilson et al., 2008).

Diabetes

According to the Centers for Disease Control and Prevention (2011), adults ages 65 and older have a 25% incidence of diabetes. Those older adults suffering from diabetes have a greater chance of co-occurring vascular and cardiovascular conditions (Brown, Mangione, & Sarkisian, 2003) and a greater rate of institutionalization and subsequent mortality. Conway et al. (2012) found that in African American and White low-income populations, mortality rates were higher for both races if the individual is suffering from diabetes. In addition, Whites with diabetes show a higher mortality rate than African Americans with diabetes when the onset occurs before the age of 65 years. Diabetes onset after 65 years of age is highest in non-Hispanic Whites (Regidor et al., 2012; Selvin, Coresh, & Barncati, 2006).

Of concern, older adults suffering from diabetes are at a higher risk for Alzheimer's disease and multi-infarct dementia (vascular dementia; see Chapter 6, Alzheimer's Disease and Other Dementias) than nondiabetic patients (Lu, Lin, & Kuo, 2009). In addition, older adults suffering with diabetes are at a high risk for depression, which may cause problems with self-care and medication compliance (Lin, Katon, & Korff, 2004; Nouwen, Winkley, & Twisk, 2010). Therefore there is a need for social workers to coordinate group meetings with family members/caregivers to offer psychoeducation, encourage medicine compliance, and provide support and, in the case of a diabetic older adult with dementia, safety education for the caregiver/family members to ensure continuity of care.

Eye Disorders

Vision loss is a significant compromise of an older adult's quality of life. Poor vision leads to accidents, dangerous driving situations, and falling, in addition to the loss of the ability to read, watch television, or fully experience social interaction (Brennan & Silverstone, 2000; Brennen, Horowitz, & Su, 2005). The most common eye disorder in older adults is cataracts. In North America, 50% of older adults between the ages of 55 and 64 and 85% of those 75 years and older will develop cataracts within a 10-year period (Klein, Klein, & Lee, 2002). Cataract surgery is cost-effective and highly successful, providing a necessary health benefit (restored sight) to a majority of older adults.

Glaucoma is an eye condition that over time damages the optic nerve, causing a progressive and, in some cases, irreversible vision loss. Glaucoma is classified as open angle (chronic) or closed angle (acute). Either can cause permanent loss of vision if untreated (Beers & Jones, 2004). Age-related macular degeneration is the progressive deterioration of the most sensitive part of the central retina. It is the most common cause of central vision loss in older adults. It is classified as dry (nonvascular) and wet (neovascular) (2004). Diabetic retinopathy is a significant problem with older adults diagnosed with diabetes mellitus. (See previous section on diabetes mellitus.) This disorder is also seen in older adults who have chronic hypertension or chronic high blood cholesterol levels (2004).

Another category of eye problems in older adults occurs when there is a disruption of blood supply to the eye. This happens when there is retinal vein blockage, retinal artery blockage, blood clots, ischemic optic neuropathy (insufficient blood flow to the optic nerve), or occipital lobe stroke (a stroke in the vision center of the brain; Beers & Jones, 2004).

Older adults may also suffer from retinal tears or detachment. A retinal tear occurs when there is an irregularly shaped tear in the retina. Retinal detachment occurs when the retina separates from the eye wall and its supporting tissues. Immediate retinal laser surgery is required to ensure a repair and stop the progression of damage (Beers & Jones, 2004).

Other eye problems affecting older adults are disorders of tear production (dry eyes or excessive tearing), extropion (the drooping of the lower eyelid), entropion (the lower eyelid turns inward), ptosis (eyelid droop), blepharitis (inflammation of the edges of the eyelids), bleohari- soasm (involuntary blinking or closing of the eyes), chalazion (swelling of the oil glands in the eyelid), stye (infected eyelid gland), and xanthelasmas (thick fatty growths on the upper eyelid; Beers & Jones, 2004).

Psychotherapeutic intervention with older adults suffering from eye disorders is important because eye disorders have multidimensional con- sequences on an older adult's life. The older adult's environmental stress- ors converging on his or her life increase exponentially with vision loss. It is reported that adults age 40 years or greater have an incidence of blind- ness of 1 million, and an incidence of low vision of 2.4 million (Congdon, Friedman, & Lietman, 2003). Eye disorders disrupt an older adult's mobil- ity, sense of self, and communication abilities (Brennan & Silverstone, 2000). Simple pleasures of reading or more important issues of reading directions on medicine bottles or dialing a telephone, all of which are instrumental activities of daily living (IADL), become impaired (Brennen et al., 2005). These impairments affect an older adult's ability to travel independently, often promoting social isolation (Long, Boyette, & Griffin-Shirley, 1996). Such environmental obstacles may lead to depression in an older adult.

Hearing Disorders

Bance (2007) finds that in older adults, clinically significant hearing loss is the most common medical condition. Bance indicates that 25% to 40% of adults over the age of 65 have hearing loss. The incidence of hearing loss in older adults increases to 50% over the age of 75 years and to 80% if older than age 85 years. Gradual loss of hearing is called presbycusis (Beers & Jones, 2004). There are two types of hearing loss: *conductive* and *sensorineu- ral*. Conductive hearing loss is a defect in the transmission of sound to the inner ear. Some pathological process in the inner ear, in the auditory nerve, or within the brain causes sensorineural hearing loss. There are many causes of hearing loss, including aging; noise exposure (whether a single very loud noise or chronic exposure to loud noises at long duration); some antibiotic therapies; some chemotherapy medications; and use of aspirin and aspirin-related compounds, diuretics, and quinine. In addition, aspi- rin is known to cause tinnitus (ringing in the ear or ears). Certain medical conditions may also cause hearing loss, including blockage of the ear canal by ear wax; rupture of the eardrum; infection; allergy; blockage of the ear canal by a foreign object (e.g., an insect lodged in the ear canal); tumor of the auditory nerve, tumor within the brain, or tumor of the Eustachian tube; strokes; and autoimmune disorder (Beers & Jones, 2004).

Hearing loss leads to dysfunction in interpersonal functioning that is manifested by social withdrawal, depressed affect and mood, reduction in daily activities, frustration in the older adult around communication, and frustration in the receivers of the older adult's communication.

Osteoporosis

Osteoporosis is a condition in which bones become less dense and more porous. This causes a weakness in the bones, making an older adult more likely to break a bone (Beers & Jones, 2004). After age 50 the lifetime risk of fractures caused by osteoporosis is 50% in women and 20% in men

(Cummings & Melton, 2002). A disturbing statistic is that 30% of older adults are noncompliant with treatment during their first year of treatment and 80% are noncompliant after 3 years of treatment (Huybrechts, Ishak, & Caro, 2006; McCombs, Thiebaud, McLaughlin-Milley, & Shi, 2004). This is an ideal opportunity for social workers to join the treatment team and intervene with group therapy oriented to compliance (Solomon et al., 2005) and individual therapy for those older adults who have co-occurring depression that is interfering with their compliance to medical treatment.

Pain

Older adults suffer from pain from a variety of causes. For example, pain can occur as part of a disease process, whether acute or chronic; from joint replacement surgery (postsurgical pain); because of a fall; and as a result of dental problems.

Medical interventions for many diseases create a paradoxical situation. A surgical procedure designed to reduce pain in the long term may cause acute pain in the short term. An example of this paradox is found in joint replacement surgery. Joint replacement surgery is gaining in popularity among older adults because it offers the opportunity to increase mobility, relieve excruciating pain, and in many cases reverse social isolation (Laskin, 1999). The paradox occurs in the postoperative period, when an older adult will experience considerable pain, which, left untreated, will delay and reduce the effectiveness of postsurgical physical rehabilitation (Devine et al., 1999; Laskin, 1999) and increase morbidity in older adults with co-occurring pulmonary and cardiovascular disease, which require increased physical activity as part of successful medical treatment. The most common pain control method employed is the use of opioid and synthetic opioid medications, which have negative side effects, including drowsiness, sedation, falling, urinary incontinence, and drug dependence. Because many older adults suffer from multiple chronic illnesses, opioid and synthetic opioid medications may exacerbate symptoms of these illnesses, as well as side effects of medications used to treat these illnesses.

As an adjuvant to opioid and synthetic opioid medications or, more important, as an alternative treatment, relaxation techniques, sometimes called guided imagery or self-hypnosis, are shown to be effective techniques for acute and chronic pain control and improved recovery from general anesthesia (Deisch et al., 2000; Nilsson, Rawal, Unestahl, Zetterberg, & Unossoon, 2001). Relaxation for pain control is not a new idea. In a meta-analysis of 191 studies, Dreher (1988) found that CBT interventions combined with relaxation techniques were effective methods for pain management. CBT interventions are an ideal opportunity for the social worker to enlist a spouse/partner, family member, or caregiver in a coaching function to help the older adult with pain control (Lingaraju & Ashburn, 2013). These authors found that this increases the older adult's likelihood of compliance with nonopioid medication regimens for pain control. Unfortunately, despite this knowledge of the effectiveness of relaxation techniques, these techniques are used on a limited basis for many older adults suffering from chronic pain (Eller, 1999). Paradoxically, this led to a trend of older adults seeking alternative or complementary therapies for pain control. These include exercise programs, relaxation techniques that were not suggested, and dietary change. Astin, Pelletier, Marie, and Haskell (2000) found that 36% of participants studied were dissatisfied with conventional medicine and 34% with conventional pain control using medication. Unfortunately, information on relaxation and hypnotic methods are rarely included in educational training for social workers.

Pressure Ulcers

Pressure ulcers are also known as decubitus ulcers or bedsores. They result from prolonged pressure on the skin and may occur with as little as 2 hours of continuous pressure (Beers & Jones, 2004). Despite common knowledge of pressure ulcers, no significant decrease in the number of pressure ulcers in older adult patients occurs in contemporary hospital settings (Whittington & Briones, 2004). Education about pressure ulcers and early intervention to avoid or minimize them are imperative for older adult patients and their relatives or caregivers. This is especially important in today's hospital environment, where short stays are more common, often breaking a comprehensive continuity of care from the hospital to the older adult's home or long-term care setting.

Sleep Disorders

Cognitive behavioral interventions are effective for sleep disorders (Gatz et al., 1998). Sharma and Andrade (2012) recommend cognitive behavioral interventions that include education, stimulus control interventions, thought reframing, and sleep restriction because these interventions are successful and cost-effective. Older clients need education about how stimulating substances such as caffeine and nicotine, alcohol, and over-the-counter sleep medications affect the sleep–wake cycle. Nutritional advice and exercise instruction must be included in an educational program for insomnia. Older clients are taught to eliminate naps and activities in bed that are not sleep related, such as watching television, eating meals, reading, or listening to music, and to monitor time spent sleeping in bed (sleep efficiency). Age-related changes in sleeping behavior need to be taught because older adults often misunderstand them.

Urinary Disorders

Urinary incontinence occurs when an older adult loses a significant amount of urine unintentionally, causing a problem for the older adult and usually identified by a nurse or caregiver (Bernier, 2002). The older adult who is incontinent often suffers humiliation and becomes isolated and stigmatized; in some cases, urinary incontinence prompts a nursing home admission. Incontinence can cause sleep disturbance, a decrease or cessation of sexual intimacy (see Chapter 9, Older Adult Sexuality), and significant emotional consequences (Bradway, Dahlberg, & Barg, 2010). Psychoeducational intervention enables the older adult to modify activities so that proper regulation of urinary evacuation can be achieved. This is most important for women, who do not have the option of a catheter, which males may employ rather than using diapers.

Interventions for Older Adults With Chronic Illnesses and Their Families

Because family members and caregivers are an integral part of the disease process an older adult experiences, psychotherapeutic and psychoeducational interventions with family members and caregivers improve medication and treatment compliance, reduce emergency room presentations, and facilitate self-care by the older adult (Glasgow, Orleans, Wagner, Curry, & Solberg, 2001; Hain & Sandy, 2013). Health education, including communication of medical diagnoses and their treatment in simple language to facilitate understanding, is an ideal task for social workers, who can integrate health education groups as part of the treatment interventions provided by physicians (Effing, Williams, & Frith, 2013). These interventions can take place in a health care facility or home setting or via telephone or Internet video conferencing. In addition, Wang and Biederman (2012) found that electronic medication checklists administered on admission to a hospital significantly decrease errors in medication history recall. This technique, facilitated by the social worker in out-of-hospital settings, increases the accuracy of medication reporting rather than using the traditional "brown bag" method (asking the older adult to put all his or her medications in a brown bag to bring to the assessment appointment) commonly employed (see Chapter 2, Assessing an Older Adult).

THE CASE OF MIGUEL

Miguel's* primary care physician felt that Miguel was becoming overly anxious about his medical conditions and referred him to a local social service agency. Miguel is a 70-year-old married man from a mixed ethnic/racial background. His mother was a Latina who emigrated from Cuba with Miguel's father, who was Chinese. Miguel recently retired (2 years ago) from a manufacturing company, where he was a bookkeeper. On retirement, Miguel moved to a gated adult community in a neighboring state, situated in a bucolic setting as opposed to the urban setting where he previously lived. When he retired, Miguel felt that living in the country would be relaxing and a much-needed relief from urban living.

Miguel was recently diagnosed with prostatitis and hypertension. Since receiving these diagnoses he has become obsessed with death, vigilantly reading obituaries in the *New York Times* every day, becoming overly concerned about any ache or pain and overly focused on the medical conditions other people speak about in his adult community. Miguel has been unable to make new friends in his community because he spends most of his time researching or worrying about disease. Miguel's wife enjoys their new community because of the many activities she is able to participate in, which is a great contrast to the isolation she felt living as a housewife in an inner-city community, where she spent most of her time at home.

On assessment, the social worker found that Miguel suffered from hypochondriasis that manifests by Miguel worrying about different diseases that he may be diagnosed with in the future. In addition, Miguel worries about his recently diagnosed hypertension and feels that at any

---

*Names and other identifying information have been changed to preserve confidentiality.

moment he might have a cardiovascular event. Miguel worries about his prostatitis and fears that it will turn into prostate cancer and cause an early death. Miguel confirmed to the social worker that he is obsessed with death, reads obituaries every day, and focuses on stories from people in his community about their illnesses or about someone in the community who recently died and, of course, what killed that person.

Once an engagement was established between the social worker and Miguel, they agreed to proceed with a cognitive behavioral therapy intervention to lessen or eliminate his anxiety obsessions. The first step in his treatment was to establish a *baseline* of how many disease and death thoughts he had each day. Disease and death thoughts were defined as any thought about a disease, whether his own or a disease he feels he might suffer from in the future, or any thoughts relating to death. Miguel's task was to make a tick mark on a pad every time he gets a disease or death thought. The next day, Miguel e-mailed the number of disease thoughts he experienced the previous day to his social worker. Miguel was able to e-mail the therapist thanks to prior computer training he had in his bookkeeping job. His social worker in turn added the daily count to a graph shown to Miguel during each weekly therapy session (Figure 7.1).

The entries on the graph indicate the number of disease or death thoughts Miguel had for 27 days. This period of observation was explained to Miguel as the baseline period. The baseline period enabled Miguel to understand precisely how many disease and death thoughts he had on a daily basis. At the start of his therapy, Miguel claimed that he had "70, 80, or more disease and death thoughts each day." In reality, the baseline data indicated that Miguel's disease thoughts ranged from two to eight disease and death thoughts each day. This insight surprised Miguel. With the knowledge derived from baseline monitoring, Miguel felt that the number of disease and death thoughts were surprisingly low and something that he might be able to change.

At the end of 27 days, Miguel began his *intervention phase*. The social worker and Miguel agreed that each time Miguel had a disease or death

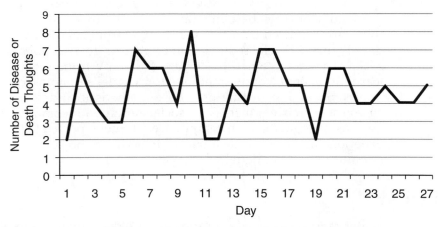

FIGURE 7.1 Baseline data showing the frequency of Miguel's disease or death thoughts on a daily basis for 27 days.

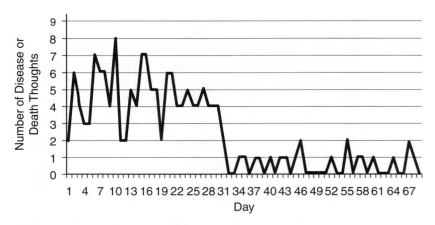

FIGURE 7.2 Baseline and intervention periods contrasting Miguel's disease or death thoughts before (days 1-27) and after the reframing intervention (days 28-69).

thought he would write the following sentences on his pad and then make a tick mark: "Having these disease and death thoughts is not healthy for me. Therefore, I will think about positive things that I can choose to occupy myself."

Miguel was instructed to just write the sentences and then repeat the sentences in his mind until any negative thought about his disease or death was absent. By writing the sentences and then thinking about it, Miguel quickly learned to reframe his negative thinking to a positive thought each time he had a negative disease or death thought. This enabled Miguel to decide to think of something else (positive change) rather than continuing to perseverate on the disease or death thought (no change). Therefore, instead of having a disease or death thought and then perseverating on it, Miguel created a break between the thought and perseveration by writing and thinking about the sentence. The social worker felt that writing and thinking about the sentence would extinguish the reinforcing property that the negative thoughts had, causing him to perseverate on his illness or anticipated illnesses.

Almost immediately, Miguel's daily rate of disease or death thoughts dropped from his baseline range of two to eight thoughts to four thoughts, followed by a rate that ranged from zero to two thoughts per day (Figure 7.2). The reduction in disease or death thoughts enabled the social worker to switch the focus of therapy from disease thoughts to learning positive coping methods for Miguel's diagnosed conditions of hypertension and prostatitis. These methods included making dietary changes, exercising, increasing socialization with community members, and ensuring medication compliance. Miguel reported feeling better and experiencing "just a little anxiety" that was of no consequence and did not interfere with Miguel's functioning.

SUMMARY

Understanding the medical problems of older adults is critical for mental health professionals because older adults with chronic medical conditions often have co-occurring psychological problems. In addition, older adults with chronic medical conditions have a dearth of knowledge about their conditions and how to care for themselves. Coordination with family members and caregivers about self-care issues, medicine compliance, safety issues, health socialization, and exercise is important because social workers often overlook psychoeducation with medically ill clients. There is a need for social workers to initiate and coordinate psychoeducational programs, psychotherapeutic interventions, and basic health care information. In addition, social workers should seek continuing education to learn about medical disorders in order to understand what an older adult experiences when suffering from a chronic medical condition.

DISCUSSION TOPICS

1. Discuss your own experience with a medical problem and how your experience was the same as or different from that of an older adult client you are counseling who is experiencing one or more medical problems.
2. Discuss at least three therapeutic interventions you would use for an older adult client who was recently diagnosed with an acute medical problem.
3. Discuss what interventions you would use when counseling an older adult who has been experiencing a chronic medical problem for several years. Indicate in your discussion whether the interventions you choose are the same or similar to those chosen by the older adult client experiencing an acute illness (see Discussion Question 2).

CHAPTER 8

Older Adult Substance Abusers

If all goes well I will write an essay on it [cocaine] and I expect it will win its place in therapeutics by the side of morphium and superior to it.
—Sigmund Freud, *Cocaine Papers: Sigmund Freud*

Historical literature on older adult substance abuse is traditionally lacking in volume and riddled with stereotypes and false information. In an early study Winnick (1962) wrongly indicated that younger adult substance abusers age out by the time they reach older adulthood, rarely showing substance-abuse problems at older ages. Peterson (1988) incorrectly indicated that a small minority of older adults abuse alcohol and that they rarely abuse any other psychoactive substance. Winnick's and Peterson's studies are typical examples of studies contaminated by ageism and false information.

Their studies neglect to recognize that older adult substance abuse preferences are cohort determined, rather than following an instinct for alcohol abuse that occurs in older age. The baby boom cohort brings with it multiple types of substance abuse. Recent studies (Gfoerer, Penne, Pemberton, & Folson, 2008; Han, Gfroerer, Colliver, & Penne, 2009) indicate that the number of older adults with substance-abuse problems is estimated to increase from 2.5 million in 1999 to 5 million in 2020. Other studies (Menninger, 2002; Pennington, Butler, & Eagger, 2000; Rigler, 2000) indicate that the baby boom generation will have an incidence of alcohol abuse between 2% and 20%. It is estimated (Colliver, Compton, Gfroerer, & Condon, 2006) that the baby boom cohort will show an exponential increase in prescription drug abuse from 1.2% in 1999 to 2.4% in 2020. In addition, the abuse of the same classes of medication off-prescription that had an incidence of 911,000 in 1999 will increase to 2.7 million in 2020. This baby boom cohort brings an historical experience of high rates of drug abuse in their youth and young adulthood that differentiates the baby boom cohort from prior older adult cohorts (Colliver et al., 2006).

In the cohort preceding the baby boom generation, substance abuse, primarily alcohol abuse, was seen as a moral failing (Marx, 2002b) because of their experience with temperance, and prohibitionist movements that developed many dry communities. The baby boom generation brings attitudes and concepts that are changing paradigms about substance use. For example, some states recently legalized cannabis use for controlling pain and nausea in many medical conditions such as cancer, Parkinson's disease, multiple sclerosis, and various chemotherapy and medical treatments. Cannabis use is predicted to increase from 719,000 older adult users in 2006 to 3.3 million older adult users in 2020 (Colliver et al., 2006). In addition, baby boomers who abused alcohol or other substances are thought to be at greater risk for increasing their substance abuse at greater rates after the age of 65 (Marx, 2002a). This phenomenon is seen primarily in the younger segment of the baby boom cohort (Jessup & Dibble, 2012). This segment of the cohort shows more substance abuse and greater co-occurring diagnoses of posttraumatic stress disorder (PTSD), depression, and anxiety, along with a greater incidence of suicidal ideation. Li-Tzy and Blazer (2011) indicate that this younger segment of the baby boom cohort, in addition to having increased rate of prior substance abuse, is also more likely to seek treatment. Li-Tzy and Blazer assert that the substances most commonly used by this cohort are opioids/synthetic opioids, cocaine, and alcohol. Another finding by Jessup and Dibble (2012) is the stratification of co-occurring psychological problems by sexual orientation. Bisexual older adults have more co-occurring psychological problems than heterosexual older adults, older gay males, and older lesbians. An interesting finding is that immigration is contributory to older adult substance abuse (Cortes et al., 2003). In their study of Puerto Rican immigration, Cortes et al. (2003) suggest that substance abuse among older adults becomes an opportunistic, maladaptive way to cope with the stress of immigration. This is an important psychosocial problem of the current waves of immigration, especially from Mexico, Puerto Rico, and other Latin and South American countries.

Often, researchers study patients admitted to substance abuse treatment centers to determine incidence rates for various types of substance abuse. This research approach is fraught with bias and skewed assumptions about older adults abusing alcohol as their primary substance of choice. A recent study (Hendersen, 2008) indicated that alcohol abuse is the primary problem of the majority of adults age 50 and older. Admission rates increased with each age group through age 74. However, this study indicated that older adults are least likely to report other substance-abuse problems or polysubstance use. Nevertheless, this study found that polysubstance use increased in adults older than age 75 to rates comparable to polysubstance use in adults 40 years and younger. This is consistent with Levin and Kruger (2000), who assert that substance use other than alcohol is an invisible epidemic. They assert that older adults' substance abuse is often misdiagnosed as symptoms of dementia or depression. Another contributor to this invisible epidemic is the lack of recognition of substance abuse in older adults by health care professionals (Kane & Green, 2009b). Other foundational variables for this hidden epidemic are barriers to substance abuse assessment and treatment such as poverty, stigma, lack of substance abuse information, and a lack of transportation availability to treatment centers (Sorocco & Ferrell, 2006). Levin and Kruger (2000) reported that 17% to 23% of older adults are prescribed various benzodiazepines (a commonly prescribed group of tranquilizers), which is consistent with Henderson (2008), who found a high incidence of polysubstance dependence that included benzodiazepines combined with alcohol or other medications in the substance-abusing older adult. Another danger in the older adult substance abuser is the combination of substances the older adult is using with other prescribed medications or herbal supplements. This phenomenon of poly-pharmacy and polyherbacy is evidenced in the current baby boom cohort (Votova, Blais, Penning, & Maclure, 2013).

CHRONIC VERSUS SITUATIONAL SUBSTANCE ABUSE

The National Institute on Aging (Koch & Benshoff, 2002) suggests that the classifications of early-onset abusers of alcohol or other psychoactive substances (before the age of 65) and late-onset abusers of alcohol or other psychoactive substances (after the age of 65) be changed to chronic abusers (before the age of 65) and situational abusers (after the age of 65). This is an important distinction because, historically, older adults were stereotyped as early-onset alcohol abusers. Although this is true with most older adult alcohol abusers (Rigler, 2000), it is not necessarily true with those who abuse prescription medications, hallucinogens, illicit substances, or other psychoactive substances. In addition, those older adults who are situational abusers tend to have a better prognosis than chronic users, having not experienced the physiological and psychological damage seen in chronic alcohol abusers (Brennan & Moos, 1996).

Furthermore, it is not appropriate to look at older adults monolithically. Dehart and Hoffmann (1997) indicated that older men will show a greater incidence of chronic alcohol abuse and older women will have a greater incidence of situational alcohol abuse. Gomberg (1995) also suggests that there are many gender differences in alcohol and alcohol/prescription drug abuse. Older women have a higher incidence of concomitant alcohol and prescription drug abuse. Older women who have alcohol abuse problems have a high incidence of widowhood, compared with older alcohol-abusing men, who tend to be married, divorced, or separated (Epstein, Fischer-Elber, & Al-Otaiba, 2007). Compared with women, older men tend to show a greater incidence of loss of social networks when abusing alcohol. Blow and Schonfeld (2004) indicate that even though substance abuse in older adults is a significant problem, most older adults do not present for treatment. Blow and Shonfeld consider substance an invisible epidemic because older adults abusing substances or alcohol tend to deny their abuse and relatives and caregivers tend to downplay any abuse in the older adults in their care (Levin & Kruger, 2000). Many older adults view symptoms of their substance abuse as a normal consequence of aging, thus eliminating any opportunity to self-identify a substance-abuse problem (Benshoff, Harrawood, & Koch, 2003).

Alternatively, the lack of identification of a substance-abuse problem might be because many older adults' substance abuse does not meet the criteria for substance abuse/dependence by traditional psychiatric diagnostic criteria, which are standardized on adolescents, young adults, and middle-aged adults (Menningger, 2002). For example, Boeri (2004) studied adults of the baby boom generation as they entered middle age. Boeri suggested that there are different typologies for baby boom heroin users and that it is an error to view heroin abuse/dependence based solely on the criteria of standard psychiatric diagnoses. These typologies are controlled occasional users; weekend warriors (loss of control or bingeing on weekends or during parties); habitués (controlled use while maintaining occupational and social functioning); marginal users; problem addicts; user dealers/runners; using hustlers/sex workers; junkies; and relapsing addicts. Further research is needed to inform social workers as to whether similar typologies exist for other types of substance abuse since the baby boom generation is beginning to comprise the majority of older adults.

ALCOHOL ABUSE/DEPENDENCE

Older adults with alcohol-abuse problems do not seek help for their problems. Rather, they are often identified as having an alcohol-use problem when seeking care for other medical or psychological problems. In addition, alcohol abuse is a major cause of acute hospitalizations in older adults (Rigler, 2000). Bleechem (2002) found that bereavement or the onset of a disability may cause an older adult to increase his or her existing substance abuse. In addition, substance abuse is often precipitated or exacerbated by co-occurring problems of depression, retirement, altered activity levels, disability, relocation of family and friends, and family dissonance (Williams, Ballard, & Alessi, 2005).

Hidden alcohol abuse is also detected by assessments that may occur in a physician's office, a home setting in which social service agencies send social workers or nurses to an older adult's home, at a social service agency, or in a social worker's private practice. An alert social worker who comprehensively assesses the older adult (see Chapter 2, Assessing an Older Adult) has a unique opportunity to help the older adult identify an alcohol problem. Through positive engagement with nonthreatening questions, an understanding of the possibility of a problem may be developed with the older adult. During the assessment, questions about alcohol use can be framed while using usual information asked of all clients. Questions can also set the stage for steering the older adult to an understanding of how alcohol may be related to his or her presenting problem.

Briggs, Magnus, Lassiter, Patterson, and Smith (2011) indicate that a social worker must develop a heightened awareness of an older adult who is presenting with depression or who has had recent traumatic events or transitions in his or her life or when hearing concerns about the older adult, usually gathered by collateral contacts with the social worker. This may indicate a possible case of an older adult experiencing alcohol abuse or about to experience alcohol abuse. Hooyman and Kiyak (2010) found that 30% of alcohol-dependent older adults have co-occurring depression (see Chapter 5, Psychopathological Problems in Older Adults) and 20% of alcohol-dependent older adults have co-occurring dementia (see Chapter 6, Alzheimer's Disease and Other Dementias). Burke, Vassilev, Kantchelov, and Zweben (2002) feel that any collateral contact should only be used for informational purposes and not for the construction of a treatment plan. When there is an indication during an initial assessment of an alcohol problem, further comprehensive assessment sessions should be planned to help the older adult understand the extent to which he or she has a problem and to motivate the older adults to accept a treatment intervention.

Social workers assessing an older adult for alcohol abuse often confuse symptoms of possible alcohol abuse with dementia (Kein & Jess, 2002; O'Connell, Chin, Cunningham, & Lawlor, 2003). This phenomenon of missed diagnosis of substance abuse while diagnosing co-occurring psychological problems prevents effective diagnosis and treatment of older adult substance abusers (Rosen et al., 2013). This often occurs because of the paucity of training in social work programs about older adult substance abuse and its co-occurrence with other disorders. To address this paucity of training, Bial, Gutheil, Hanson, and White-Ryan (2012) instituted a program in which graduate social work students were recruited and received special training to work with older adults. The social work students interviewed older adults who had extensive substance-abuse histories. They then created life narratives for each older adult based on the interviews. These narratives were then used to infuse information about adult substance abuse into the graduate social work curriculum. This infusion is part of an effort of the GeroEd initiative sponsored by the Hartford Foundation ("CSWE Gero-Ed Center," 2013) to enhance gerontological knowledge across undergraduate and graduate social work curriculums. Briggs et al. (2011) reviewed research articles on substance abuse in older adults between the years of 1999 to 2009 and found only two research studies focused on how to increase learning for health care professionals about older adult substance abusers. Kane and Green (2009a) found that social work students feel treating older substance users is a waste of limited resources because older adults do not benefit from treatment. Paradoxically, these authors found that older adults drinking more than two drinks per day develop alcohol-abuse problems. These older adults were found to be using alcohol to self-medicate symptoms of depression and loneliness. Therefore the assumption by social work students that older adults need not be serviced for substance-abuse problems is incorrect.

Patterson and Jeste (1999) suggest that standards for recognition and definition of alcohol problems in younger adults are not necessarily accurate for the assessment of alcohol problems in older adults. Inaccurate assessment, when a social worker often diagnoses a co-occurring psychopathological problem and misses an alcohol abuse/dependence diagnosis, occurs because most social workers and other health care workers are inadequately trained to assess addiction in older adults (Sorocco & Ferrell, 2006). In addition, health care professionals are often reluctant to recognize alcohol problems in an older adult because of the confusion in the social workers' lives between what is socially acceptable and what is problematic (Stewart & Olsin, 2001). Most older adults being treated for alcohol abuse who have a chronic history (whether early or late onset) have initial treatment in an in-patient setting (Kraener, Conigliaro, & Saitz, 1999). This is to help prevent delirium tremens, seizures, and falls and to treat co-occurring medical and cognitive decline conditions.

Another important aspect of a social worker making an accurate assessment of alcohol abuse by an older adult is the phenomenon of *alcohol use disorder* (AUD; Wiktorsson, Runeson, Skoog, Ostiing, & Waern, 2010). An older adult experiencing AUD is at risk for attempted or completed suicide. As indicated in Chapter 2, Assessing the Older Adult, an older adult contemplating suicide may not volunteer this information on assessment unless the social worker asks direct exploratory questions on suicidality (Sher, 2006; Wilcox, Connor, & Caine, 2004).

NONALCOHOL SUBSTANCE USE DISORDERS

An unfortunate consequence of older adults being the largest cohort of prescription drug misusers/abusers (Culberson & Ziska, 2008) is a virtually hidden epidemic of prescription drug abuse (Finlaysoon & Davis, 2004). Unfortunately, health professionals unfamiliar with substance-abuse problems in older adults often confuse substance abuse symptoms for signs of aging or misdiagnose it as a psychological disorder (Epstein et al., 2007; Han et al., 2009). Prescription drug abuse can occur with a single drug, polydrug prescriptions, or co-occur with alcohol abuse. The most abused prescription drugs are benzodiazepines and opioids/synthetic opioids (Culberson & Ziska, 2008). In addition, older adults abuse prescription drugs without the intention of wanting to abuse them (Jensen, Lukow, & Heck, 2012). This occurs because of these older adults experiencing co-occurring psychological problems of anxiety and depression (see Chapter 5, Psychopathological Problems in Older Adults) and co-occurring dementia (see Chapter 6, Alzheimer's Disease and Other Dementias). Alemagno, Niles, and Treiber (2004) find that policy changes are needed to institute a national computer database that cross-matches medications that older adults are using to prompt intervention in instances of unintentional misuse.

A surprising clinical intervention is that of *life circumstance*. Atchley (1997) finds that an older adult with a chronic debilitating illness or an acute illness tends to stop abusing alcohol or other psychoactive substances because these substances interfere with needed medications. In addition, when medical conditions cause the placement of an older adult in a facility that prohibits the use of psychoactive substances, lack of access to these substances causes the older adult to stop his or her abuse.

Benzodiazepine Abuse/Dependence Disorders

Longo and Johnson (2000) indicated that benzodiazepines are often prescribed to older adults for anxiety and insomnia. Levin and Kruger found that benzodiazepines comprise 17% to 23% of the prescriptions written for older adults (2000). These prescriptions are an addition to the polypharmacy found with many older adult patients. Polypharmacy is a concern because many older adults have multiple co-occurring medical illnesses that are being treated with several medications. This puts these older adults at risk for a greater number of side effects, treatment failures, and increased morbidity (Linnebur, O'Connell, & Wessell, 2005).

Marienfeld, Tek, Diaz, Schottenfeld, and Chawarski (2012) found a growing trend of psychiatrists reporting a reluctance to prescribe benzodiazepines to older adult patients with a history of substance abuse. Reluctance is based on a high probability that these older adults may be manipulating the psychiatrist, seeking to divert prescribed benzodiazepines to other substance abusers, or that by prescribing benzodiazepines the psychiatrist may be initiating dependence in the older adult. If this trend to resist prescribing benzodiazepines to older adults were sustained, it would contribute to addressing a major social problem facing older adults (Preville et al., 2012). Moos, Brennan, Schutte, and Moos (2004) indicated that alcohol and polydrug use is an escalating trend that increases morbidity and mortality in older adults and, from a policy prospective,

simultaneously increases health care costs. Most of the health complications arising from inappropriate prescribing are a consequence of adverse
drug reactions (Lazarou, Pomeranz, & Corey, 1998).

Older adult benzodiazepine abusers are at risk for hip fractures from
falls. The greatest periods of risk are within 2 weeks of initiation of use and
4 weeks after cessation of use (Cumming & Le Couteur, 2003). In addition,
benzodiazepine abuse increases age-related cognitive impairment and exag-
gerates dementia (Longo & Johnson, 2000). Another concern with benzodiazepine abuse is with the older driver. When using benzodiazepines the older
adult should be carefully evaluated for temporary driving suspension or,
in the case of chronic use, permanent driving suspension. Benzodiazepine
use and abuse increase the likelihood of automobile accidents (Sadock,
Sakock, & Ruiz, 2009). Unfortunately, when an older adult is advised to dis-
continue benzodiazepine use, he or she will most likely find another physician and reinstitute use. Social workers who see older adults in a social
service agency, institutional setting, assisted living setting, or private practice should be in contact with prescribing physicians to ensure proper use
or successful withdrawal from the older adult's prescribed benzodiazepine.

Opioid/Synthetic Opioid Abuse/Dependence Disorders

Prescribing opioids and synthetic opioids to an older adult is complicated.
Many older adults experience chronic pain from cancer, arthritis, postsurgical pain, or injuries (Cummings & Cooper, 2011). Opioids and synthetic
opioids are also used in end-of-life cases. Paradoxically, in end-of-life cases
many older adults are underprescribed for fear on the physician's part of
causing an addiction. For example, 80% of patients in long-term care suffer
from substantial pain, yet 25% do not receive pain medication or nonmedication treatment (Won, Lapane, & Vallow, 2004). In some cases, long-term
use is warranted and can be done safely when overseen by a pain specialist or oncologist. The prevalence rate of pain in older adults living within a
community is 25% to 50% and in nursing homes increases to 70% (Furlan,
Sandoval, & Mallis-Gagnon, 2006). Most older adults who experience
chronic pain do not develop addiction (Liorente, Oslin, & Malphurs, 2006).
Clark (2006) found that 44% of older adults who are prescribed nonsteroi-
dal anti-inflammatory drugs (NSAIDs) are also prescribed opioid and synthetic opioid medications. Fentanyl patches may be effective in managing
pain, as opposed to oral or intravenous opioids and synthetic opioids, and
show a greater degree of safety with reference to addiction (Zuurmond,
Davis, & Vergidis, 2002).

Alternatively, opioids and synthetic opioids have an increased probability of causing dependence and co-occurring delirium in older adults
(Briggs et al., 2011; Culberson & Ziska, 2008). Opioid and synthetic opioid
use in older adults has two additional potential dangers. Tolerance and
dependence occur more rapidly compared with younger adults. In addition, initial pharmacological action of the opioids and synthetic opioids is
slower than in younger adults, but the duration of the substance effect is
longer than in younger adults (F. C. Blow, 1998). If used clinically, administration of opioids and synthetic opioids should be done as a team effort
including an addiction specialist, physician, and social worker.

AN EXISTENTIAL ANALYSIS OF OLDER ADULT SUBSTANCE ABUSE/DEPENDENCE

An older adult can suffer from many forms of inner tension. The older adult may feel oppressed by poverty, medical illness, bereaved through loss of significant others, loss of functioning, or isolation, among other significant psychosocial stressors. A significantly disturbing psychosocial stressor or the convergence of two or more psychosocial stressors can reduce older adults' resilience (Kane, 2008; Morgan, Brosi, & Brosi, 2011) to psychosocial stressors, producing an existential vacuum. Because of this existential vacuum, the older adult may choose a *purpose substitute* in lieu of purpose or positive forward movement with his or her life (see Chapter 3, Intervention Theories Informing the Clinician Treating Older Adults). With respect to this chapter, the older adult chooses compulsive use of psychoactive substances as a purpose substitute. Most psychoactive drug users quickly progress to dependency. However, a weakness in this orientation is noted by Weinberg (2000), who suggests that drug abusers are identified as those who have lost control of their use, ignoring a subgroup of psychoactive drug users that are occasional substance abusers. Unfortunately, older adult substance abusers resist or refuse traditional substance-treatment venues such as rehabilitation facilities, 12-step programs, and psychotherapeutic settings, which view a substance abuser as one who loses control (Grant, Schreiber, & Odiaug, 2013; Kane & Green, 2009a). In addition, family members of the substance-abusing older adult are considered codependent (Ligon, 2013). This may explain why many older adult substance abusers are not identified as having a substance-abuse problem.

This author suggests the following explanation for older adult substance abuse. Once the older adult chooses a psychoactive substance (or several substances) as a maladaptive response to biopsychosocial stressors, the older adult enters a cyclic phenomenon (Figure 8.1) that starts with a resilience reduction to inner tension, leading to the choice of engaging in repetitive, compulsive psychoactive substance ingestion. This compulsive behavior creates a temporary state of disorientation that enables the older adult to be temporarily relieved from the distress emanating from the biopsychosocial stressors that caused the initial resilience reduction. By not dealing with the biopsychosocial stressors, the older adult experiences punishment from the compulsive psychoactive substance ingestion. Punishment can take many forms: The older adult can experience a medical emergency, can be arrested, can have severe interpersonal dysfunction leading to relationship problems and isolation, can experience financial hardships, and any other imaginable consequences of substance abuse/dependence. These punishments bring the older adult back to his or her state of resilience reduction, which is now exacerbated by the consequences of his or her substance abuse/dependence. The exacerbation of the psychological distress the older adult experiences causes him or her to re-engage in the compulsive psychoactive substance ingestion that begins the cyclic phenomenon again. As noted earlier, this dalliance in substance abuse can be occasional or can lead to clinical substance dependency.

A social worker intervenes in this cyclic phenomenon by introducing the concept that the psychoactive substance ingestion is a maladaptive choice in response to the reduction of resilience to known biopsychosocial stressors. Therapy proceeds by examining other choices that address the psychosocial stressor (or stressors) that would lead to a positive resolution

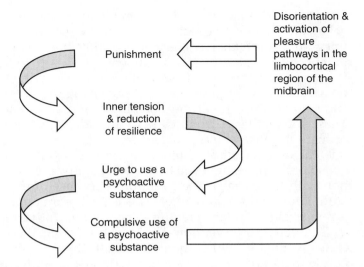

FIGURE 8.1 The cyclic phenomenon of older adult substance abuse that leads to substance dependence.

(see different psychotherapy strategies listed in subsequent sections). The social worker helps the older adult identify other problem-solving strategies that he or she employed in the past to solve egregious problems in his or her life. This identification helps the older adult to muster his or her strength (strength perspective; see Chapter 3, Intervention Theories Informing the Clinician Treating Older Adults) and develop a sense of empowerment during the process of learning to effectively deal with the identified psychosocial stressor (or stressors).

A parallel effort is made to have the older adult achieve a state of sobriety that may entail medical intervention, a rehabilitation program, or 12-step support groups as a critical adjuvant to the older adult's psychotherapy. Unfortunately, most social workers make attendance at 12-step programs mandatory, disregarding that not everyone is suited for 12-step intervention (D. D. Koch & Benshoff, 2002). In addition, many older adults who attend 12-step meetings do not feel engaged with the younger people in the meeting, feeling that their concerns and consequences from substance abuse are different and that age-related hearing problems and disabilities and lack of transportation are barriers to regular attendance at meetings (2002).

It is critical that the short-term goal is cessation of ingesting the psychoactive substance (or substances) in order to achieve a state of abstinence. The long-term goals are to maintain abstinence and to learn to deal with psychosocial stressors effectively without turning to the substitute purpose of using a psychoactive substance (or substances).

MOTIVATIONAL INTERVIEWING

Miller and Rollnick (2002) suggest the importance of using motivational interviewing to heighten the awareness of a substance abuser about his or her addiction and to produce an internal motivation to accept treatment.

Cooper (2012) suggests combining motivation interviewing with cognitive behavioral therapy (see sections on Cognitive Behavioral Interventions and Integrating Motivational Interviewing With Other Therapeutic Modalities) for effective substance-abuse treatment.

In the first aspect of motivational interviewing, the social worker uses interactive interpersonal skills to engage an older adult with open-ended questions, reflective listening, validation, and summarization. These interactive techniques help an older adult learn to discuss his or her substance-abuse problem from his or her perspective. By doing this, the older adult develops a heightened awareness of the substance-abuse problem being discussed. Reciprocally, the interpersonal interaction with the social worker reinforces a sense of engagement between older adult and social worker. This aspect of motivational interviewing is remarkably similar to reminiscence and narrative therapies discussed in Chapter 3, Intervention Theories Informing the Clinician Treating Older Adults, in which the older adult, through his or own life story, is able to identify problems and rewrite the narrative to facilitate cognitive change.

The second aspect of motivational interviewing, again using interactive interpersonal techniques, entails targeting the desire to make change and commit to cessation of substance abuse, which is strengthened. Glasner (2004) indicates that in this phase the social worker creates a cognitive dissonance through dialogue with the client, highlighting the contrast between the older adult's substance abuse and the positive aspects of his or her aspirations, self, and purpose for moving forward with his or her life. In other words, the older adult is slowly moved through a cost/benefit analysis of limiting his or her substance abuse or achieving cessation of substance abuse and finally a state of abstinence.

COGNITIVE BEHAVIORAL INTERVENTIONS

Bartels, Blow, Brockman, and Van Citters (2005) find that older adults who are alcohol dependent drink in response to inadequate social supports, loneliness, and depression. This suggests that cognitive behavioral interventions can be effective for older adult problem drinkers with treatment focused on increasing social contact, improving intimacy in interpersonal relationships, and increasing participation in recreational activities. Schonfeld and Dupress (1995) feel that cognitive behavioral interventions produce significantly better results in older drinkers when compared with 12-step programs. Cognitive behavioral therapy (see Chapter 3, Intervention Theories Informing the Clinician Treating Older Adults) is effective for substance abuse in general and not exclusively for alcohol abuse (Cooper, 2012; Grant, Donahue, & Odlaug, 2011).

Many older adult substance abusers do not have available transportation to treatment facilities or are disabled and unable to travel (Morgan & Brosi, 2007). In addition, many older adults have a poor understanding of their substance abuse, and the health care professionals treating them often lack an understanding of the relationship of aging and substance abuse (Ligon, 2013). Addressing the problems of isolation from services and the dearth of understanding and information on substance abuse, researchers are experimenting with reaching these older adults via the mail (Parr, Kavanagh, Young, Stubbs, & Bradizza, 2013) or a website to provide cognitive behavioral therapy (Parr, Kavanagh, & Young, 2011). This research is in a preliminary stage and to date is not recommended as an effective cognitive therapy tool. However, with the new baby boom cohort aging, use of Internet-related therapeutic tools may prove to be successful interventions unto themselves or useful adjuncts to existing cognitive behavioral therapy techniques

INTEGRATING MOTIVATIONAL INTERVIEWING WITH OTHER THERAPEUTIC MODALITIES

Combining motivational interviewing with cognitive behavioral therapy is shown to be more effective for treating substance abuse that either therapeutic modality alone (Moyers & Houck, 2011). The motivational interviewing therapeutic component is used for initiating and maintaining a motivated response in the older adult substance abuser. The cognitive behavioral therapy component is used to give the older adult the psychological tools to make alternative changes to thoughts and behaviors to initiate and ensure compliance with abstinence from substance abuse (Burke, 2011). Marlatt and Donovan (2005) extend this model by suggesting that motivational interviewing is effective for managing resistance to treatment while building motivation in the older adult. In addition, Marlatt and Donovan (2005) suggest that motivational interviewing serves as a foundation for the integration of other therapeutic modalities, not restricting this integration to cognitive behavioral therapy, as Moyers and Houck (2011), and Burke (2011) suggest.

Morgan et al. (2011) feel that narrative therapy (see Chapter 3, Intervention Theories Informing the Clinician Treating Older Adults) is an appropriate therapeutic component to combine with motivational interviewing. By doing so, the social worker enables the older adult substance abuser to understand the oppressive aspects he or she experienced from addiction. This in turn reinforces the cost/benefit analysis of motivational interviewing by having the older adult re-author his or her story by focusing on the benefits of abstinence and incorporating past skills and strategies to overcome conflicts and adversity experienced during the older adult's history. Miller, Forcehimes, and Zweben (2011) suggest an existential approach by combining motivational interviewing with existential techniques of empathy, support, and ability to chose positive responses to psychosocial stressors rather than engaging in substance abuse. These authors feel that it is important for the social worker to view an older adult who breaks abstinence with an empathic response and supportive suggestions, reminding the older adult that he or she still has a repertoire of positive coping responses to employ that would enable restoration of abstinence. This is in contrast to 12-step programs that view a lapse in sobriety as a relapse, suggesting failure to the older adult. Finally, Marlatt, Bowen, and Chawla (2010) encourage incorporating mindfulness therapy with motivational therapy. Mindfulness therapy teaches the older adult substance abuser how to heighten his or her awareness of thoughts and feelings, integrates relaxation techniques as a substitution for substance-abuse behaviors, and reinforces the concept of positive choices (Bowen, Witkiewitz, Chawla, & Grow, 2011; Germer, Siegel, & Fulton, 2013; Nickoletti & Taussig, 2006) that are available to the older adult.

THE CASE OF PAULINE

Pauline* is an 87-year-old Caucasian woman living in a continuing care community. Pauline has been a resident for the past year. She is chronically ill with Parkinson's disease and diabetes. Because of these conditions, Pauline is prescribed multiple medications by her internist and her neurologist.

Pauline was referred to a social worker at the continuing care medical center because she was complaining of anxiety. Her internist was concerned that Pauline was insisting he prescribe Xanax for her because in the past she had been prescribed Valium and then Xanax by different internists in the community where she used to live. Pauline claimed that she just "ran out of her drugs" and insisted that she was always prescribed 120 pills at a time. Pauline indicated to her new internist that she had been taking benzodiazepines for the past 20 years. This alarmed her internist, causing him to make the referral to the social worker.

On assessment, Pauline explained that she is always anxious and needs the medication to feel "level." When asked by the social worker to explain what she means by "always anxious" Pauline spoke in general terms that she feels nervous and only feels calm when she takes Xanax. The social worker had consulted with the internist when he made the referral and was told by the internist that he would only prescribe 30 pills at a time on the condition that Pauline attend psychotherapy sessions on a regular basis. The social worker told Pauline this condition and she agreed to begin attending weekly sessions.

After 8 weeks of psychotherapy, Pauline and the social worker had made a strong engagement with each other. Pauline, feeling safe in her relationship with the social worker, confessed that she was augmenting the prescription from the internist by seeing three other internists in the area who were not part of the continuing care medical facility. When the social worker questioned Pauline about how she knew about these internists, she told her that other residents are doing the same thing because doctors are "clamping down on how many pills we can get." When questioned about her dosage, Pauline indicated that the community care internist prescribed 1 mg four times per day. Pauline said that she was used to 3 mg four times per day and that was why she was going to the other doctors.

The social worker told Pauline that what she was doing was medically dangerous and that the doctors would have to be informed about the multiple prescriptions. In addition, the social worker told Pauline that she would have to coordinate treatment with an addiction specialist who would help Pauline return to a safer dose and eventually be withdrawn from Xanax because she had developed a benzodiazepine dependency.

Subsequently, Pauline was seen by the social worker three times per week for a period of 8 weeks to facilitate psychoeducational learning about addiction. Going to a 12-step program was suggested to Pauline, and she tried an open meeting. After the meeting, Pauline told the social worker that the "place was full of young addicts and drunks" and that she could

---

*Names and other identifying information have been changed to preserve confidentiality.

not relate to anyone in the room, let alone ask anyone to be a sponsor. Pauline agreed with the social worker that they would proceed by having her continue to attend individual psychotherapy sessions where motivational interviewing techniques were combined with cognitive behavioral therapy and narrative therapy. In addition, weekly she would attend group therapy sessions that focused on support and psychoeducation about addiction. The group therapy sessions would have group members in the same age cohort as Pauline and with similar substance dependencies. In addition, Pauline would see an addiction specialist for medication management. It was also agreed that Pauline did not have to return to the 12-step program.

Using motivational interviewing techniques, the social worker was able to get Pauline to understand and cooperate with a plan to slowly withdraw her from benzodiazepines. In addition, the addiction specialist initiated a plan to transition Pauline from benzodiazepines to an antidepressant (Zoloft, an antidepressant and antianxiety agent that is not addictive) to help manage her withdrawal from Xanax and to address any subsequent anxiety symptoms.

In addition to the interventions from the addiction specialist, Pauline's social worker began a process of teaching Pauline relaxation techniques based on Ericksonian hypnotic techniques (see Chapter 3, Intervention Theories Informing the Clinician Treating Older Adults). From the first session, Pauline felt a sense of relief of her anxiety and was eager to continue learning the techniques. Using her hypnotic relaxation techniques and cooperating with a slow withdrawal from Xanax over a period of 5 months enabled Pauline to address the interpersonal and intrapersonal conflicts she was experiencing. As problem resolution proceeded, Pauline reported a gradual lessening of her anxiety. She even remarked to the social worker, "Why didn't anyone take the time to figure out my problems before? All they did was just throw pills at me."

SUMMARY

Contrary to conventional wisdom, there is an escalating incidence of substance abuse in older adults. The current cohort of older adults, the baby boom generation, is making a profound change in the culture of substance abuse in older adults. Unlike prior cohorts whose primary substance-abuse problem was alcohol abuse and dependency, the baby boom generation brings polysubstance experience. Projections indicate that the incidence of substance abuse will more than double by the year 2020.

This brings a special challenge to social workers who are the primary gatekeepers on the front line to recognize substance abuse and dependency in the older adults they serve and to implement treatment interventions. All social workers need additional training in substance-abuse treatment with older adults.

Another mission of these gatekeepers is to educate and coordinate with the physicians prescribing polypharmacy to their clients. In addition, an advocacy imperative is needed to change state laws to seek mandated centralized recording of controlled substances in a national database to eliminate the ability of older adults to seek prescriptions from multiple physicians, both in and out of state.

DISCUSSION TOPICS

1. Discuss the different types of substance abuse you have encountered working with older adults.
2. Discuss the different types of substance abuse you have encountered working with adolescents, young adults, and middle-age adults.
3. Discuss what interventions you used for each age group.
4. Discuss which interventions were the same and which were different for each age group.

CHAPTER 9

Older Adult Sexuality

What most people in our culture mean by being lovable is essentially a mixture between being popular and having sex appeal.
— Erich Fromm, *The Art of Loving*

From the Middle Ages to today, sexuality between older adults has been considered by some religions as immoral and by most younger people as nonexistent—promoting the stereotype that older adults do not engage in sexual activity (Convey, 1989). Because most adults in the past did not live past 65, discussion about and interest in older sexuality was virtually nonexistent (Tien-Hyatt, 1986–1987). Historically, many mental health professionals and health care providers were judgmental about an older adult's sexuality in institutional settings (LaTorre & Kear, 1977). Fournier (2000) calls this phenomenon the *cringe factor*.

Today, older adults, when questioned about their sexuality, indicate that sexual activity is a pleasurable and positive aspect of their lives (Beckman, Waern, Gustafson, & Skoog, 2008; Bouman, 2008; Rosen & Bachman, 2008). This dispels the myth that older adults are not interested in or do not engage in sexual activity (Lochlainn & Kenny, 2013). Sexuality in old age needs to be viewed as unique to older adults, rather than an extension of youthful sexuality (Hajjar & Kamel, 2003). Shaw (2012) feels that a research initiative needs to begin to further studies of normal sexual functioning in older adults.

In older adults, sexual activity declines as a result of multiple causes such as medical illness, disability, psychological problems, and social constructs that exist in institutional settings (Lindau et al., 2007). One basis for a stereotype of older adults not being interested or engaged in sexual activity may come from the negative correlation that as one ages, the distress felt by a decline in sexual activity or dysfunction decreases. Therefore, older adults may not complain to a social worker about a decline in sexual activity for lack of information about older adult sexuality and lack of the knowledge of the possibility of experiencing satisfying sexual activity, thus buying into the stereotype by experiencing self-stigma (see Chapter 4, Stigma and Older Adults). Older women are found not to confide in their physicians about sexual problems unless the discussion is initiated by the physician, in contrast to older men, who speak more freely about their sexuality (Sadovsky et al., 2006).

Another phenomenon of older adult sexuality is that many older adults are aging without major health problems that would limit their sexual functioning. Therefore, their aging process occurs as a healthy integration of biological, psychological, and social spheres in their lives. In addition, these adults value the benefits of sexual activity and how it influences their quality of life (Davis, 2012). When sexual activity declines in this relatively healthy group, concern is raised and solutions are sought. Many older male baby boomers use sexually enhancing medications that treat sexual dysfunctions, and older baby boomer men and women seek psychotherapeutic knowledge and available information on older sexuality when addressing sexual dysfunctions (Bitzer, Tshudin, & Adler, 2008; Montague et al., 2005).

Historically, this concept of declining sexuality in a relatively healthy older adult population was called the *interest–activity gap* (Pfeiffer, Verwoerdt, & Davis, 1972; Pfeiffer, Verwoerdt, & Wang, 1969). This interest–activity gap finds the older adult interested in sexual activity even though for a variety of reasons sexual activity is decreased. Kalra, Subramanyam, and Pinto (2011) find that 72% of adults younger than 60 report being sexually active, in contrast to 57% of adults older than 60. Many adults from both groups reported periods of sexual abstinence during their adult lives. Sexual decline was found to be greater in women. Decline in sexual activity or desire was not attributed to chronic illness.

MEN

Avis (2000) indicates that sexual interest and activity is higher in men when compared with women throughout the developmental stages from age 35 to old age. Men tend to maintain interest in sexual activity well into advanced age (Laumann et al., 2006). However, men, like women, report declining sexual activity as they age, despite continued interest in sex. Most older men attribute the decline in their sexual activity to erectile dysfunction (Tressel et al., 2007). This subgroup of older men who experience erectile dysfunction, which has a prevalence rate of 52% to 64%, still have desire for and interest in sexual activity (L. J. Smith, Mulhall, Deveci, Monaghan, & Reid, 2007). Other symptoms of problems that contribute to the decline in sexual activity are decline in erection frequency, decline in sexual desire, and problems associated with ejaculation (Bacon, Mittelman, Kawachi, & Giovannucci, 2003).

Older men often reveal their problem with erectile dysfunction to a health care provider or social worker (Ayta, McKinlay, & Krane, 1999). With the introduction of oral medications for erectile dysfunction, men are most likely to present for treatment (Marshall, 2010). However, these medications are not a magic cure for erectile dysfunction because approximately one third of older adult men being treated with oral medications do not respond to treatment (Corona, et al., 2010; Hatzimouratidis & Hatzichristou, 2005). This may be due to older males having one or more co-occurring medical problems (see Chapter 7, Medical Problems in Older Adults) that physiologically interfere with the pharmacotherapy treatment. In addition, pharmaceutical interventions for male sexual functioning inadvertently have caused a phenomenon called *medicalization of sexuality* (Conrad, 2005). This phenomenon is driven by capital markets, rather than by health care professional initiatives. Aggressive advertising drives consumer demands that support and further medicalization of older adult male sexuality. In addition, a phenomenon of *virility surveillance* is created whereby normal sexual function is considered healthy and any deviation from normal functioning is considered a sign of disease or disorder (Marshall, 2010). Virility surveillance infers that functional changes that occur in normal aging are an indication of a sexual disorder.

However, for gay men, changes in erectile functioning are experienced as unacceptable and especially problematic to their lifestyles (Adams, 2003). Adams claims that change in erectile functioning causes a conflict that is deeply rooted in the youthful sexual prowess that underlies gay male culture, which over a gay man's development stresses multiple sexual encounters and sexual vigor. This conflict in older gay men is further complicated by co-occurring medical problems. Social workers treating older gay men for erectile dysfunction need additional training about understanding gay male culture (see Chapter 11, Gay Male, Lesbian, Bisexual, and Transgender Older Adults).

Erectile Dysfunction Treatments

There are multiple approaches to treating erectile dysfunction in older men. The first and primary intervention is referral to an urologist. The urologist has many options for treatment. These include medications, natural supplements (e.g., yohimbine), vacuum constriction devices, and surgical intervention (penile prosthesis; Montague et al., 2005).

Social workers often receive referrals from urologists, family physicians, and geriatricians for older men suffering from erectile dysfunction. Psychotherapy and sex counseling are often needed as an adjunct to medical interventions. The psychosocial aspect of erectile dysfunction is as important to address as the medical aspect. Therapy is oriented to eliminating unrealistic expectations about any of the medical interventions returning sexual performance to that of a younger adult. Focus is also on the benefits of noncoital sexual activity and how those behaviors may also produce sexual gratification (Korfage et al., 2009). In addition, the older male adult's social worker can address lifestyle changes (Eposito et al., 2004) that may have a positive effect on erectile functioning. These include pursuing a smoking-cessation program and enlisting the help of a nutritionist, if the older adult is obese, to facilitate a weight-loss program and with medical guidance to initiate an exercise program. Therefore, smoking cessation, improved nutrition, and increased exercise are reasonable goals for improving erectile functioning.

WOMEN

Women are more likely than men not to report sexual activity, making them harder to study. However, like men, women attribute declining sexual activity to a least one sexual problem (Tressel et al., 2007), usually the lack of a partner. Loss of a partner for women is more traumatic than for men because women tend to outlive men. Therefore, finding a new partner is competitive and it is unlikely that a partner will be available. Hypoactive sexual desire is the most reported sexual dysfunction in older women (Laumann, Paik, & Rosen, 1999). Other functional sexual problems reported are difficulty with vaginal lubrication and inability to achieve orgasm. Women report that a decline in sexual activity starts as early as the late 30s or early 40s, with an increasing decline in sexual interest and desire as they age (Hayes & Debbersteub, 2006). Older adult women also attribute a decline in their sexual activity to lack of social opportunity (Tressel et al., 2007).

Older heterosexual women report that a precipitator of decline in their sexual activity is a reaction to sexual dysfunctions in their male partners, or the loss of a sexual partner, who is usually the spouse (Blumel, Castel-Branco, Cancelo, & Romero, 2004). Functional problems that contribute to the decline in sexual activity of older women include co-occurring anxiety or depression (see Chapter 5, Psychopathological Problems in Older Adults), urinary incontinence, and thyroid conditions (Shifen, Monz, Russo, Segreti, & Johannes, 2008). Additional psychological problems that are contributory to sexual decline include being a victim of sexual abuse or domestic violence, abandonment by a sexual partner, negative body image, eating disorders, and poor sense of self (Wiegel, Scepkowski, & Barlow, 2006).

Another factor often misunderstood that leads to a diagnostic opinion of pathology in sexual desire and activity in older adult women is that women's sexual activity, unlike men's sexual activity, is initiated by arousal behaviors rather than sexual drives (Basson, 2000). Arousal emanates from signals of a partner's receptivity, seductive behavior by the woman or her partner, or a conscious perception of arousal. Unfortunately, most older women were socialized to be passive to a male partner (Baldissera, Bueno, & Hoga, 2012). Most older men were not socialized to be romantic to a partner, invest time in foreplay, and have the knowledge of what a woman needs to achieve orgasm. In order for older adult women to overcome the male-dominated barriers to their sexual satisfaction they need to enhance their self-esteem and overcome loneliness by increasing socialization in pursuit of a sexual partner, no longer viewing men's sexual satisfaction as a woman's obligation. These steps will help older women overcome social constructs that have inhibited or impaired their sexuality.

GAY MALE AND LESBIAN COUPLES

See Chapter 11, Gay Male, Lesbian, Bisexual, and Transgender Older Adults.

HETEROSEXUAL COUPLES

Heterosexual couples react to a decline in sexual activity in several characteristic ways. Many couples will slowly see a decline in their sexual activity with a result of complete abstention from sexual activity. If other aspects of their relationship are positive, then the lack of sexual activity is not a threat to the integrity of the couple.

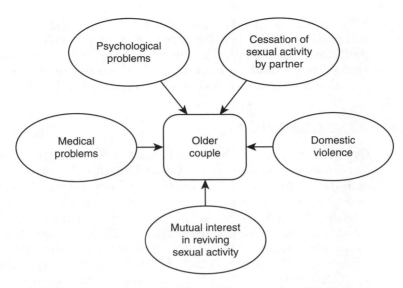

FIGURE 9.1 Types of variables that affect sexual activity in couples.

However, lack of sexual activity can cause dysfunction in a coupled relationship that may threaten the integrity of the couple (Figure 9.1). When one partner ceases any desire for sexual activity while the other still wants to engage in sexual activity, the homeostasis of the couple becomes threatened, often leading to an extramarital affair by the sexually active spouse. This type of problem is often a cause of presentation by either partner, for his or her own reasons, for psychotherapy. The nonsexual spouse may discover the affair or be complaining about the lack of closeness (nonsexual) in the relationship. The spouse engaged in the extramarital affair may present with feelings of guilt, wanting to leave the relationship, or wanting to repair the relationship.

Another presentation often seen by social workers is a couple presenting for help because there is a mutual interest in reviving their sexual relationship. A typical presenting problem is a long history of routine, predictable sexual activity without any perception of passion and excitement. An older couple may present with a dilemma of one partner having a functional problem or disability that requires a new approach to sexual interaction with each other. In addition, many older adult couples present with a problem of poor communication with each other about sexual needs, desires, and fantasies. All these presentations are amenable to psychotherapeutic intervention.

Serious psychological problems in one or both partners may be the reason for requesting counseling (Kalra et al., 2011; Shifen et al., 2008). These problems may be co-occurring with functional problems or may be the primary reason for dysfunction in the sexual relationship. Anxiety and depression are common presentations (see Chapter 5, Psychopathological Problems in Older Adults). Personality disorders, often not diagnosed in older adults, are the foundations for difficulties in successful psychotherapeutic intervention. This is because a personality disorder is ego-syntonic to the older adult. Therefore, he or she has little insight into his or her problem, often blaming the other for the lack or dysfunction in sexual activity.

This is often seen when an older adult has a narcissistic or obsessive-compulsive personality disorder (Althof et al., 2005; Wiegel et al., 2006). Additional psychological problems that are contributory to sexual decline among couples include being a victim of sexual abuse or domestic violence and abandonment by a sexual partner (Wiegel et al., 2006).

SEXUALITY AND DEMENTIA

Contrary to popular belief, when an older adult experiences dementia, the dementia does not necessarily eliminate sexual desire or sexual activity. Many older adults suffering from various forms of dementia (see Chapter 6, Alzheimer's Disease and Other Dementias) become sexually disinhibited and show increasing hypersexuality as their cognitive deficits increase (Alagiakrishnan et al., 2005). In contrast, some dementia patients show a diminishment of sexual desire and sexual activity (Vioeberghs, Van Dam, Franck, Staufenbiel, & De Deyn, 2007).

Dementia patients presenting with hypersexuality exhibit a high sexual drive that causes sexual behaviors that interfere with their activities of daily living (ADLs) or is actuated with unwilling partners (Higgins, Barker, & Begley, 2004). The inappropriate sexual behaviors include unwanted touching, groping, public masturbation, public disrobing, and public sexual verbalizations (Alagiakrishnan et al., 2005). Gender determines the type of hypersexuality. Men usually act out physically, whereas woman usually act out verbally (Onishi et al., 2006). Patients with dementia who are aging in place are often transferred to assisted living centers or nursing homes because of the increased distress placed on caregivers stemming from these inappropriate sexual behaviors (Alkhalil, Tanvir, Alkhalil, & Lowenthal, 2004).

Inappropriate sexual behaviors in patients with dementia have a prevalence rate of 7% to 25% (Guay, 2008). A common stereotype is that inappropriate sexual behavior is seen only in Alzheimer's disease. This is incorrect; inappropriate sexual behavior is seen in many types of dementia (Meston & Frohlich, 2000). However, the most common dementia showing inappropriate sexual behaviors, aside from Alzheimer's disease, is vascular dementia (2000).

Di Napoli, Breland, and Allen (2013) formed focus groups with nursing home staff members to understand their attitude about the sexuality of residents experiencing dementia. Contrary to the stereotype that staff members are uninterested in residents suffering with dementia being sexual, this study revealed that staff members feel a need for more training and interventions that would enable residents to sexually express themselves in a positively managed way. The staff members' attitudes toward residents were neutral about sexuality, which enabled the expression of need for further educational interventions.

CAREGIVER SEXUAL EDUCATION FOR DEMENTIA PATIENTS

Social workers have an opportunity to provide psychoeducation to families and caregivers in managing hypersexuality exhibited by patients suffering from dementia. In addition, training programs need to be established for staff members in assisted living and nursing home facilities to teach procedures and management techniques for humanistic treatment of older patients experiencing dementia who act out sexual behaviors (Bauer, McAuliffe, Nay, & Chenco, 2013; Beebe & Mills, 2013). These authors found that social workers face resistance from staff members of facilities who tend to dismiss the need for knowledge about older adults' sexuality. This psychoeducation is needed so that staff members may help patients with dementia understand their sexual needs and help them incorporate appropriate sexual behaviors, when possible, to continue to enjoy normal sexual functioning. Bauer et al. (2013) found that staff members were more permissive with residents in long-term-care settings and, in addition, had less negative views of same-sex couples.

HIV/AIDS

Many older adults remain sexually active throughout the life span, well into their 80s (Schick, Herbenick, & Reece, 2010). Approximately 16.5% of these older adults are diagnosed with HIV infection, and, surprisingly, 5% of older adults over 60 die from HIV infection. This occurs in geographic areas where there is a high prevalence of HIV infection (Prejean et al., 2011). This breaks the stereotype that HIV infection occurs in young gay men because these are older adults, men and women, heterosexual and gay (Onen, Shacham, Stamm, & Overton, 2010).

Older adults who are HIV infected tend to be divorced or recently have had a spouse or partner die, do not have a good understanding of how HIV is spread, and do not use condoms (or their partners do not use condoms) or sporadically use a condom (Savasta, 2004; Schick, Herbenick, & Reece, 2010; Schick et al., 2010). Widowhood is associated with an increased risk of sexually transmitted infections (STIs) for men (K. P. Smith & Christakis, 2009). Most of this increased risk occurs within 6 months of wives dying. Older adult men who suffer from erectile dysfunction now have access to medications that improve sexual performance. This enables older men who may have been avoiding sexual activity to accelerate opportunities for sexual activity, mostly without condoms.

Older adult women, because they are postmenopausal, are not concerned about becoming pregnant. This lack of concern about pregnancy facilitates a casual orientation to sexual activity that produces little perceived need for or concern about condom use (Lindau, Leitsch, Lundberg, & Jerome, 2006). Older men who have sex with men are at considerable risk for exposure to HIV and, as with younger men who have sex with men, must consider condom use to help avoid HIV infection. Alternatively, the older male adult, if HIV positive, may avoid infecting others by using a condom.

Another contributor to the incidence of HIV infection in older adults is health care workers, especially physicians. Many health care providers have an ageist view of older adults and feel that they are a low-risk group for HIV infection because they feel older adults are uninterested in sexual activity or are not sexually active (Loeb, Lee, Binswanger, Ellison, & Aagaard, 2011). This puts older adults at considerable risk for HIV infection or other sexually transmitted diseases. Conversely, older adults fearing stigmatization from health care providers do not seek guidance about sexual activity and are hesitant to bring sex-related issues into conversation during routine physical checkups or appointments for other co-occurring problems (Lindau et al., 2007). However, African American older women are significantly more apt to discuss sexual activity with their physicians than White women (Lindau et al., 2006). Because of this dysfunction in sexual health care communication between health care professionals and older adults, there is a need for a policy initiative to develop sex education programs for older adults and their health caregivers (Levy, Ory, & Crystal, 2003; Tabnak & Sun, 2000).

The current older adult cohort comprises at least 10.8% of newly diagnosed HIV infections in the United States. This alarming statistic warns of a health problem that is projected to increase exponentially in the coming years (Prejean et al., 2011). Within this group, older male African Americans who have sex with men are 12.5 times more likely to have HIV infection when compared with White older men who have sex with men. Latino older men who have sex with men are five times more likely to have HIV infection when compared with White older men who have sex with men (Linley, Prejean, An, Chen, & Hall, 2012).

NURSING HOMES

A significant percentage of the residents in nursing homes remain sexually active or desire sexual activity (Richardson & Lazur, 1995). Di Napoli et al. (2013) found that the most frequent sexual contact reported among residents in a nursing home setting was older adult males not experiencing dementia with older adult females not experiencing dementia (67.5% of this subgroup). Older adult males experiencing dementia having sexual contact with older adult females experiencing dementia comprised 53.6% of the subgroup. Katz (2013) found that many staff nurses in nursing homes are uncomfortable with the notion of residents engaging in sexual activity. Katz attributes this negative attitude to the nurses psychologically denying that residents did indeed have an active sexual history as middle-aged adults and young adults. This is consistent with Williams, Ylanne, and Wadleigh (2007), who found that young people deny older adults' sexuality through a defense called *intrinsic unwatchability*. Fortunately, Di Napoli found that nursing home staff members are open to psychoeducational interventions designed to give staff members the information and interventional tools needed to help residents learn to engage in appropriate sexual activities with fellow residents.

In nursing homes where staff are not given the opportunity to experience psychoeducational programs on resident sexuality, a problem arises when staff members view older adult patients as asexual and view any presentation of sexual desire or sexual activity as problematic or inappropriate. When staff limit or prevent normal sexual activity in residents, staff members unwittingly provoke sexual responses in residents when providing intimate care such as bathing dressing, and bathroom assistance because staff may be of the opposite gender (when helping a heterosexual patient) or of the same gender (when helping a gay male or lesbian patient; Peate, 2004).

OLDER ADULT SEXUALITY AND RELIGION/SPIRITUALITY

As adults age, there is a tendency to find religion or spirituality a significant aspect of life (Wink & Dillon, 2002). This tendency to find religion in late life may be explained by terror management theory, which describes the chronic death anxiety all people experience and the subsequent defenses used to relieve this anxiety (Greenberg & Arndt, 2011). This chronic death anxiety is further exacerbated by the reality of an older adult's pending mortality (Dalby, 2006). Unfortunately, there is a dearth of research about the relationship of older adult sexuality, leaving social workers to extrapolate the relationship between religion and spirituality from research on younger adults. The consequent effect that religion and spirituality may have on older adult sexuality is not clearly defined. Because religion/spirituality is a significant aspect of the biopsychosocial assessment of an older adult, along with questions about the older adult's sexuality (see Chapter 2, Assessing the Older Adult), a research agenda is needed to investigate this relationship.

THE CASE OF LIM AND JUN

Lim and Jun* are a Chinese American married couple. Lim is a 78-year-old woman and Jun is an 84-year-old man. Lim and Jun are currently living in a apartment complex for senior citizens in Southern California. They went to a local social service agency that has outpatient counseling services for older adults.

At their initial session, they indicated to the social worker that they were having marital conflicts regarding their intimate relationship. When asked to describe what they meant by "intimate," Lim indicated that she was concerned that her husband wanted to be unfaithful to her by seeing other women. Jun indicated that he had no interest in other women but that he felt that Lim was not interested in him sexually.

When asked to define what he meant by "not interested in him sexually," Jun said that he felt Lim was turned off to him because she did not want to engage in sexual activity with him. Lim said that they had not been sexual with each other for the past 10 years and that up until this moment it had not been a problem in their marriage. She felt that they both had been content with each other, feeling close, and that their marriage did not have any problems. Jun said that she was correct about the past 10 years, that he would say that overall they had a good marriage, and that he was content with Lim as a spouse throughout their marriage.

When asked what was different now that made the lack of sexual activity a problem, Lim blurted out "that damned Viagra." When asked what she meant, she said that ever since Jun was given a prescription by their family doctor things had not been the same. Jun indicated that he used to enjoy masturbating on a weekly basis; however, for the past 3 years he'd had trouble achieving or maintaining an erection. Now, since Viagra, he did not have trouble achieving an erection.

---

*Names and other identifying information have been changed to preserve confidentiality.

Jun went on to indicate that maybe this was his fault because he made the decision to take Viagra. Now that he had erections without a problem, he also felt that he would like to engage in sexual activity with Lim. He thought perhaps it was not fair to Lim to suddenly change how they were living.

During subsequent sessions, Lim and Jun explored whether Lim was willing to address returning to sexual activity with Jun. Lim and Jun were also referred to a sex therapist for psychoeducation on what sexual options were available that did not require coitus. This referral was made because Lim and Jun indicated that their sexual history consisted of a quick experience of sexual intercourse with little or no foreplay, causing Lim to feel a paucity of arousal. Therefore they were devoid of any comprehensive sexual knowledge of each other and did not understand what activities were available that would give them mutual satisfaction. Lim and Jun also indicated that they were virgins when they met and neither had had sexual experience with other people, aside from basic kissing and some fondling.

After six meetings with the sex therapist, Lim and Jun began engaging in various types of noncoital sexual activity. In addition, Lim consulted her gynecologist about using a hormonal vaginal suppository to help with vaginal lubrication. They were able to have successful intercourse, but Lim still preferred to engage in noncoital sexual activity. Jun indicated that if he had his preference, he would prefer to compliment the noncoital sexual activity with sexual intercourse more frequently. However, he was rejoicing that Lim was willing to re-engage in sexual activity and that in itself was gratifying to Jun.

SUMMARY

Although most people recognize adolescent and adult sexuality as a normal basic drive, when it comes to older adults, sexuality is stereotyped as nonexistent. In reality, older people do enjoy a sexual life, want to engage in sexual activity, and feel a loss when functional problems or social stressors, such as divorce or death of a spouse or partner, intervene. Biological factors causing sexual decline include chronic illness, dementia, and surgery, as well as pharmacy and polypharmacy side effects (Figure 9.2). Unfortunately, when older adults experience a decline in sexual desire or sexual activity, they experience fear, anxiety, depression, boredom, and disenfranchised grief.

Help for declining sexual desire or declining sexual activity is often not sought for two reasons. First, older adults, because of self-stigmatization and fear of humiliation, tend not to ask health care professionals for help. Second, many health care professionals view older adults as asexual—having no interest in sexuality. Therefore, health care professionals or social workers rarely ask older adults, during health or psychobiosocial assessments, about their sexual activity or lack thereof. Because of this, there is an increasing need for sexual education in older adults from the baby boom generation, as well as psychoeducational programs for the health care and social workers who serve these older adults.

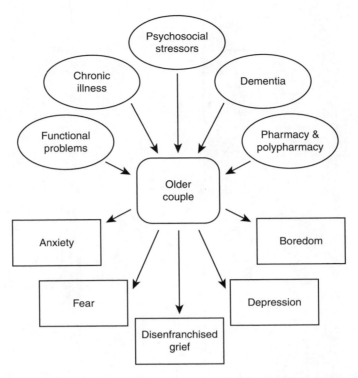

FIGURE 9.2 Factors causing decline in sexual activity and their consequence.

DISCUSSION TOPICS

1. Discuss your feelings about older adult sexuality.
2. Discuss how you have handled older adult sexuality issues in your fieldwork or practice.
3. Discuss any conflicts you have experienced within yourself while counseling an older adult experiencing sexual problems.

CHAPTER 10

Older Adult Abuse

Researchers have repeatedly found violent families, whether rich or poor, to be characterized by high levels of social isolation, rigid sex-role stereotyping, poor communication, and extreme inequalities in the distribution of power among family members.
> — M. F. Belenky, B. M. Cindy, N. R. Goldberger, and J. M. Tarule,
> *Women's Ways of Knowing: The Development of Self, Voice, and Mind*

The roots of older adult abuse, also called elder abuse, can be seen historically. In medicine, elder abuse was called *battered old person syndrome* (Butler, 1975). In older social work literature, older adult abuse was linked to informal care providers (Lau & Kosberg, 1978). Older adult abuse is often associated with explanations borrowed from domestic violence and criminal justice literature (B. K. Payne, 2005; B. K. Payne & Gainey, 2006; Straka & Montminy, 2006). In time, older adult abuse has evolved from a social problem existing between caregivers and the older adults they help to a public health concern and a criminal problem. This transition in thinking comes from an integration of ecology theory and person-in-environment theory (Walsh, Olsen, Ploeg, Lohfield, & MacMillan, 2011). Brownell and Berman (2004) suggest that victimization by loved ones and caregivers is not only dangerous but may also be life threatening (Dong et al., 2011). Older adult abuse is no longer considered limited to caregiver distress (Brandl & Raymond, 2012). There are many variables in the abuser, ranging from psychological problems to criminal intent. In addition, older adults may engage in self-neglect behaviors and self-harm (see the section Older Adults' Self-Abuse; Figure 10.1).

Older adult abuse is a multifactorial problem that includes problematic relationships among the older adult and spouse/partner, cohabitating with adult children, and caregivers left unsupervised with an older adult (Abolfathi Momtaz, Hamid, & Ibrahim, 2013; von Heydrich, Schiamberg, & Chee, 2012). In addition, these authors found that abuse occurs when there is pressure by an abuser to force an older adult to give access to finances or valuables, from other interpersonal psychosocial forces that

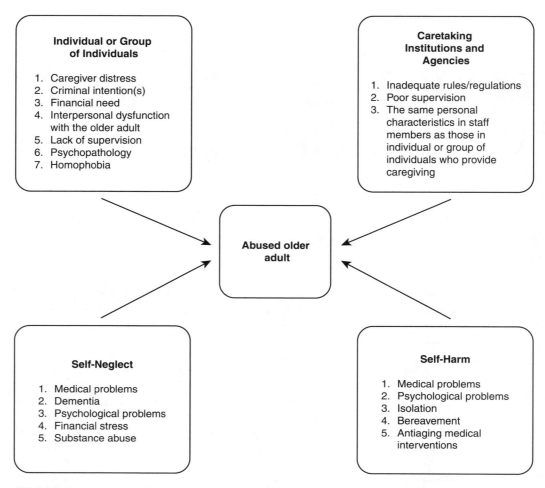

FIGURE 10.1 Some variables that contribute to the process of older adult abuse by individuals or by institutions and agencies.

occur among the older adult and caregiver, institutional staff, or opportunistic criminals. Researchers focusing on the etiology of abuse of older adults need to place a greater emphasis on the characteristics of the abuser as a predicting variable rather than the characteristics and stereotypes of the victim as the responsible predictor of the abuse (Brownell & Berman, 2004). In addition, Schiamberg and Gans (2000) and Walsh et al. (2011) indicate that it is important to take a person-in-environment perspective to understand the biopsychosocial stressors converging on abusers that are the etiological roots for their abuse. This is important because the ultimate cure for older adult abuse will be derived from addressing these precipitating biopsychosocial factors.

Paradoxically, a barrier to studying the characteristics of an older adult abuser is the older adult. Victims of abuse, especially older adult women, have difficulty identifying that abuse is occurring or deny it because of embarrassment or a sense that others will not believe that abuse occurred (Dienemann, Glass, & Hyman, 2005; Powers, et al., 2009). Abused older adults may fear additional violence or that reporting violence may narrow their scope of independence (Higgins & Follette, 2002). Some Caucasian American younger adults are potential older adult abusers because of the current cohort's lack of respect for older adults (Hudson, et al., 2000). Childs, Hayslip, Radika, and Reinberg (2000) find that many younger adults have ageist views of older adults and feel that they are deserving of abuse and do not deserve respect (Palmore, 2001; Figure 10.2).

Another precipitator of abuse is the financial stress felt by lower income families who are having difficulty coping financially and then are burdened with the added financial distress of having to care for an older family member (Angel, Angel, Aranda, & Miles, 2004). In addition, when older adults, because of lack of income, need help, they are forced to seek help from others, making them vulnerable to abuse (Fulmer, Guadagno, Bitondo-Dyer, & Connolly, 2004). However, financial abuse is often driven by greed (MetLife Mature Market Institute, 2011) and is not limited to poor families. Greed is seen in rich families as well, as evidenced by the recent case of Brooke Astor, the philanthropist of the Astor family fortune, whose older adult son was imprisoned for grand larceny (Peltz, 2009).

PREVALENCE OF OLDER ADULT ABUSE

Acierno et al. (2010) surveyed 5,777 respondents and evaluated the prevalence of older adult abuse over a 1-year period. Older adult abuse was divided into the following categories, each indicating a prevalence rate. Emotional abuse had a prevalence rate of 4.6%, 1.6% for physical abuse, 0.6% for sexual abuse, 5.1% for neglect, and 5.2% for financial abuse by a family member. These authors found the most common etiological factors explaining these prevalence rates were poor social supports and exposure to prior traumatic events.

Another study by Lachs and Berman (2011) found equivalent rates. These authors surveyed 4,156 older community-dwelling adults living in New York and 292 agencies serving these older adults. They found a self-reported older adult abuse rate of 7.6%, and a 4.2% rate of financial abuse. A compelling finding is that these rates are 24% to 44% greater than the number of cases reported by the social service agencies serving these older

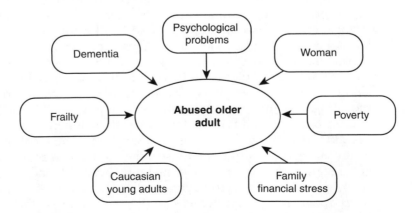

FIGURE 10.2 Variables that put an older adult at risk for abuse.

adults. This suggests that the recognition of older adult abuse by service providers is inadequate and more effective assessment initiatives must be developed.

Nursing homes are notorious for incidences of older adult abuse. Schiamberg et al. (2012) surveyed 452 family members of older adult nursing home residents. They found an older adult abuse rate of 25%. Types of abuse discovered were forced restraint, physical mistreatment, and sexual abuse. Page et al. (2009) surveyed 718 family members and caregivers of older adults in nursing homes. They found a prevalence rate of 30% of reported incidences of elder abuse. This abuse included neglect as the most common abuse and sexual abuse as the least common. Abusers were staff members.

PERPETRATORS OF OLDER ADULT ABUSE

The perpetrators of abuse against older adults, in most cases, are those who have an interpersonal relationship with the older adult. These relationships may be between an older adult and a family member, caregiver, spouse, or adult child, usually male (Nelson, 2002). Hooyman and Kiyak (2010) find that 70% to 80% of frail older adults' caregivers are family members. Caregivers often abuse older adults by actively neglecting them. This occurs when the caregivers do not provide adequate food, do not maintain proper hygiene for the older adult, provide a hazardous environment that can cause harm, or disregard the older adult by having little interaction. In addition, caregiver distress causes many negative consequences in the caregiver (Brintnall-Peterson, 2012). These include social isolation, depression, anxiety, substance abuse, and overeating. These symptoms are exacerbated by chronic medical and psychological problems the caregiver experiences. However, although the majority of abusers are caregivers, abuse is not limited to caregivers (Fulmer et al., 2004).

ASSISTED LIVING FACILITIES AND NURSING HOMES

A scathing newspaper report (Barry, Sallah, & Miller, 2011) finds that many residents are being abused in assisted living facilities in Miami, Florida. These abuses include a 71-year-old woman who was left in a bathtub of scalding water; a 74-year-old woman who was left in tight restraints that produced a blood clot that caused her death; and a 75-year-old man, an Alzheimer's disease patient, who wandered from a facility to be eventually killed by an alligator. These offenses occurred despite the fact that Florida has very strict laws pertaining to elder abuse.

Paradoxically, older adults who are abused have a high rate of admission to nursing homes (Dong & Simon, 2013), where in turn they are further abused. In nursing homes and assisted living facilities, the majority of abusers of the older adult residents are staff members (Burgess, Dowdel, & Prentky, 2000; Burgess & Morgenbesser, 2005). The most frequent targets of abusers of older adults are those older adults who are hostile to caregivers or staff or those who have dementia. Those older adults who are more cognitively intact tend to have a higher frequency of verbal abuse with consequent anxiety and depression (Begle et al., 2011; Tatara, 2001).

Nurses are in an ideal position to be vigilant about the status of older adults under their care, evaluating risk factors for abuse on assessment of the older adult, as well as looking for signs of abuse during their care (Wieland, 2000). However, Wieland indicates that in order to be effective, programs need to be developed to train nurses in how to detect abuse and not mistake signs such as bruising, unexplained vaginal bleeding, and unexplained injuries, among others. In addition, training programs are effective for staff interventions to reduce resident-to-resident elder mistreatment (Teresi et al., 2013).

Older adults who have psychological problems such as anxiety disorders or depression (see Chapter 5, Psychopathological Problems in Older Adults) or psychological problems co-occurring with dementia (see Chapter 6, Alzheimer's Disease and Other Dementias) are at high risk for abuse. Many older adults in need of psychological care do not seek it because of poverty, lack of knowledge about available services, fear of stigmatization, or cultural stigma (Bowes, Avan, & Macintosh, 2012). This is especially true in Latino populations (Morano & Bravo, 2002). Further compounding this lack of mental health care is the lack of emphasis by nursing homes and residential care facilities to provide psychotherapy services. Paradoxically, older adults who previously have been a victim of abuse by a relative or caregiver have a high probability of suffering from posttraumatic stress and of being placed in a nursing home. This is because the emotional and physical damage from the prior abuse make the older adult more frail and in turn in need of nursing home placement (Lachs et al., 2004; Lachs, Williams, O'Brien, & Pillemer, 2002).

LONG-TERM CARE AT HOME

Aging in place (see Chapter 12, Care and Residential Settings for Older Adults) is an alternative way to care for older adults who do not want to go to an assisted living facility, long-term-care facility, or nursing home. These types of care are constructed by the limitations set by insurance providers, Medicaid, and Medicare. Hospital stays are shortened; long-term-care facilities are becoming harder to access and are too expensive for many older adults. Therefore, home care services are being provided by social service and private for-profit agencies. These agencies provide trained staff, some of whom are licensed, if required by state law. Home care agencies indicate that the staff they send to the older adult's home for caregiving is also there as a safety measure to look for signs of abuse. However, Carp (2000) found that bringing outside caregivers into the home creates the possibility and opportunity for abuse of the older client. Abuse patterns in in-home care by outside service professionals are the same as those occurring in institutional care. A possible remedy is being developed in New York City, sponsored by the Harry and Jennette Weinberg Center for Elder Abuse Prevention at the Hebrew Home at Riverdale (New York), where doormen, concierges, porters, and other building staff across New York City are being trained to identify signs of older adult abuse (Winnie, 2013). These service providers become watchful eyes for older adults living in the apartment buildings where they work. These providers learn to identify whether outside service providers for elderly residents are removing valuables from the residents' apartment and whether residents show signs of physical abuse, look malnourished, seem to be isolated in their apartments, or look sickly or dehydrated.

OLDER ADULTS' PERCEPTIONS AS POTENTIAL CRIME VICTIMS

Older adults are usually viewed as victims of crime, rather than perpetrators of crime. This perception emanates from the stereotype that most criminals "age out" of crime. However, the growing population of older adult inmates has piqued the interest of researchers to reassess the notion that older adults are victims and not perpetrators (Powell & Wahidin, 2006). Whether the majority of older adults are victims of crime or not, the fear of crime is a significant factor in the minds of many older adults (Farrall, Jackson, & Gray, 2009; Fitzgerald, 2008). The etiology of the fear of crime in older adults comes from two sources: their own sense of vulnerability and fragility and environmental triggers such as news stories about local crime that highlight visible symbols of crime (vandalism, street prostitutes, gangs in poor neighborhoods, etc.; Kohm, 2009). This is an example of older adults caught in the intersection of fear of crime, poverty, and relative isolation. Social workers must take into consideration that many older adults suffer from anxiety (see Chapter 5, Psychopathological Problems in Older Adults), thus making the uncertainty about being a crime victim feel real, as opposed to being confronted with a reality-based trigger that causes fear. For example, reality-based triggers are an older adult witnessing an assault or hearing about a violent crime on the television news. Anxiety is the fear of the unknown; fear is the response to an imagined threatening situation.

SEXUAL VIOLENCE

Burgess and Morgenbesser (2005) suggest that most people, young and old, find it incomprehensible that older adults, women or men, are sexually abused. In addition, older adults who are sexually abused are reluctant to report such abuse because of personal shame and fears of stigmatization. Although not widely studied, Cook-Daniels and Munson (2010) report that there is a high incidence of sexual violence in transgender older adults, but accurate prevalence rates are unknown. This is consistent with a finding that fewer than 1% of cases reported and investigated by Adult Protective Services (APS) are for sexual abuse of all categories of older adults (Teaster, 2003) This hesitation to report is the same for physical and emotional abuse of disabled persons (Dienemann et al., 2005; see Disabled Older Adults).

Nursing homes and long-term care facilities are notorious environments for sexual abuse and exploitation. Burgess, Dowdel, and Prentky (2000) find that victims of sexual abuse in a nursing home studied were predominantly older adults, had different levels of cognitive decline, and evidenced posttraumatic symptoms consistent with rape. However, most sexual abuse does not consist of sexual intercourse, but instead consists of inappropriate fondling and kissing (Cook-Daniels & Munson, 2010; B. Payne & Civokie, 1996). Signs of sexual abuse in older adults include torn or bloody underwear or bedding, bruises in genital areas or on breasts, bleeding vaginally or anally, and newly diagnosed sexually transmitted infections.

Bonnie and Wallace (2003) indicate that older adults who have cognitive decline or are disabled, and especially those in nursing homes or residential care facilities, are at significant risk for sexual abuse. The majority of these sexual abuse victims are older adult women who are disorientated in one or more spheres (person, place, time), have lost most executive functions, and are disabled, or have difficulty ambulating (Burgess et al., 2000).

DISABLED OLDER ADULTS

Discrimination that women endure on a regular basis occurs in the workplace, in social policies, in medical research, from being impoverished and isolated, and in other aspects of their lives. Disabled women experience a greater frequency of violence and abuse when compared with nondisabled women (Brownridge, 2006; Casteel, Martin, Smith, Gurka, & Kupper, 2008; Martin et al., 2006; Powers, Curry, Oschwald, Saxton, & Eccles, 2002; Smith, 2008). Having a disability also increases the probability of mortality (Schofield, Powers, & Loxton, 2013).

Unfortunately, there is a dearth of research with a specific focus on older adult disabled women. Studies are needed similar to research studies that indicate older adult abusers are not limited to intimate partners or family members (Brownell & Berman, 2004; Brownell, Berman, Salamone, & Welty, 2002). Hassouneh-Phillips and McNeff (2004) reported that potential abusers include other persons who disabled people depend on. These potential perpetrators are health care professionals, home companions, home health aides, transportation drivers, and other service personnel.

OLDER ADULT PRISONER ABUSE

The majority of incarcerated older adults show evidence of accelerated aging caused by histories of alcohol and substance abuse and the harsh conditions of prison life (Beiser, 1999). This exacerbates the physical and emotional abuse they also sustain from younger prisoners. Crawley (2005) indicates that prison routines and rules are based on convenience to the system, ignoring the special needs of older adult inmates. This produces an institutional construction of abuse of older inmates. Alternative solutions may be incarceration in halfway houses, specialized geriatric centers, or some other way to accommodate older adult inmates, especially those who are frail and are no longer a threat to society.

Historical Programs to Address Older Adult Prisoner Abuse

In 1999 the first privatized prison for older adult inmates was opened by a company called Just Care, Inc. (Beiser, 1999). A concern about this new initiative of privatizing prisons for older adult inmates is whether corporate profits dominate the initiative and cut back on the much-needed medical and psychological care this vulnerable population requires. After all, this new concept arose from the needs of state and county governments to cut back on expenses. This graying population of inmates has the same comprehensive medical needs as those of their cohort in nonimprisoned communities.

In nonprivatized prisons, older inmates have greater access to medical care. Drummond (1999) indicated that these inmates receive better care than equivalent older adults who often cannot afford to have necessary medical care outside of prison. Collins and Bird (2007) suggested that policy should be enacted to allow geriatricians and gerontological social workers to make penitentiary visits in order to provide equity of access for standard health care services to older inmates. This is important because of increases in the aging population of prison inmates. Fazel, Hope, O'Donnell, Piper, and Jacoby (2001) find that 85% of respondents reported one or more major illnesses during their incarceration, with at least one of the illness classified as chronic. Mental illness and substance abuse/dependence problems affect more than 50% of older adult inmates (James & Glaze, 2006). Both medical and mental health problems, when not given proper care, are further examples of older adult inmate abuse.

One innovative program for older male adult prisoners is called POPS (Project for Older Prisoners; Will, 1998). This program chooses male inmates 55 or older for release from prison. Although the program releases only a small number of inmates (less than 200 at its initiation), it is an excellent model of a progressive initiative to remove older adult inmates from an environment where they are threatened with physical, sexual, and emotional abuse from younger inmates. After all, prisons are environments not constructed for the health needs and activities of daily living (ADLs) for older adults. Will (1998) reported that the recidivism rate for inmates in the POPS program was zero. Since its initiation, the program expanded to many law schools whose students help inmates obtain paroles, pardons, or alternative forms of incarceration; locate housing; and prepare the inmate for a parole hearing.

OLDER ADULTS' SELF-ABUSE

Self-Neglect

Self-neglect in older adults takes many forms, both medically and physically, leading to increased morbidity and higher rates of mortality when compared with nonself-neglect in older adults (Burnett et al., 2012; Dong et al., 2009). Self-neglect is a significant predictor for subsequent elder abuse reports to protective service agencies (Dong, Simon, & Evans, 2013). These older adults have a high incidence of co-occurring chronic medical problems (see Chapter 7, Medical Problems in Older Adults), medical problems with co-occurring dementia (see Chapter 6, Alzheimer's Disease and Other Dementias), psychological problems (see Chapter 5, Psychopathological Problems in Older Adults), and psychological problems with co-occurring medical problems. When these problems are untreated, or the older adult does not comply with treatment or medication compliance, there is an increased risk of mortality (Abrams, Lachs, McAvay, Keohane, & Bruce, 2002; Turner, Hochschild, Burnett, Zulfiquar, & Dyer, 2012).

Self-neglect also affects an older adult's ability to successfully engage in ADLs, which leads to potentially dangerous situations or financial problems. This failure is linked to cognitive deterioration (see Chapter 6, Alzheimer's Disease and Other Dementias). Symptoms include not eating or drinking fluids on a normal basis, poor hygiene, failure to pay bills causing disruption in utility services, failure to shut off burners on stoves, failure to turn off electrical appliances and devices, maintaining a dirty or cluttered residence, and an inability to discern potential financial exploitation by others (Tierney, Snow, Moineddin, & Kiss, 2007).

These failures for an older adult to maintain ADLs are attributed to the deterioration and sometimes complete loss of executive functioning, causing the older adult to no longer appreciate or execute the processes of goal-directed behavior (Dong, Simon, Wilson, & Mendes de Leon, 2010; Dyer, 2005; Dyer, Goodwin, Pickens-Pace, Burnett, & Kelly, 2007; Insel, Morrow, Brewer, & Figueredo, 2006). This lack of properly executed goal-directive behavior includes not performing ADLs, noncompliance with medical instructions, and not taking prescribed medications. Because older adults experiencing cognitive decline are rarely aware of these changes in executive functioning, self-neglect behaviors often occur for a long time until an outsider, usually a friend, relative, or caregiver, observes these changes.

As discussed in Chapter 6, Alzheimer's Disease and Other Dementias, depression is often a precursor to cognitive decline. In addition, depression is a significant predictor of dementia and substance abuse in an older adult. Therefore, Dyer, Pavlik, Murphy, and Hyman (2000) indicate that depression alone, or co-occurring with dementia, is a significant predictor of self-neglect. Unfortunately, this study did not focus on the relationship of depression with co-occurring substance abuse (see Chapter 8, Older Adult Substance Abusers) as a predictor of self-neglect.

Self-Harm

Self-harm is a problem usually associated with young people and rarely thought of as occurring with older people. However, even though the incidence in adults older than 65 is approximately 5%, it does not mean that self-harm is not a significant problem for older adults (Dennis, Beach, Evans, Winston, & Friedman, 1997; Hawton & Fagg, 1990; Owens, Dennis, Jones, Dove, & Dave, 1991). It is important for a social worker to be alert to evidence of self-harm because self-harm in older people is a significant predictor of suicidal intent (Harwood & Jacoby, 2000). More specifically, a social worker must be alert to an older adult's struggling with a medical illness or with psychological problems that may or not be co-occurring with a medical illness. These older adults include those who are isolated by choice or by circumstance and those who experience bereavement or disenfranchised grief (Doka, 2002; Salib, Tadros, & Cawley, 2001; Suominen, Isometsa, & Lonnqvist, 2004). The reason for the need of alertness is that too many causes of suicidal intent are retrospectively identified after a successful suicide or an unsuccessful attempt.

Another form of self-harm is what occurs in the relationship with purveyors of antiaging interventions and vain older adults seeking to recapture their youth. This takes many forms. Whether the physicians believe in antiaging interventions or are practicing self-harm by proxy is yet to be determined. There are several examples of antiaging medical interventions that cause harm in older adults. Many older adults seek antiaging hormone treatment to retard the progression of their aging bodies. These hormone treatments can cause diabetes and glucose intolerance (Blackman et al., 2002; Janssens & Vanderschueren, 2000). Hormone replacement therapy for postmenopausal older adult women can increase the probability of coronary heart disease, stroke, pulmonary embolism, and breast cancer and may be a major contributor to dementia in older women (Shumaker et al., 2003). In addition, the current trend, seen mainly in older adult men, of growth hormone injections to increase vitality causes these older adults to have an elevated risk of cancer (Chan et al., 1998). Excessive plastic surgery procedures are also an increasing trend in baby boom older adults. Studies are needed to determine whether these procedures are harmful or helpful.

INTERVENTIONS FOR OLDER ADULT ABUSE, SELF-NEGLECT, AND SELF-HARM

Social workers are in an ideal professional position to discover and to intervene in elder abuse, self-neglect by an older adult, or self-harm in an older adult. In addition, social workers often take the lead in establishing safeguards for an older adult to help prevent elder abuse, older adult self-neglect, or older adult self-harm. When assessing an older adult, the social worker must be do the following as needed:

1. Discover what support systems are available to an older adult. These may include available caregivers, local social service agencies, home health care and companion agencies, physicians, and dentists.
2. Develop a comprehensive understanding of the older adult's financial situation. Sometimes this requires a collateral informant if the older adult appears unaware of his or her financial status. Signs of financial abuse include large withdrawals from bank accounts that are not consistent with prior banking activity, endorsements on checks that do not match the older person's signature, and an increase in ATM cash withdrawals that do not match prior banking activity.
3. When necessary, contact the local Adult Protective Services (APS) agency. Contacting local APS requires an investigation by APS whether the complaint is made by a service provider, a related party (relative, spouse, caretaker), or the older adult (Teaster, 2003).
4. Act as a coordinator, or second voice, for the older adult needing any of the services listed here.
5. Initiate psychotherapy (see Chapter 3, Intervention Theories Informing the Clinician Treating Older Adults, and Chapter 5, Psychopathological Problems in Older Adults) for depression when depression is diagnosed.
6. Initiate psychoeducational support groups for the older adult and his or her family/caretaker to facilitate better self-care and to create a safe environment for the older adult.

7. Develop a comprehensive understanding of the older adult's culture. This is important for the service provider to make a positive engagement through the awareness of cultural difference (Angel et al., 2004; Dong et al., 2011; Tatara, 2001; Walsh et al., 2011).
8. Check for signs of self-neglect or self-abuse. These include sudden weight loss, extreme thirst, bedsores or unattended wounds, poor hygiene, and obvious body odor (see Chapter 2, Assessing an Older Adult).
9. Check for signs of physical abuse. These include bruising, ropes marks on wrists or ankles, unexplained injuries, and refusal to seek medical help for injuries.
10. Check for signs of sexual abuse. These include torn or bloody underwear or bedding, bruises in genital areas or on breasts, bleeding vaginally or anally, and newly diagnosed sexually transmitted infections.

These types of initiatives tend to decrease the probability of older adults engaging in self-neglect or self-harm or being a victim of elder abuse. In addition, these initiatives may be lifesaving when such abusive behaviors are already occurring (Alexopoulos et al., 2002; Alexopoulos, Raue, & Arean, 2003; Arean, Hegel, Vannoy, Fan, & Unuzter, 2008; Bartels, Haley, & Dums, 2002; Birrer & Vemuri, 2004; Grek, 2007; Hawthorne, 2006; Minicuci, Maggi, Pavan, Enzi, & Crepaldi, 2002).

Another type of initiative has been in existence since 1991. It is called the Friends for Folks program (Clayton, 1999). This program makes an unusual alliance between incarcerated adults and nonincarcerated seniors. Inmates, who are screened to make sure there is no history of animal abuse, adopt stray, abandoned, and abused dogs for a short period. These inmates learn grooming skills, first aid, recognition and treatment of parasites, basic housebreaking of the dogs, and on- and off-leash obedience training. Once trained, the dogs are given to older adults living alone to help them cope with loneliness and possibly as a proactive step to avoid depression or to improve depressed states. Dogs are also placed in assisted living facilities and nursing homes. Positive changes in behaviors have been observed in the inmates participating in the program. For older adults, the dogs provide companionship, reducing the risk of self-harm, self-neglect, and depression.

Many older adults do not know who to reach out to for help when they recognize that they are in an abusive interpersonal relationship. Therefore, there is a need for social workers and community relations officers in local police departments to educate older adults in their practices and to educate community members about service providers that exist to help older adults. Research has identified physicians, police, friends, relatives, social workers, clergy, confidants, and nurses as providers most likely to be in a position to help (Podnieks, 2003; Pritchard, 2000).

THE CASE OF GLORIA

Gloria* is an 82-year-old Caucasian female aging in place in an apartment in Chicago, Illinois. Gloria's husband died from pancreatic cancer 5 years ago. Gloria has a daughter (Tina) who lives in Scarsdale, New York. Her daughter visits Gloria three times a year and coordinates caretaking from Scarsdale by telephone with an agency that provides home companions. Tina has a general power of attorney for Gloria and manages her finances remotely via computer with Gloria's bank.

Tina became alarmed one afternoon when Gloria's bank manager called her and indicated that Gloria came to the bank with two adults that the manager did not recognize and insisted on cashing a check for $1,000. Tina thanked the bank manager for calling and immediately contacted Gloria by telephone asking her why a check for such a large amount was cashed. Gloria replied, "It is my money and I needed it for my expenses." Tina was unable to get any further information from Gloria as to what her expenses were. Tina contacted Gloria's home companion, who said that she had no knowledge of Gloria going to the bank with anyone. Tina contacted the home companion agency and the director indicated that she would investigate. The director returned a call to Tina saying that there didn't appear to be any problem and that Gloria is cognitively impaired and must just be confused.

Tina was not satisfied with what she was hearing and decided to review Gloria's bank account for the past few months. Tina had not been monitoring it aside from making sure deposits were made to Gloria's checking account from an investment account, Social Security, and a small pension. Tina discovered that Gloria was paying the home companion as required but also writing checks to another person with the same last name. Tina called the home companion to ask about the other person. The home companion indicated that the other person was her daughter, who was a qualified home companion and sometimes looked after Gloria when she was unable to be there or had to go out on errands. The director of the agency that contracted with the home companions claimed no knowledge of such substitutions and promised to visit Gloria to make sure everything was all right. The agency director informed Tina that a visit was made to Gloria and everything was fine. In addition, she said that the home companion was instructed not to allow her daughter to substitute for her.

During a telephone call with Gloria, Gloria indicated to Tina that she'd driven down to Evanston to visit her old neighborhood. Tina was concerned because Gloria was too cognitively impaired to drive, despite the fact that Gloria refused to surrender her car. Tina called the doorman at Gloria's apartment building and inquired about Gloria taking the car from the garage. The doorman told Tina that on numerous occasions, Gloria and her companion, and a man unknown to the doorman, would take the car for the day and return at night. Tina called Gloria and asked her about this. Gloria said that only once or twice had she returned to the old neighborhood and then rambled on about the different landmarks she remembered from her travels.

---

*Names and other identifying information have been changed to preserve confidentiality.

Tina decided to travel to Chicago to see the situation firsthand. Tina was horrified with what she found. In the trunk of the car she found personal belongings of people other than her mother. All of Gloria's jewelry was missing, and approximately $6,000 from her bank account was unaccounted for. The home companion was off the day Tina arrived. Tina promptly call the agency and told them she no longer wanted their services and that the home companion should not return the next day. One of Gloria's neighbors told Tina about an agency that a member of her church owned, vouching that he was honest and reliable. She had used his services when her husband had a stroke and never had a problem with the agency. Tina called this new agency and arranged for a home companion for her mother.

Tina then went to the local police department to file a complaint against the home companion and the agency. In addition, Tina hired a local lawyer to contact the agency and threaten a lawsuit. After 3 weeks the police indicated that they had interviewed the home companion, who denied any wrongdoing. They checked local pawnshops and did not find evidence of Gloria's stolen jewelry. The home companion agency denied any fault with their home companion, and the home companion's lawyer indicated that there was not sufficient evidence to support a suit. Tina felt that this was a terrible injustice but also felt that she had some responsibility by being too absent in the overseeing of Gloria's caregiving.

Aggravated and frustrated, Tina decided to take steps to ensure Gloria's safety. First, Tina convinced Gloria to have her car removed from the apartment building, to be sold. Next, Tina investigated several continuing care centers in the immediate neighborhood because Gloria did not want to move from Chicago. After several visits to several centers, Gloria finally agreed to move to a continuing care center that impressed her. Tina helped Gloria put her apartment up for sale so that the proceeds would support Gloria in the continuing care center. Tina felt that Gloria's move to the continuing care center would keep her safe and be a transition step to assisted living, which was anticipated when Gloria's dementia process progressed. In addition, Tina vowed to herself to monitor Gloria's finances on a regular basis.

The problem in this case is that Tina did not seek the guidance of a social worker who would have helped her coordinate the living-in-place care of Gloria. Part of the coordination of services would be overseeing staff brought into the house, monitoring the care given, and assessing whether any abuse or neglect was occurring. In addition, when abuse was discovered, a social worker would have advised Tina to involve Adult Protective Services. Possibly APS's involvement would have produced a more comprehensive investigation from the police department. In addition, Tina would have been instructed to file a formal complaint with the state agency that licenses the home companion agency. Finally, the social worker could have helped to coordinate Gloria's transition process from aging in place to the continuing care facility.

Fortunately for Tina and Gloria, the continuing care facility had a staff social worker who provided psychotherapy and case management services. This ensures that Gloria's future treatment will be humanistic and that Gloria's human rights will be protected.

SUMMARY

Older adult abuse, often called elder abuse, is a hidden epidemic in the United States. Caretakers, including adult children, a spouse or partner, a hired home companion, staff at an institutional setting, or other family members or friends, may abuse older adults. Abuse may be physical, financial, emotional, or sexual. Most older adults are too frightened, embarrassed, demented, medically ill, or depressed to report abuse. In addition, many older adults fear that reported abuse would result in limiting what freedom they have by causing them to be put in a more restrictive setting.

Another form of older adult abuse is self-harm or self-neglect. Unfortunately, an older adult is not often aware of his or her self-harm or self-abuse. Therefore, vigilance is required by health care providers, family members, friends, and staff members of institutions to recognize signs and symptoms of self-abuse and self-harm. This is an ideal opportunity for social workers and nurses to provide psychoeducational training for recognition of these self-abuses.

Rather than focusing on multiple personal characteristics of older adults that put them at risk for abuse, it is suggested to focus on the personal characteristics of the abusers. This removes blame from older adults for *causing the abuse* because of their multiple vulnerabilities. The abusers have the primary responsibility for the abuse. Abusers may be criminals, family members under financial distress exploiting the older adult's finances, staff members who are sexual predators, older adult children who have a dysfunctional relationship with their parent or parents, or caregivers or staff members who react poorly to an older adult's abusive or condescending behavior. As in self-abuse cases, abuse of older adults by others requires psychoeducational programs to sensitize family members, health care providers, and staff members to the recognition and remediation of older adult abuse.

DISCUSSION TOPICS

1. Discuss any incidences of abuse of older adults that have occurred in your family.
   A. What type of abuse occurred?
   B. How was it discovered?
   C. Was the abuse reported?
   D. What were the characteristics of the perpetrator(s)?
2. Discuss any incidences of older adult abuse you have discovered in your fieldwork or practice.
   A. What type of abuse occurred?
   B. How was it discovered?
   C. Was the abuse reported?
   D. What were the characteristics of the perpertrator(s)?
3. Discuss what you feel are the most effective means for detecting older adult abuse.
4. Discuss what you feel would be an effective way to educate older adults about elder abuse.

CHAPTER 11

Gay Male, Lesbian, Bisexual, and Transgender Older Adults

When highly stigmatized, a component of one's self is difficult to present, and managing the presentation is especially daunting.
—Erving Goffman, *Stigma: Notes on the Management of Spoiled Identity*

The concept of being an old gay male adult, old lesbian adult, old bisexual adult, or old transgender adult is remote and insignificant to most people. There is an abundance of literature about the younger lesbian, gay, bisexual, and transgender (LGBT) community and a dearth of literature about the older LGBT community. However, this abundance is limited when compared with the overall social and psychological literatures, which tend to omit LGBT populations in their studies (Van Voorhis & Wagner, 2001). This is especially egregious in social work literature, which prides itself on inclusion and sensitivity to diversity. In addition, *intersectionality theory* suggests that there are significant cultural, social, and psychological differences within each subcategory of LGBT (Cronin & King, 2010). This is a much-needed area for future research because researchers tend to categorize LGBT as a population sharing similar dynamics rather than highlight the richness of diversity within this group. Recognizing this richness in diversity, social workers may adapt person-in-environment therapeutic interventions from LGBT social work with adolescents (Crisp & McCave, 2007) to older adults.

Cahill, South, and Spade (2000) indicate that the number of older gay males and old lesbians is estimated to range from 1 to 2.8 million. This is only an estimate because respondents vary when they disclose their sexual orientation to a researcher depending on many methodological variables in research studies. Berger (1996) coined the term *gay and grey* to describe the current gay male cohort. However, *gay and grey* is also aptly applied to the current aging LGBT cohort. Cluse-Tolar, Lambert, Ventura, and Paspuleti (2004) indicate that 2.5% to 9% of men and 1.5% to 4% of women in the United States are gay or lesbian. They suggest the probability of social workers encountering older gay and older lesbian adult clients is highly likely. Furthermore, most social workers have a positive attitude toward LGBT clients when compared with other health care professionals.

However, little is known about this older LGBT population. Cahill et al. (2000, 2007; Cahill & Valadez, 2013) feel that this lack of knowledge is due to differences of self-identification among this cohort and lack of institutional interest in funding research on LGBT older people. Unfortunately, the focus of most research literatures is on older gay men and older lesbians, neglecting older bisexual and older transgender adults (Davies, Greene, Macbridge-Stewart, & Sheperd, 2009). There is also a dearth of literature on older transgender adults. Older transgender adults include those who made gender transitions early in life, those who transitioned their gender later in life, and those who never transitioned their gender.

This is not to be confused with intersex individuals, who are often referred to as suffering from disorders of sex development (DSD). These people have reproductive and/or sexual anatomy and/or chromosomal anatomy that does not define the traditional gender categories of male or female. Older transgender adults are usually lumped with older gay and older lesbian adults as having the same problems with discrimination and oppression. However, this is a misconception, because older transgender adults have a unique set of problems, which lead to their own oppression.

This lack of interest in the LGBT population is seen in governmental policy and attitude. President George Bush in a State of the Union address emphasized that citizens should value the institution of marriage by defining it as the union of a man and a woman, setting the stage for banning gay marriage (Anonymous, 2004) in many states. In contrast, the 2005 White Conference on Aging (Cahill, 2007) urged policy makers to "expand the definition of minority populations to include gays, lesbians, bisexuals, transgender people, and seniors with disabilities, and increase federal funding to the National Institutes of Health (NIH), Centers for Disease Control and Prevention (CDC), Title 3 and other federal agencies to reduce health disparities and promote health programming for all minority populations" (p.19). In 1952 the American Psychiatric Association (APA; in the first edition of the *Diagnostic and Statistical Manual of Mental Disorders*) labeled homosexuality as a *sociopathic personality disturbance*. In contrast, in 1973 the APA delisted homosexuality as a psychopathology (Kochman, 1997).

Quam (1993) felt that research on older gay males and older lesbians was biased, focusing on gay urban centers (New York, San Francisco, Chicago, and Los Angeles) containing mostly middle-class old gay men and old lesbians who are predominantly European Americans. This type of skew was also reported by Porter, Russell, and Sullivan (2004), who found most research on populations of gay males and lesbians were on those living in cities and well educated. Literature on older transgender adults is sparser because of stigmatization, causing most transgender people to keep their identities hidden, making them inaccessible for research studies.

COMING OUT IN LATER LIFE

Coming out is a difficult process for anyone, at any developmental stage. It is most difficult when old gay men or old lesbians do not initiate a decision to disclose their sexual identity until late life. Altman (1999) indicates that there are negative psychological consequences to not deciding to make this late disclosure. Not coming out, or pressure to come out causes increased anxiety (Perez & Amadia, 2004). Older adults not publicly acknowledging their gay male or lesbian lifestyles create a situation of isolation, preventing themselves from engaging in and experiencing intimate relationships (friendship or romantic) with other people regardless of sexual orientation. Cultural bias to heterosexual lifestyles, family discord, and fears of violence and discrimination are foundational to delaying the coming-out process (Haldeman, 2007). This bias assumes that one is heterosexual unless one discloses a different sexual orientation. Wallace, Carter, Nanin, Keller, and Alleyne (2002) advocate for educating families to increase family support for the LGBT lifestyles and to increase awareness in service providers so that they may be another source of positive support.

The coming-out process often intersects with racism, gender discrimination, and ageism. Many minority families tend to maintain a strong bias against LGBT lifestyles, preferring a strong heterosexual orientation to family (Rosario, Scrimshaw, & Hunter, 2004). This intersection of discrimination against LGBT lifestyles includes the intersection of racism and LGBT discrimination from the White majority. In contrast, Perez and Amadia (2004) and Katz, Joiner Jr., and Kwon (2002) reported positive feelings after coming out. These positive findings were confirmed by Fannin (2006), who indicated that slightly more than 47% of respondents studied reported positive feelings about coming out with their gay identities.

Ram Dass (Richard Alpert), the spiritual guru of the 1960s, did not hide the fact that he is gay but felt that he should not emphasize that he is gay in his writings because it would limit the number of people he would reach (Bradley, 2000). This deemphasizing of his sexual orientation is most evident in his book *Embracing Aging, Changing and Dying* (Dass, 2000). In addition, Dass feels that openness about his sexual orientation contributed to his firing from Harvard University (2000) .

Most often neglected in the research literature is the coming-out process of transgendered individuals. Transgender is not a sexual orientation but a gender issue created by the societal value of having only two genders, male and female. A recent report from the National Center for Transgender Equality and National Gay and Lesbian Task Force indicates that 70% of transgender older adults avoided gender transition because of past discrimination in employment (Grant et al., 2011). This type of discrimination is a major contributor to the lack of coming out of transgender individuals throughout adulthood.

OLDER LGBT SEXUALITY AND HIV

Older adults with HIV disease are a significant subpopulation of the current older adult cohort (Cahill & Valadez, 2013; Justice, 2010). Justice indicates that by the year 2050 at least half of the adult population living with HIV will be 50 years or older. Transgender older adults are more likely to have a history, as compared with nontransgender people, of sex work, substance and alcohol abuse, and depression. This is contributory to an increased incidence in HIV infection from unprotected sex and non–health care professional injection of silicone and hormones (Bockting, Robinson, & Rosser, 1998; Clements-Nolle, Marx, Guzman, & Katz, 2001). Whether an older gay male, older lesbian, older bisexual, older transgender adult, or heterosexual older adult, little information is know about the incidence of HIV infection in these older adults. This is because they traditionally are not screened for HIV infection by health care professionals, who assume that these older adults are not interested or engaged in sexual activity (Jacobs & Kane, 2010; Lindau, Schumm, & Laumann, 2007; see Chapter 9, Older Adult Sexuality).

Within the minority population of LGBT, gay men have the highest rate of HIV infection. Black Americans have the highest rates of new HIV diagnoses when compared with other racial categories. Black Americans currently represent 12% of the general population and have an incidence of 50% of currently diagnosed HIV infections (Hall, Song, Rhodes, & Janssen, 2008). Latino older adults have a 2% incidence of HIV compared with the general population (CDC, 2010).

Currently there is a cohort of older gay men who have outlived many of their cohorts who died when HIV transmission routes were unknown at the time HIV infection was first discovered. These gay men are also faced with the exponential loss of partners and caregivers because of the early high rate of death from HIV infection (Herek, 1998; Meyer, 1995, 2003). Researchers indicate that those LGBT persons who are able to accept the coming-out process have a lower risk for HIV infection than those who conceal their sexual orientation (Cole, Kemeny, Taylor, & Visscher, 1996; Kennamer, Honnold, Bradford, & Hendricks, 2000; Peacock, 2000). For those who are diagnosed with HIV infection, strength is seen in older LBGT adults, when compared with adults under age 30. Older LGBT adults are more positive about their attitude being HIV positive, are more likely to seek support, and are more knowledgeable about their health needs (Fritsch, 2005). This may be a cohort effect of the baby boom generation who are now aging. This is an area for more study.

SUBSTANCE ABUSE

Sumerskill (2012) finds that older LGB people (it did not include transgender older adults) are more likely than heterosexual older adults to abuse substances (see Chapter 8, Older Adult Substance Abusers). Sumerskill surveyed single LGB older adults (11% surveyed) compared with LGB older adults in partner relationships (7% surveyed). In this study, 14% of LGB older adults had abused substances compared with 7% of heterosexual older adults. Comparison was also made on alcohol drinking. Sumerskill found that 35% of older gay men and 19% of older lesbians drank alcohol "every day" or at least "5 to 6 days" a week. Heterosexual older adult males (25%) and heterosexual adult females (15%) drank alcohol at a similar frequency. Although not directly concluded from this study, it can be assumed that the social forces of discrimination, stigmatization, violence, poor family relationships, loss of independence, increased morbidity, and housing problems all converge on older LGB and cause a substance- and alcohol-abuse response as a maladaptive attempt to cope with these pressures (Jessup & Dibble, 2012; see Figure 11.1). These maladaptive responses are more common in bisexual older adults. Transgender adults over 65 report a 16% incidence of substance and alcohol abuse. These adults use substances- and alcohol- as a maladative coping response to the social oppression, discrimination, and abuse suffered because of their transgender status (Annonymous, 2012).

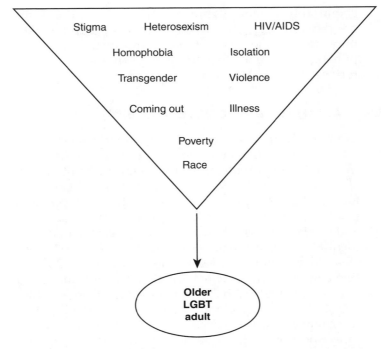

FIGURE 11.1 Some examples of psychosocial stressors converging on older LGBT adults that are contributory to substance-abuse problems.

OLDER GAY INMATES

Harsh treatment, rape, solitary confinement, and guards soliciting sex have long been common phenomena for gay inmates, who are often placed in segregated sections of a prison. In Los Angeles, California, this segregated section is called a *queens tank* (Andreoli, 2004). This puts older gay male and older lesbian inmates at considerable risk for sexual, emotional, and physical abuse (see Chapter 10, Older Adult Abuse).

Clinical Intervention

A pioneering program was initiated called SMART (Social Mentoring and Academic Rehabilitative Training Program; Andreoli, 2004). Andreoli explains that sheriff's deputies who were concerned by the high recidivism rate of LGBT inmates initiated this program. The recidivism rate for LGBT inmates before the initiation of this social education service was 94% as compared with straight inmates' recidivism rate of 65%. Five years after the inception of SMART, the recidivism rate for LGBT inmates dropped to 30%. Andreoli feels that self-esteem issues, substance abuse, and homelessness contribute to the incarceration of LGBT inmates. The program addresses those issues by introducing education programs that enable LGBT inmates to complete high school or beyond and providing anger management classes, testing for sexually transmitted diseases, safe-sex education, and substance-abuse treatment. In addition, LGBT inmates are provided with useful, crime-prevention tools. Because the LGBT inmate community is small (approximately 300 in this setting), these services are economically feasible. Intervention programs like this are especially important to older LGBT inmates who are the most vulnerable of the LGBT inmate population. Extending the same services to non-LGBT inmates represents a fiscal challenge.

CONCERNS ABOUT HEALTH SERVICE DELIVERY

Brotman, Ryan, and Cormier (2003) found social service and health care workers insensitive and intolerant of homosexuality, which compromises their ability to provide care. This is because health care facilities are *settings of heterosexuality*, inherently discriminating against gay, lesbian, bisexual, and transgender patients (de Vries, 2005). Shippy, Cantor, and Brennan (2001) indicate that 75% of respondents report not fully disclosing their gay and lesbian lifestyles to health care workers. Not disclosing gay or lesbian identity causes a phenomenon of being *invisible*, which is found in older closeted gay male and lesbian adults (Ramello, 2013). Fear of discrimination because of their sexual orientation causes many older LGB people not to use available health care services (Anetzberger, Ishler, Mostade, & Blair, 2004). This is a reaction to a general fear in the LGBT community of being discriminated against when receiving or asking for health care or social services (Johnson, Jackson, Arnette, & Koffman, 2005). In addition, it must be noted that potential caregivers, at times, are often hesitant to help because of the stigma attached to the HIV-positive older LGBT adult or homophobic pressures from the surrounding community (Wright, 2002).

Heaphy, Yip, and Thompson (2004) indicate that older gay men are similar to older lesbians in choosing friendships or choosing kin as caretakers. Consequently, friends and kin become their source for emotional and health care support rather than available social services. This helps dispel the myth that older gay men are isolated from social networks. However, the type and extent of social networks and family support for older gay men have not been comprehensively studied (Grossman, D'Augelli, & Hersberger, 2000), although Grossman, D'Augelli, and Hersberger found that 33% of respondents did rely on siblings for their care and social networks.

In addition, health needs of LGBT older adults are virtually absent from most social policies (Annoymous, 2011). This is because older adults are often looked at as a homogenous group, which neglects the importance of the various subgroups in this population (Bayliss, 2000; Harrison, 2001; Hughes, 2007b). Donahue and McDonald (2005) feel that clinical social work focuses on symptoms of homosexuality rather than the root issues of discrimination and stigmatization that the LGBT community currently faces.

Cooper (1988) described younger lesbian social workers stigmatizing older lesbian clients as needy and defenseless. This is analogous to the *new ageism* described in Chapter 1, Theories to Inform the Clinician Practicing With Older Adults. Cooper suggested that older lesbians must take an advocacy approach to confront ageism in younger lesbians with the goal of promoting greater understanding of aging and identify commonality between younger and older women, with a special emphasis on lesbians. This is important because older lesbians, when compared with older gay men, have greater concerns about declining physical and mental health, loss of cognitive abilities, and limited independence in old age (Quine & Morrell, 2007).

Transgender older adults routinely find discrimination and hostility in hospital emergency rooms, drug treatment centers, mental health agencies, and when seeing other health care professionals (Grant et al., 2011). Grant et al. indicated that 19% of transgender adults report denial of health care services because of their transgender status. Some of the older transgender respondents report that health care workers subjected them to physical assault (Cook-Daniels & Munson, 2010). This discriminatory treatment by health care workers causes many transgender older adults to become isolated and avoid health care treatment leading to increased morbidity and mortality (Kimmel, Rose, & David, 2006). A further exacerbation of discrimination of older transgender adults is found in Latino transgender older adults, who have the highest rate of unequal health and mental health care compared with older White adults. In addition, African American transgender older adults are the population most vulnerable to assault by health care workers (Grant et al., 2011). Altogether, Fredrisken-Goldsen et al. (2011) indicate that transgender older adults, regardless of race or socioeconomic status, are twice as likely to experience domestic violence than older gay male, older lesbian, or older bisexual adults. Furthermore, Fredrisken-Goldsen et al. report that 22% of transgender older adults are too poor to seek health care, regardless of their state of health.

Interventions

Many years ago, Berger (1977) developed an advocacy model for social work intervention. This model can be adapted to meet the social and clinical needs of the LGBT community. This is accomplished by extending Berger's model to employ professionals in social agencies who have expertise in LGBT issues to form groups, organizations, and services that support the LGBT community. Social workers on a macro level need to advocate for laws to give rights, privileges, and protection to the LGBT community.

MENTAL HEALTH ISSUES

It was not until 1973 that the APA declared that homosexuality was not a mental illness (Kochman, 1997). Before this, the mission of social workers was to help an LGBT person make the journey to a *normal sexuality*, that of being a heterosexual, because homosexuality was considered a sociopathic personality disturbance (APA, 1952). Unfortunately, some Christian-oriented psychotherapists still adhere to this misguided mission of sexual-orientation conversion. To this day, heterosexuality is considered the norm by most of the population. This consideration rewards heterosexuals with privilege at the expense of nonheterosexual people, who are, in turn, stigmatized and oppressed for their sexual orientation (Woodford & Bella, 2003).

Unfortunately, Woodford and Bella indicate that heterosexism is still a force that causes bias in some social workers and limits their ability to help LGBT clients. Sexual orientation discrimination is still a problem in many institutional, community, and social environments (Brotman, Ryan, & Cormier, 2003; Cahill et al., 2000). Appeals for advocacy for LGBT people have been ongoing for more than 30 years, as identified in an old study (Dulaney & Kelly, 1982), and continue today, another 30 years later.

Many community organizations have developed programs to promote services that focus on advocacy, psychoeducational programs, and research geared to promoting maximum health and positive interventions for the LGBT community (Old Lesbians Organizing for Change, 2012; Pride Senior Network, 2012; SAGE, 2012).

Decker (2004) presents a case study of a lesbian therapist working with an older lesbian patient who starting therapy at age 70 and ended with her therapy at age 80. Her initial reason for coming into therapy was her suffering from a depression and having suicidal ideation. This is a unique window into the therapeutic process of a lifetime of being stigmatized because of gender and sexual orientation. Therapy became her vehicle for healing the wounds of discrimination and to eliminate a *fictitious identity* created during her long struggle to come out and to own that she was a lesbian.

Caregivers helping older LGBT adults show significantly higher levels of psychological distress and a more pessimistic outlook on life when compared with noncaregivers (Broe et al., 1999). This may not be accurate because Brotman (2007) found that caregiver distress working with LGBT older adults is equivalent to working with the general heterosexual population. However, the causes of distress for caregivers of LGBT older adults are different (Grossman et al., 2000). These caregivers are faced with the social pressures of stigmatization, homophobia in the general population, discrimination, HIV fears, and other pressures shared in kind with the older LGBT adults receiving care.

Unfortunately, the mental health establishment view transgender older adults as having a gender identity disorder rather than being part of a third gender category, having equality with male and female older adults. This would enable most older transgender adults to be viewed by the psychiatric establishment as normal, despite a smaller subset of older transgender adults who experience mental health issues (Vance, et al., 2010).

Transgender older adults suffering from depression show a 16% incidence of suicide attempts during their lifetime (Grant et al., 2011). Another report indicated that 71% of transgender older adults reported having suicide ideation or suicide attempts, which is significantly higher that the incidence of 35% to 40% reported by older gay male, older lesbian, and older bisexual older adults (Fredrisken-Goldsen et al., 2011). However, there is a lack of significant evidence to suggest that suicide rates for LGBT individuals are higher than the population in general (Maris & Berman, 2000; Westfield et al., 2000). Therefore, suicide rates determined by LGBT status may be an artifact of methodological problems in reported research studies.

LGBT older adults are more likely than heterosexual older adults to have a history of being diagnosed with depression (Logie & Gadalla, 2009). This phenomenon of a depression diagnosis arises from the psychological distress caused by the stigma of being LGBT and presents a potential risk for suicide, especially in the older adult transgender population (Haas et al., 2011; Oswalt & Wyatt, 2011). Older gay men and older bisexual men show a greater rate of depression diagnosis (40%) than older heterosexual men do. Older lesbians and older bisexual women show a closer comparison to older heterosexual women, that being 40% and 33%, respectively (Sumerskill, 2012). Depression is often a co-occurring diagnosis with HIV/AIDS diagnoses (Emlet, 2007; Grov, Golub, Parsons, Brennan, & Karpiak,

2010). Therefore, an initiative must commence to motivate physicians treating older adults for various medical conditions to screen for HIV-related conditions and to screen for depression (Henry, 2009).

Anxiety diagnoses show a similar pattern with LGBT older adults having a greater frequency of diagnosis than do older heterosexual adults. Older lesbians and older bisexual women show a diagnosis rate of 33% compared with 26% in older heterosexual women. Older gay men and older bisexual men show greater rates for anxiety diagnoses than older heterosexual men do. This is a similar trend to that seen in depression. Older gay men and older bisexual men show a 29% rate of anxiety when compared with older heterosexual men, who show a 13% rate (Sumerskill, 2012). These results are consistent with theories of how social stressors can be harmful to one's mental health (Dohrenwend, 2000). This is especially understandable when considering the stress burden experienced by LGBT older adults and their caretakers (Meyer, 1995, 2003).

RETIREMENT AND HOUSING

Retirement is a difficult transition for older people. For the LGBT older community, this transition is more arduous because there are few precedents to guide them (Beeler, Rawls, Herdt, & Chohler, 1999). Johnson, Jackson, Arnette, and Koffman (2005) indicate that older LGBT people face discrimination from administration, care staff, and residents of retirement facilities. Research on housing needs for older LGBT adults is biased toward the economically advantaged, neglecting the needs of poor LGBT older adults (Addis, Davies, Greene, Macbride-Stewart, & Shepherd, 2009).

Johnson, Jackson, Arnette, and Koffman (2005) suggest that education programs be developed to address awareness and acceptance of LGBT retirees as a potential intervention in a majority heterosexual retirement community. Increasing awareness of gay, lesbian, bisexual, and transgender lifestyles in a heterosexual retirement community or a heterosexual community containing many older retirees is called *queering* of the elder housing and care environment (Cahill, 2002). Alternatively, establishment of LGBT-exclusive or LGBT-friendly retirement and care facilities may be preferable. The advent of LGBT-exclusive and LGBT-friendly retirement and care facilities is an attempt to combat the fears of a reduced social life, disenfranchisement of the gay community, and loneliness that often occurs when LGBT adults age (Heaphy et al., 2004; Hughes, 2007a; Meyer, 2001). Unfortunately, LGBT residents of gay retirement communities face a threat to this special lifestyle. Because gay retirement communities are a relatively new concept, they may not have the financial reserves that older heterosexual retirement communities have to cope with the current economic crisis in the United States (Frosch, 2011).

Most LGBT older adults prefer gay-specific housing (Fannin, 2006). Those LGBT older adults in retirement who need in-home health care or some caregiving assistance prefer gay-friendly or gay caregivers (Fannin, 2006). Cantor, Brennen, and Shippy (2004) found that most older gay, older lesbian, older bisexual, and older transgender adults are involved in caregiving to family members or partner's relatives or gay and lesbian friends. Older lesbians tend to focus their social lives around friends in lieu of maintaining close family relationships (Goldberg, Sickler, & Dibble, 2005).

In addition, older lesbians avoid using heterosexually dominated senior social service agencies because of stigmatization and discrimination experienced throughout their lives. Answering this call, Hilda Rush, Santa Fe's oldest living lesbian, established the first full-service gay retirement housing development, which provides housing for independent living and assisted living (Allen, 2005). In addition to independent and assisted living facilities, there is a need for advocacy for LGBT older adults to be able to engage in sexual activity with partners in long-term care facilities (Brotman et al., 2003; Cahill et al., 2000). Ironically, institutional restriction of sexual activity with partners is also a long-standing policy pertaining to heterosexual partners in these institutions (see Chapter 9, Older Adult Sexuality).

THE CASE OF SHERI AND CAMILA

Sheri and Camila* are a lesbian couple who have been living together for the past 27 years. Sheri is an 82-year-old White woman and Camila is a 79-year-old Latina women. They have been living in a gay retirement community for the past 10 years. One day they presented at a local social service center seeking couples therapy. During the intake session, Sheri and Camila described multiple verbal fights that have been occurring weekly for the past 8 months. They indicated that the tension is so great that they are sleeping in separate bedrooms, Sheri feeling depressed and Camila feeling anxious about their future together.

After 3 weeks of counseling, Sheri and Camila discovered the roots of their dysfunction. What precipitated the urgency to seek counseling was that their gay retirement community was going bankrupt because the community did not have enough reserve capital to maintain its financial obligations. Therefore, Sheri and Camila were given notice that they had to move within the next 3 months. Because they were renting their unit, they had little recourse and suddenly had to decide where to live. The gay retirement community was their reason to leave friends and family and move to Florida from New York City. This change in living status was a significant part of what they were disagreeing about, and what prompted their arguments was where to move.

Complicating the decision of where to move were two factors. They discovered that there were no other gay retirement communities that had available housing in Florida. They did not want to move away from the East Coast. In addition, a more significant problems was that Sheri had never come out and was terrified about being discovered as a lesbian if they moved to a straight (heterosexual) community. For many years Camila had felt that Sheri's reluctance to come out limited their intimacy. They could never show affection toward each other in public. They gave ridiculous excuses to people as to why they lived together—*they were cousins, they were college friends, for economic reasons they shared a residence, they both experienced traumatic relationship breakups and decided to live together,* and so on.

---

*Names and other identifying information have been changed to preserve confidentiality.

After doing some extensive research on retirement communities, Sheri and Camila found a beautiful community that had all the amenities they enjoyed just two towns away from where they were now living. Camila found out through a friend that there were five lesbian couples and three gay male couples living in that community. Camila's friend told them that the community was gay tolerant and that they would not feel the discrimination that would probably occur in a strictly heterosexual community.

However, Camila insisted that she would not move to this community or any other community with Sheri unless Sheri came out and they got married. Complicating this, Florida recently banned gay marriage, so Camila suggested an alternative move to Vermont because Vermont had legalized gay marriage. The reason Camila wanted to be married was to have financial and health care rights available to them that were not available to them as unmarried partners. They'd vacationed in Vermont many times, and they especially liked the town of Burlington because it is a college community with many cultural benefits.

Sheri was willing to move to Vermont but remained unwilling to come out. This caused many tense counseling sessions. The social worker suggested that Sheri and Camila should make a practice trip to Vermont, and since no one knew them, they might try experimenting with a public display of affection by holding hands when walking around Burlington. Sheri finally agreed to visit Burlington and look at communities where they might live. Sheri also said that she would try holding hands as long as the reaction from other people was not hostile, even though she was terrified at the thought of doing that.

On returning to therapy after their visit to Vermont, Sheri surprised the social worker when she indicated that their experiment with public affection (holding hands) went surprising well. No one seemed to react poorly, and Sheri said that after a few days she actually enjoyed the experience. Now she was wondering why she had been so scared for so many years. Sheri also agreed with Camila that they were becoming frailer and that being married would enable either one of them to be a health advocate if the other was hospitalized; and when one of them died, the other would have financial security. Even though they did not know whether a small retirement condominium community they saw had any gay couples, their experience walking around the community and chatting with the residents was positive and very welcoming. In addition, they found out from a university professor Camila's niece knew, who was coincidently a gay man, that there were health care providers who were gay friendly and that Burlington had a small gay community that was very supportive and included many gay and lesbian older adults who were retired. They were not centered in a retirement community like in Florida, but Burlington was a small city and everyone in the gay community seemed to know each other.

SUMMARY

Being old and a gay male, lesbian, bisexual, or transgender adult is finding oneself at the intersection of being older and LGBT, making one vulnerable to discrimination and stigmatization. Add in race, medical illness, mental health problems, or other vulnerabilities and that can cause a very difficult older adulthood, leading to a need for ongoing research on the older LGBT population and the development of psychoeducational training for social workers about the special needs of the older LGBT population. In addition, social workers need to take the lead on advocating for policy changes to ensure that the human rights of older LGBT people are protected.

Housing communities need to be developed that are at the minimum gay friendly. In addition, new research should be done and policy changes made regarding the housing of aging gay inmates, who are vulnerable to abuse and neglect because they are LGBT and old in a young and heterosexually biased system. This would include the development of special security housing for older LGBT inmates who have special emotional, medical, and psychological needs.

The same problems must be addressed for noninmate LGBT older adults who need to be in a continuing care facility, assisted living facility, or nursing home. There is a need for institutions that are LGBT friendly or exclusively LGBT that will provide a safe environment to meet the needs of these residents. For all these types of communities, LGBT-friendly health care services, mental health services, legal services, and other needed providers should be identified and encouraged through advocacy, policy changes, and psychoeducational programs.

DISCUSSION TOPICS

1. Discuss any experiences you have had working with older gay male, older lesbian, older bisexual, and older transgender adults.
2. Discuss the interventions you used with these older LGBT adults and how these interventions were the same or different from those you use with older heterosexual adults.
3. Discuss how your sexual orientation influences your work with older LGBT adults.

CHAPTER 12

Care and Residential Settings for Older Adults

A house is not a home unless it contains food and fire for the mind as well as the body.

—Benjamin Franklin, *The Leading Mind*

Housing communities for older adults are not a contemporary concept. Tinker (1997) indicates that housing communities for older adults date back to the Middle Ages in England. The guiding concept of creating older communities is the desire to give older adults an alternative concept of housing that will allow them to sustain themselves economically, while giving choice and an element of control over their health care, social networks, and physical environment (Berglund & Erricsson, 2003; Bowers et al., 2009). These communities facilitate a sense of empowerment in older adults if given a sense of choice between more independent living in a retirement community and more restricted living in an assisted living facility (Peace, Wahl, Oswald, & Mollenkopf, 2007). The most restricted option for older adults is placement in a nursing home (Figure 12.1). Rowles and Bernard (2013) suggest revisiting the environment where older adults live and their surrounding public space. Instead of a negative focus on what is wrong with these environments and how they limit the world of older adults, these authors encourage revisiting the design of private and public spaces to enhance meaning in older adults' lives. This includes creating opportunities in the public spaces for multigenerational communication to help break the isolation of older adults by integrating them with younger cohorts. This will have a reciprocal effect of sensitizing younger cohorts to older adults, which would help diminish the inherent ageism normally found in younger cohorts (see Chapter 1, Theories to Inform the Clinician Practicing With Older Adults).

Obviously, the degree of choice narrows as the effects of co-occurring chronic and acute illness, disability, and frailty increase (Clegg, Young, Iliffe, Rikkert, & Rockwood, 2013). In the past, for most older adults the types of continuing care they received were not made by choice or forward planning but instead by failing health and frailty (Longino, Perzynski, &

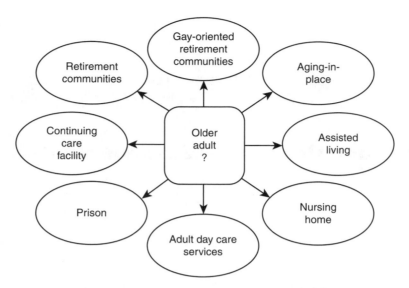

FIGURE 12.1 Care and residential choices for older adults.

Stoller, 2002). Co-occurring chronic or acute illnesses happen when two or more medical illnesses occur at the same time. An older adult experiencing co-occurring illnesses has an increased risk for disability and mortality, a considerably higher risk than from any one medical illness (Cacioppo et al., 2002; Holt-Lunstad, Smith, & Layton, 2010). Disability occurs when an older adult has difficulty with or loses the ability to independently engage in activities of daily living (ADLs; Nagi, 1991). Disability is a multidimensional phenomena that takes place at the intersection of social, medical, economic, and psychological forces (Fried & Guarlnik, 1997; Stuck et al., 1999). In addition, disability sets the stage for future functional and medical complications. Frailty occurs when an older adult becomes at high risk for further deterioration in health, needs increasing help with ADLs, falls often, and has an increasing probability of mortality (Clegg et al., 2013). Older adults reach a state of frailty in nursing homes and assisted living facilities (Slettebo, 2008). The underlying cause of frailty in older adults occurs when multiple systems (physiological and psychological) are involved and the older adult is no longer able to regulate them. This is called *dysregulation* (Bortz, 2002; Lipsitz, 2002).

RETIREMENT COMMUNITIES

Retirement communities began to gain popularity in the 1920s by providing a choice for older adults who were healthy and high functioning to live together to maintain social networks and provide an environment for a range of physical and social recreational activities (Hunt, Feldt, Marans, Pastalan, & Vakalo, 1984). These are relatively large in scale as compared with assisted living facilities or nursing homes. In addition, most retirement communities offer housing that enables older people to downsize, reducing in-home maintenance chores as well as reducing financial burdens of upkeep (Erikson, Krout, Ewen, & Robison, 2006; Krout, Moen, Holmes, Oggins, & Bowen, 2002). Many older adults choose retirement communities for an added sense of personal security and continued independent living as a beginning preparation for their ultimate mortality (Pinquart & Sorensen, 2002).

Gay-Oriented Retirement Communities

At 93 years of age, Hilda Rush, Santa Fe, New Mexico's oldest lesbian, was present at the opening of the first full-service, gay-oriented retirement housing community, consisting of independent and assisted living apartments and condominium residences (Allen, 2005). See Chapter 11, Gay Male, Lesbian, Bisexual, and Transgender Older Adults, for a more detailed discussion of gay retirement communities.

AGING IN PLACE

A contemporary trend is to have older adults age in place. Aging in place encompasses an older adult staying in his or her home throughout the aging cycle or moving to housing that provides limited services such as an option for communal dining, cleaning services, and transportation. The theory underlying aging in place is to reduce admissions to continuing care centers, assisted living facilities, and nursing homes by extending the ability of older adults to live as independently as possible for as long as possible (Oldman, 2000; Verkerk, 2001).

Underlying the success of aging in place is the ability to create an informal support system in which older adults help each other along with assistance from family and younger friends (Novak & Campbell, 2006). Social support includes supporting one another emotionally; giving assistance with ADLs; and more comprehensive assistance by caregivers for older adults suffering from chronic illness, requiring medical interventions, or continuing care for a chronically ill or disabled older adults (Chappell, McDonald, & Stone, 2010).

A criticism of aging in place is that this approach to housing serves older people who are of the young-old cohort, are relatively healthy, have virtually no cognitive impairment, and have few if any disabilities (Darton et al., 2011). Without comprehensive services such as in-home health care and physician visits (Guerriere, Zagorski, & Coyte, 2013) for those aging in place, a threshold for no longer aging in place is always anticipated or reached, forcing the older adult to seek more restrictive housing (Frank, 2001; Krout et al., 2002; Longino et al., 2002). Therefore, with respect to this criticism, planning and policies need to be initiated to provide services and assistance to older adults aging in place as their health care needs and frailty increase and cognition further deteriorates.

The decision to abandon aging in place for a community care facility with access to assisted living is usually made by the older adult. This decision commences when the older adult develops a chronic debilitating health problem, has environmental physical barriers in the home that would require expensive remodeling, develops safety concerns after an injuring fall, and has decreased mobility or experiences cognitive decline (Biggs, Bernard, Kingston, & Nettleton, 2000; Evans, 2009; Kingston, Bernard, Biggs,

& Nettleton, 2001; Vallelly, 2002). For older adults suffering from a health problem or mobility problems, who have a healthy spouse or partner as the primary caregiver, a decision to move is often instigated not by declining health or frailty but by environmental factors such as property maintenance, or the acute disability or death of the caregiving spouse or partner (Krout et al., 2002). Ironically, this anticipated loss of independence and social stimulation by leaving their aging-in-place residence is more fearful to these older adults than their mortality (Prince & Butler, 2007; Tuckett, 2007).

Another alternative for those older adults aging in place who, because of being impoverished, do not have the alternative to transition to a continuing care or assisted living facilities was described by Myerhoff (1978). This classic study described a community of elderly Jewish immigrants who lived in Venice, California, a small, impoverished seaside town. Being poor, unable to move, lacking financial support from their children, living in shoddy housing, and having no hope to address their situation by leaving for a continuing care facility, this community organized to face and solve their problems of basic living together. Their organization centered around a community center where they socialized, provided needed food, looked after each other's safety, and supported those with special needs created by chronic illness and disability.

In effect, they reproduced their own Eastern European ghetto, similar to those they escaped from many years before or during the Holocaust. Ironically, at the edge of the boardwalk is a residential care facility that only a few of their original members were able to transition to because of financial means. For the rest, this residential care facility was just too close and yet, too far. This study demonstrates the importance of resilience to environmental obstacles that grew out of a high degree of group cohesiveness and group relatedness.

ADULT DAY CARE SERVICES

Adult day care services is a loosely defined term describing centers that are opening up at an exponential rate to serve older adults who are physically or medically disabled, or in various degrees of cognitive impairment, and those suffering from Alzheimer's disease. These centers enable caregivers to have respite during daytime hours while the older adults are in a safe and stimulating environment (Bradsher, Estes, & Stuart, 1995). These centers are not merely a repository for older disabled or older adults experiencing dementia; they are a place where these older adults can have a stimulating environment, rather being isolated and sedentary at home. Some centers have adopted Montessori-based techniques to actively engage older adults who suffer from Alzheimer's disease (Judge, Camp, & Orsulic-Jeras, 2010).

A downside to adult day care services is the significant probability of nursing home placement of older adult males compared with older adult women, which is positively correlated with the number of days in adult day care. Though no predictor variables were identified to explain this phenomenon, it is thought that placement in a day-type institution may be transitional for the caregivers and may facilitate placement in nursing homes (McCann et al., 2005). An upside for adult day care services is seen by the caregivers. Gaugler et al. (March 2003) indicated that caregivers who placed older adults in day care centers reported fewer behavioral problems with the older adults when compared with caregivers not availing themselves of adult day care. Providing respite for the caregivers enabled them to feel relief from the burden of caregiving for a time.

CONTINUING CARE AND ASSISTED LIVING

Like aging-in-place strategies, continuing care and assisted living facilities provide medical and nonmedical living services to older adults who are unable to live independently because of medical illness, cognitive decline, or disability. The premise of continuing care is to provide, as much as possible, independence, quality of life, socialization, purpose, meaning, and individualization to the highest degree (Agich, 2003; World Health Organization [WHO], 2000). The decision to move to a continuing care facility or assisted living facility is extremely difficult for older adults used to living independently by either aging in place or living in a residential retirement community (Frank, 2001).

Assisted living facilities have now surpassed the number of nursing home facilities currently in the United States (Stevenson & Grabowski, 2010). Most older adults prefer to transition from aging in place to continuing care or assisted living facilities, rather than to nursing homes as their older cohort did (Eckert, Carter, Morgan, Frankowski, & Roth, 2009). Addressing this need, many states allow Medicaid coverage in continuing care facilities and assisted living facilities, making these centers an alternative to the traditional route to a nursing home, which tends to have more excessive costs (Mollica & Johnson-Lamarche, 2005). This is not a guarantee for the older adults placed in assisted living in lieu of a nursing home that they will be able to remain there; many older adults must move on to a nursing home because most assisted living facilities are not able to manage the complex needs of older adults who have worsening chronic illnesses or advanced Alzheimer's disease (Zimmerman et al., 2005).

Most assisted living facilities also have a continuing care center for those who do not need the more intensive care provided by an assisted living facility. In addition, many assisted living facilities have a rehabilitation unit on premises. These additional resources address the needs of older adults transitioning from aging in place to continuing care who are still relatively independent yet need some support services. Therefore, by providing an interim continuing care facility, these older adults have their own apartments yet have communal dining available and access to health care services (Edelman, Guihan, Bryant, & Munroe, 2006). Other older adults transition to assisted living because of medical conditions and cognitive decline that cause functional impairments.

Many older adults are serviced by social agencies that provide in-home counseling for older adults aging in place. These social workers are the first to advise older adults living at home on their anticipated transition to a continuing care or assisted living facility. Recognizing this aspect of social work counseling, many continuing care and assisted living facilities employ social work staff who provide psychotherapy and counseling services to help older adults transition from aging in place to continuing care and assisted living (Tuckett, 2007).

There are multiple problems when older adults transition from aging in place to a more formal care setting. Problems arise ranging from exacerbation of preexisting psychological problems, anxiety or depression instigated by the move from aging in place, adjusting to a new community, learning new or reviving old social skills, dealing with the loss of proximity to family, and dealing with disenfranchised grief issues (see Chapter 13, Dying and Death; Doka, 2002; Kenndey, Sylvia, Banni-Issa, Khater, & Forbes-Thompson, 2005; Kling, Ryff, Love, & Essex, 2003). In addition to psychotherapy services, social workers initiate psychoeducational interventions to assist family members and the older adults in transition so that they may understand the new lifestyle the older adult is facing, his or her care plan, and what services are available (Coleman & Boult, 2003; Naylor & Keating, 2008).

After all, transitions for older adults, especially when moving from a familiar environment and losing local and medical social support to a new environment, cause distress that makes these older adults vulnerable for psychological and medical consequences (Naylor & Keating, 2008). These transition issues are similar to those consequences an older adult experiences transitioning between a hospital and residential care during acute exacerbations of medical conditions.

Social work interventions are also needed on an ongoing basis in community care and assisted living facilities because the majority of older adult residents, like residents in a nursing home, spend their time isolated in their rooms, watching television, or eating in the dining room (Harper Ice, 2002). These older adults rarely attend recreational activities (2002). Therefore, counseling, psychoeducational groups, recreational therapy, and art and music therapy are much-needed interventions to break the isolation and sedentary behaviors of these older adults.

Another reason for social work intervention is the mental health problems of residents in continuing care facilities and assisted living facilities, which are either preexisting from before the transition was made or occur during the older adult's stay. It is estimated that between 66% and 81% of older adults in these facilities experience depression, anxiety, or dementia (Gruber-Bakdini, Boustani, Sloane, & Zimmerman, 2004). Rather than viewing this as a routine occurrence of aging or restricting intervention to psychopharmacotherapy, ongoing individual and group counseling should be provided to older adult residents and, when necessary, to their family members or caregivers to alleviate these psychological problems (see Chapter 5, Psychopathological Problems in Older Adults; Zarit & Femia, 2008). Social work psychotherapeutic interventions with older adult residents help prevent another transfer for the older adult to a nursing home or a psychiatric facility (Cummings, Chapin, Dobbs, & Hayes, 2004; Dobbs, Hayes, Chapin, & Oslund, 2006). In addition, social work interventions with staff using psychoeducational groups and workshops help the staff recognize psychological problems in residents, help them develop an empathic understanding of the residents' experiences of psychological problems, and help to increase referrals for psychotherapeutic care (Abendroth & Graven, 2013).

HOUSING FOR AGING INMATES: A NEW TYPE OF AGING IN PLACE

In 1999, Just Care, Inc. was established as privatized prison for older adult and critically ill inmates (Beiser, 1999). Since then, other privatized institutions have been created to provide similar care as an effort to control escalating medical expenses in state and federal prison facilities. This is a parallel problem to escalating medical problems seen in the current non-inmate baby boom population. The same concerns exist for both aging inmates and noninmate aging older adults. Are medical services being adequately provided? Is there a rationed strategy to cut costs (for state and federally funded medical services) or to increase profits (in privatized institutions)?

NURSING HOMES

Older adults are at risk for placement in a nursing home when ADLs are significantly limited, these older adults are of advanced age, they do not have a social support system, and they do not have available financial resources for in-home caretaking (Lindrooth, Hoerger, & Norton, 2000; Taylor Jr., Osterman, Acuff, & Ostbye, 2005). If one is an older woman, the likelihood is high that at some time nursing home placement will occur because women outlive men and with longer aging have the above-mentioned risks for nursing home placement (Tuckett, 2007). Ironically, older men have a greater chance of not being placed in a nursing home because their spouses, who are women, are usually their caregivers (Lindrooth et al., 2000; Miller & Weissert, 2000; Taylor Jr. et al., 2005). It is unclear whether the same is true for gay male marriage/partnership or lesbian marriage/partnership because of the lack of research regarding these couple types (see Chapter 11, Gay Male, Lesbian, Bisexual, and Transgender Older Adults). There is some evidence of a current trend indicating that African Americans have a higher frequency of placement in nursing homes compared with Whites (Ness, Ahmed, & Aronow, 2004). However, it is unclear whether this is because of financial status or some reason relating to race.

Chronic illness, functional impairments, cognitive decline, bereavement, and disenfranchised grief are also predictive factors for nursing home placement (Choi, Ranson, & Wyllie, 2008; Cole & Dendukuri, 2003; Darton et al., 2011). Disenfranchised grief occurs when an older person loses a meaningful attachment that is not recognized as significant by others. Examples are loss of a pet, loss of a gay or lesbian partner who is not recognized because of heterosexualism in others, loss of a caregiver or medical providers, or loss of any other significant relationship for the older adult that is not validated or recognized by others. This leaves the older adult to suffer in silence without any emotional support (Doka, 2002).

Older adults suffering with chronic illness, functional impairments, cognitive decline, bereavement, and disenfranchised grief more often than not have co-occurring depression (Choi et al., 2008; Cole & Dendukuri, 2003; McCusker et al., 2005; Noel et al., 2004). In addition, older adults who have cardiovascular and vascular disease and live in nursing homes are at high risk for co-occurring depression (Cervilla, Prince, & Rabe-Hesketh, 2004;

Van der Kooy, van Hout, Marwijk, Stehouwer, & Beekman, 2007). The incidence of depression with these risk factors is higher in nursing home residents when compared with community-dwelling older adults. This may be due to the stressful environment of a nursing home and more advanced states of medical illness and disability. Unfortunately, instead of providing social support from staff and encouraging social interaction with fellow residents, nursing home staff stereotype the residents as less worthy than healthy and socially disengage these older adults because of their frailty, medical illness, and disabilities (Palmer et al., 2013). As a consequence, these staff members act condescendingly toward these older adults, often infantilizing and patronizing them, causing them to lose their status as adults (Tuckett, 2007). Therefore there is a need for staff training programs that infuse gerontological concepts and information in nursing and social work curriculum and that stress interprofessional collaboration in on-site training workshops (Abendroth & Graven, 2013; Dufrene, 2012; Interprofessional Education Collaborative, 2011).

Most older adults in nursing homes are relatively safe but struggle with loneliness and the paucity of social interaction (Slettebo, 2008; Victor, 2012). Older adults in nursing homes have little motivation or institutional forces needed to foster meaning in their lives (Blazer, 2002; Franklin, Ternestedt, & Nordenfelt, 2006; Haugan & Moksnes, 2013). In addition to loneliness, these older adults spend most of their waking hours bored, with little social stimulation, facilitating depression and a general sense of helplessness (Choi et al., 2008).

GOALS FOR IMPROVED EXPERIENCES IN ALL TYPES OF CARE AND RESIDENTIAL SETTINGS

A communication pattern (Figure 12.2) between the caregiver and older adult that ultimately treats an older adult as a child happens when there is a one-way communication from caregiver to the older adult. Ryan, Giles, Bartolucci, and Henwood (1986) describe this as an *active–passive* style of communication. Whether the caregiver is motivated to act paternalistically toward the older adult in care or not, the ultimate dynamic that is established places the caregiver in the dominant role and the older adult in the passive role.

Many social service agencies send social workers into the homes of older adults aging in place. This is a great opportunity to engage the caregiver and the older adult in discussion about how they perceive their relationship (Verkerk, 2001). Problems with caregiver communication can be reduced if the roles of caregiver and the older adult are discussed and agreed on before care giving commences. Social workers overseeing caretakers or those working with families and/or older adults must teach positive communication skills to both the caregiver and older adult (Li, 2004). By restructuring communication (Figure 12.3), the older adult may share as equally as possible in decision making with the caregiver

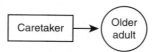

FIGURE 12.2 Active–passive communication between caretaker and older adult.

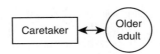

FIGURE 12.3 Equality of communication between the caretaker and older adult.

(Daveson et al., 2013; Haggstrom, Mamhidir, & Kihlgren, 2010; Hain & Sandy, 2013; McCormick, 2001). This causes a phenomenon of *symbiotic niceness* whereby the older adult and caregiver each benefit by creating a positive relationship (Li, 2004). Many times decisions are routinely made by the caregiver, without consultation with the older adult in care. Examples are arranging for prescription delivery from the pharmacy, paying bills that were authorized by the older adult, or a family member overseeing the finances of the older adult without consultation with the older adult.

Implicit in the negotiations of the caregiver–older adult relationship, in addition to focusing on protecting the dignity and meeting the needs of the older adult, is the importance of meeting the needs of the caregiver (Beauchamp & Childress, 2009; McCormick, 2001; Oosterveld-Vlug, Pasman, Gennip, Willems, & Onwuteaka-Philipsen, 2013; Verkerk, 2001). Emphasis should be placed on the older adult recognizing the need of the caregiver to be respected by him or her and agreeing on a strategy of what to do when a conflict arises with the caregiver (Forsgard, Westman, & Jansson, 2002). This is another opportunity for social work intervention. When there is a recognized conflict, the social worker may be called in to mediate the interpersonal problem, or the older adult and caregiver, for future mediation purposes, may identify another third party.

Older adults should enjoy the same social and emotional benefits that they had before aging (Phelan, Anderson, LaCroix, & Larson, 2004; Rim Shin, Kim, & Kim, 2003). There should be no differentiation of these benefits by age brackets. Older adults, especially those in continuing care, assisted living, or nursing home facilities, should be encouraged to maintain their sense of selves, finding meaning and purpose in their lives, and feel a sense of individualism (Haugan & Moksnes, 2013). This can be achieved by enlisting older adults in care facilities to engage in activities within the institution other than limited recreational activities like arts and crafts, singing groups, or watching movies or television (Flatt & Hughes, 2013). These older adults could do volunteer work within the facility where they assist in helping others, provide entertainment, help care for the grounds, or help with housekeeping and meal preparation (Pinquart & Sorensen, 2001; Robichaud, Duran, Bedard, & Ouellet, 2006; Tse, 2010).

Social integration of residents in continuing care centers, assisted living, or nursing homes is imperative to preserving psychological health. By forming caring relationships within their institutional community, those who are separated from family or friends from home can replace these lost or diminished social experiences. Increased intimate socialization facilitates a greater sense of self, improved psychological and medical health, and a more normal experience of the aging process. By establishing a strong social community, the debilitating effects of loneliness can be mitigated (Fessman & Lester, 2000; Pinquart & Sorensen, 2001).

Another aspect of socialization is providing residents of institutions with home-like settings (Edelman, et al., 2006). Most continuing care facilities provide residents with their own rooms where they can bring some furnishings from their homes. Also, in addition to private rooms, some continuing care communities also have a limited number of apartment and condominium residences. Nursing homes, instead of providing ward-like rooms with more than one resident, could be restructured to give residents a sense of privacy and home like those in continuing care facilities. Providing private space for entertaining friends and family is as important to residents of institutions as to those older adults living independently (Barba, Tesh, & Courts, 2002; Bowers et al., 2009; Robichaud et al., 2006).

Psychoeducational programs for all levels of staff, from physicians to nurses to housekeeping, must be instituted to facilitate a rich interpersonal encounter between staff and older adult residents. By increasing their gerontological knowledge, staff will view residents more realistically, rather than through a lens of stigma and false information (see Chapter 4, Stigma and Older Adults). This will promote a positive interpersonal experience in staff when interacting with residents, which in turn produces a shared experience of meaningfulness and purpose. The underlying theoretical foundation to achieve these goals is the person-centered model of care for older adults (Jones, 2011).

THE CASE OF ADANNA

Adanna* is an 81-year-old African American woman living in a continuing care facility. She currently has co-occurring medical problems. Adanna is diabetic, has Parkinson's disease, and was recently diagnosed with Alzheimer's disease. Even though most of Adanna's care is provided by the continuing care center, Adanna's daughter, Melea, is active in her caretaking by overseeing the care she receives in the continuing care center, visiting often, and when possible taking Adanna on trips to a shopping mall, to a movie, or to a restaurant. However, Adanna's dementia is progressing and Melea finds it difficult to continue activities with her outside of the continuing care center.

Melea received a call from the social worker at the continuing care center indicating that the center's internist referred Adanna to him because she was exhibiting signs of a possible depression. The social worker told Melea that for the past 3 weeks Adanna had refused to leave her apartment to participate in activities. When asked why she did not leave, Adanna indicated that her daughter visits her every day and she speaks to her daughter by telephone every evening. She said that she was tired and socialized enough with her daughter.

The social worker made an appointment to speak with Melea to collect collateral information about Adanna. The social worker had Adanna's permission for this meeting. At the meeting, Melea expressed guilt about wanting to not see Adanna on a daily basis because Melea felt that she "no longer had a life." Melea indicated that she retired from her job as a third-grade teacher 3 years ago, and at the same time her husband, a transit

---

*Names and other identifying information have been changed to preserve confidentiality.

worker, decided to retire. She indicated that they both worked throughout their adult lives, and now was their opportunity to travel and see some of the world. She said that her husband was becoming increasingly frustrated with the amount of time she spent caretaking Adanna and that her caretaking was putting an awful strain on her marriage. However, any thought of reducing the frequency of her visits or telephone calls caused Melea to feel guilty and depressed.

The social worker suggested to Melea that she seek individual counseling and gave her a referral to a social worker familiar with problems associated with caregiving to older adults. The social worker further suggested coordinating counseling with Adanna with the social worker Melea agreed to see. As part of the process, the social worker asked Melea to start limiting her visits to every other day so that the social worker could work with Adanna to increase her socialization and participation in the center's activities. He explained that this was important because Alzheimer's disease patients improve cognitively, while in an early stage of the disease, by participating in stimulating activities such as art therapy, music therapy, and an exercise class, all of which was available to Adanna at the center.

Melea entered therapy and began a positive adjustment to cutting back the time she spent with her mother. This immediately made an improvement in her relationship with her husband, and surprisingly, the social worker was able to get Adanna to attend activities at least twice per week. All seemed to be going well until Melea got a call from the social worker that Adanna was found leaving her room naked on two occasions and that Adanna was showing deficits in her ADLs. These deficits included not bathing, having an offensive body odor, falling on occasion (thought to be caused by her Parkinson's disease), and having bladder-control problems. In addition, Adanna once again was refusing to leave her apartment and was losing weight from not eating properly. Even though Adanna had a small kitchenette, she also had access to the dining room at the center. Adanna was now unable to cook for herself but was resistive to going to the dining room. The social worker felt that it was time to transition Adanna to the assisted living facility within the continuing care complex.

Melea felt reluctant to have Adanna transferred to the assisted living facility and asked the social worker if there was an alternative. The social worker said that he felt the transfer would be the best decision because Adanna's dementia symptoms were increasing in intensity and frequency and her co-occurring diabetes and Parkinson's disease further complicated Adanna's circumstance. The social worker expressed much concern about Adanna's recent falls and her deficits in ADLs.

Hearing Melea's reluctance to initiate the transfer, the social worker suggested an alternative strategy. He indicated to Melea that because Adanna had long-term care insurance and had the financial resources from the sale of her home, Adanna could begin a slower transition process by having the necessary physical therapy done in her apartment. If Melea would agree to have a 24-hour home companion move in with Adanna so that she would be served meals in her home, her walking would be monitored, she would be fed on a regular basis, and necessary hygiene needs would be properly fulfilled. The social worker felt that if this strategy was employed, Adanna would become accustomed to more direct care, easing her transition to the assisted living facility, which in the near future would become necessary because of her escalating dementia and increasing symptomatology from her Parkinson's disease.

The second plan was initiated. At the beginning, Adanna was resistive to having a stranger live with her. However, after a few days Adanna seemed to benefit from the socialization with the home companion and ceased to complain about this change in her living status. After 9 months, Adanna's memory began to deteriorate and she experienced five more falls, which her physician felt was from her Parkinson's disease, and possibly the Alzheimer's disease as well. Therefore, for safety purposes Adanna was transferred to the assisted living facility. The social worker facilitated the transfer by counseling Adanna about the benefits of the transfer, into which she, because of her Alzheimer's disease, had little insight. In addition, the social worker took Adanna on several visits to the assisted living facility to familiarize her with the room where she would live. In addition, the social worker had Melea move some of Adanna's personal possessions and furniture to the room at the assisted living facility because she had a private room, which was a positive aspect of the center's policy for residents.

To everyone's surprise, the event that cinched the deal and made Adanna excited to transfer to the assisted living facility was a therapy dog that lived at the facility. When Adanna met the dog, whose name was Brownie, Adanna gave Brownie a new name and called her Bentley. Even though staff corrected Adanna, she insisted on calling Brownie Bentley. Bentley became a close companion for Adanna, spending an hour each day with her. This intervention of a therapy dog seemed to mitigate the resistance Adanna traditionally experienced regarding change of place and functional changes from her co-occurring diseases.

SUMMARY

There are many housing opportunities for older adults, including aging in place, retirement communities, continuing care communities, and nursing homes. For some older adults, there is no choice because they are incarcerated in prisons. Gerontological social work practice with older adults requires that the social worker has a comprehensive knowledge about these housing opportunities in order to be able to advise older adults and their families on what type of housing is the best fit for themselves or their loved ones. Another imperative for social workers is to advocate for appropriate housing of older adult inmates to provide a more humanistic environment that addresses their special needs and to advocate for release of some older adult inmates who no longer represent a threat to society.

No matter what the choice of housing for an older adult, more often than not the older adult will need some type of caregiving assistance and special housing arrangements.

DISCUSSION TOPICS

1. Discuss any experiences you have had in fieldwork or a job working in a continuing care facility, assisted living facility, or nursing home.
2. Discuss how you envision possible interventions to increase a sense of meaning in nursing home residents, who are usually isolated, bored, and lack stimulation.
3. Discuss what interventions you would develop to enhance nursing home staff members' sensitivity to and interest in their older adult residents.

CHAPTER 13

Dying and Death

The act of dying is one of the acts of life.

—Marcus Aurelius, *Telling It Like It Is*

Death is a difficult phenomenon for most people. Because of this, and the current emphasis on positive aging and empowerment of older adults, death and dying does not have a significant emphasis by researchers and clinicians. Death is especially difficult and fear inducing in younger and middle-aged adults. For older adults, the phenomenon of death is accepted and does not induce the fear experienced by younger adults (Fortner, Neimeyer, & Rybarczyk, 2000; Thorson & Powell, 2000).

However, Cicirelli feels that fear of death to a lesser extent does indeed occur in older adults in mid-old age (75–84 years of age), compared with those older adults who are younger and older (65–74 years of age and 85 years and older; 2002). One reason postulated for fear of death in the 75 to 84 and older adults is that this life stage is when one's life expectancy is likely to end, causing a heightened awareness of coming death in that age bracket. The heightened awareness of coming death finds many older adults in an existential crisis whereby they lose their sense of purpose and forward movement in their lives (see Chapter 1, Theories to Inform the Clinician Practicing with Older Adults). After this age bracket, older adults may sense that they cheated death and now any further life is a gift and deserves gratitude. Other older adults may feel that the loss of functioning and chronic health problems are now an unnecessary burden and that death is welcomed as relief for their existential anguish (Gott, Small, Barnes, Payne, & Seamark, 2008; Ternesterdt & Franklin, 2006).

END-OF-LIFE PLANNING

There are formal and informal end-of-life planning activities that older adults and their significant others initiate (Ai, Hopp, & Shearer, 2006). This initiation usually occurs when there is a change in the older adult's condition that causes concern about the future quality of life for the older adult (Coyne & Lyckholm, 2010). The focus on planning is to ensure the best quality of life for the dying older patient, and a better quality death (Detering, Hancock, Reade, & Silvester, 2010). Married older adults and older adults who have children have a greater probability of initiating end-of-life planning (Carr & Khodyakov, 2007; Treas & Marcum, 2011). Older adults who witness a painful death of another older adult also have a higher probability of end-of-life planning as a way to prevent a *bad death* (Carr & Khodyakov, 2007).

Most older adults who are highly educated, have strong social support, are White, and are of European descent initiate end-of-life planning (Kwak & Haley, 2005) . Approximately one third to one half of older adults make end-of-life plans, also known as advanced care planning (ACP; Silveira, Kim, & Langa, 2010). Compared with Whites, non-White minorities and lower economic status (LES) older adults tend not to initiate advance directives (Kwak & Haley, 2005). However, African Americans prefer life support (McKinley, Garrett, Evans, & Danis, 1996). This is consistent with a finding by Kaufman (2005) that if life-sustaining techniques exist, then older adult patients want them made available. Educational interventions with the older adult and his or her family members are used to encourage end-of-life planning (Moorman, Carr, Hammes, & Kirchhoff, 2012). Older adults experiencing death anxiety tend to discourage themselves from end-of-life planning (Ditto, Hawkins, & Pizzaro, 2006; Kübler-Ross & Kessler, 2005; Zimmermannm, 2007).

Older adults who do not engage in end-of-life planning may receive unwanted, unnecessary, costly, and painful medical interventions or withdrawal of desired treatment (Silveira et al., 2010). In addition, the lack of end-of-life planning causes a burden to family members that promotes intrafamily conflict. Asian Americans and Latino Americans compared with Whites tend to rely on family decision making (Kwak & Haley, 2005). Blacks tend to have more aggressive end-of-life care when compared with Whites (Hanchate, Kronman, Young-Xu, Ash, & Emanuel, 2009). In addition, poor older adults also tend to have more aggressive end-of-life care than wealthier older adults do.

Advanced directives are a formal active way for older adults and their families, spouse/partner, and caregivers to plan for death and dying. Advanced directives have been shown to increase the quality of life, while reducing the use of intensive life-sustaining medical interventions (Wright et al., 2008). This is especially true when family members are active in the planning (Mitchell et al., 2009). A consequent effect is a reduction in unnecessary hospital admissions. Physicians, nurses, social workers, and family members perceive advanced directives as helpful to the older adult patient and themselves (Buiting, Clayton, Butrow, van Delden, & van der Heide, 2011; Detering et al., 2010; Rurup, Onwuteaka-Philipsen, Pasman, Ribble, & van der Wal, 2006). An incentive for physicians to be more involved with end-of-life planning is their recent ability to bill Medicare for doctor/patient advanced care planning (Pear, 2010).

There are gender differences regarding the decision to allow medical interventions to prolong life or to not elect medical interventions to prolong life (Arber, Vandrevala, Daly, & Hampson, 2008; Seymour, Gott, Bellamy, Ahmedzai, & Clark, 2004). Older men tend to choose to stay alive by any means necessary regardless of the distress this decision may cause others. In contrast, older women are more concerned about the experience of others, which motivates them to oppose the use of medical interventions to extend life. Paradoxically, when it comes to their husbands (in a heterosexual marriage), they advocate for life-extending measures.

There are also additional considerations for planning dying and death that are considered formal activities (Lloyd-Williams, Kennedy, Sixsmith, & Sixsmith, 2007; Seymour et al., 2004). These include advanced funeral arrangements, giving away belongings or designating belongings for others after the older adult's death, and writing of wills. Those older adults who engage in formal arrangements for dying and death tend to be concerned with reducing or eliminating any burden that their dying process and death will have on others. Wealthy older adults tend to vigorously focus on financial planning and estate planning for the end of their lives, yet tend to lessen their focus on end-of-life medical planning (D. Street & Desai, 2011).

Older adults planning their dying and death also engage in informal planning activities (Ai et al., 2006; Bryon, Dierckx de Casterie, & Gastmans, 2011; Pang et al., 2012). These include discussing feelings about death with family members, spouse/partner, close friends, or caregivers; discussing dying and death with a religious advisor; and discussing desired religious or nonreligious aspects of their anticipated funerals and burial, types of tombstones, and epitaphs. In addition, those older adults who make living wills are encouraged to engage in informal conversations with family members to help clarify their wishes because living wills are more often than not ambiguously written (Doukas & Hardwig, 2003). In some cases, family members may override the older adult patient's advanced directive if they feel there are other alternative treatments that may improve the quality of life for the older adult (Kwak, Tang, & Woo, 2001).

A curious phenomenon occurs with physicians. Aita et al. studied physicians who ordered *external feeding* (feeding tube) for their older adult patients, yet when asked whether they would want external feeding for themselves indicated that they would refuse this intervention (2007). In another study, Golan et al. (2007) found that physicians ordering end-of-life interventions for older adults experiencing co-occurring dementia felt that the interventions ordered for the older adults under their care would not be acceptable for their family members. These are examples of ethical decision-making issues (Brooks, 2011) that need further study, especially regarding those older adult patients who are experiencing dementia and are unable to contribute to decision making.

END-OF-LIFE PALLIATIVE CARE

"A hospice is a program of palliative and supportive services which provides physical, psychological, social and spiritual care for dying persons and their families" (Munley, 1983, p. 79). End-of-life planning, mentioned earlier, causes a higher frequency of use of hospice care by older adults (Nicholas, Langa, Iwashyna, & Weir, 2011). For a dying older adult, the dying process can be facilitated by professionals who are motivated to address end-of-life issues with the older adult, have positive attitudes about the dying process, and are able to address and support the emotions of a dying older adult. Palliative care is considered a characteristic of a *good death* (Steinhauser et al., 2006).

Unfortunately, most physicians and other medical professionals do not address these needs with a dying older adult because of their own emotional difficulties with the dying process and lack of training in their medical education (Curtis, Engelberg, Nielsen, Au, & Patrick, 2004; Fraser, Kuter, & Pfeifer, 2001). A consequence would be situations that commonly occur during the last 3 months of life; caregivers often call emergency services, causing the older adult to be hospitalized unnecessarily in an acute emergency hospital setting, where the older adult dies (Abel, Rich, & Griffin, 2009; Baxter et al., 2013). This is thought to be a product of limited discussions by medical staff and family physicians with caregivers and the older adult patient (Vittica et al., 2010; Whitehead, O'Brian, & Jack, 2011). If more information were communicated by these medical professionals, caregivers and older adults would have a better understanding of end-stage illness, enabling the older adult to remain at home with in-home care. A remedy for this lack of information is for social workers to initiate educational interventions that inform the dying older adult, his or her family members, and the health care professionals treating the older adult (Moorman et al., 2012),

Specially trained health professionals and volunteers provide hospice services at home and in institutional settings to assist an older adult in the dying process by addressing his or her emotions, help the older adult understand the dying process, and provide medical interventions to lessen the pain and anguish associated with medical symptoms experienced during the dying process. Shallcross (2010) indicates that the ethical position of health care workers and social workers must be placing the patients needs ahead of the their personal values.

Palliative care is the treatment of choice for most older adults facing end-of -life care (Teno et al., 2004). Under the umbrella of end-of-life care are two distinct pathways that physicians and families need to choose. Should life-prolonging procedures be performed, or should palliative care be instituted? This is a common dilemma that confronts nursing home residents, their families, and physicians, because most nursing home residents die in their respective nursing homes (Hanson, Henderson, & Rodgeman, 1999; Kayser-Jones, 2002; Teno et al., 2004). In order to initiate this decision making, families, and physicians need to evaluate a constellation of symptoms that have a high probability of indicating that death may occur within 2 years. These symptoms include difficulty breathing, significant weight loss, significant chronic pain, functional decline, cognitive decline from a baseline state, and verbal or physical agitation (Covinsky, Eng, Lui, Sands, & Yaffe, 2003; Schonwetter et al., 2003). No symptom, on its own, is sufficient for making this 2-year prediction of death. Most symptoms must occur in a cluster to make this determination. Having most or all of these symptoms, an older adult will most likely die in less than a year from the initial projection of 2 years.

Palliative care is instituted when an older adult is no longer responsive to curative treatment (Gott et al., 2008). Many older people feel that the goal of palliative care is to make the best possible dying experience for the older adult and his or her family. This best possible dying experience is thought of as a *good death* (Broom & Cavenaugh, 2010; Lloyd-Williams et al., 2007; Seymour et al., 2004). In addition, most older adults prefer to die at home, not in the hospital (Bell, Somogyi-Zalud, & Masaki, 2009).

This is because dying in a hospital causes an older adult to experience poor end-of-life care ("Dignity and nutrition for older people," 2011). Some older adults use palliative care as a means of holding on, so that family members, spouse/partner, or close friends may lessen their suffering and worry about the anticipated older adult's death, thus making the eventual death a good death (Broom & Cavenaugh, 2010). Dying is the last life experience for anyone.

Therefore, many social workers lend credence of this life stage by emphasizing the importance of assessing the quality of life during palliative care (Richards & Ramirez, 1997). An older adult patient's experience of quality of life when receiving palliative care is an aggregation of many psychosocial components (Cohen, 1992; Cohen, Mount, Tomas, & Mount, 1996; Singer, Martin, & Kelner, 1999). They include the satisfaction with the palliative care, degree of independence, experience of pain, cognitive health or decline, status of family and social relationships, spiritual well-being, religiosity, existential issues of life and dying (Hack et al., 2010), and quality of support (Figure 13.1). It is important to understand that the quality of life for a dying older adult is not a static event or measurement, it is a phenomena that is in constant change with a downward trajectory as the dying process progresses (Lo et al., 2002).

For many older adults, intractable pain and intractable symptoms that cause anguish are dealt with by their physicians using sedation as a means of reliving their existential suffering. This is a controversial decision because it may be argued that using sedation hastens death, thereby being physician-assisted suicide (Wein, 2000). Is the intention of a physician using this intervention to relieve existential suffering, or is the intention of a physician to hasten death? According to the rule of *double effect*, if the intention of a physician is to relieve suffering, then subsequent death is considered moral. If the intention of a physician is to cause death to relieve suffering, then the subsequent death is consider immoral (Quill, Dresser, & Brock, 1997; Figure 13.2).

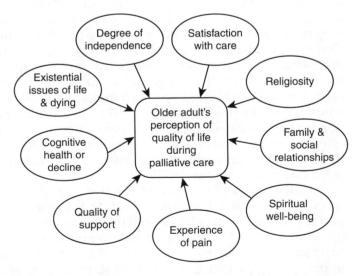

FIGURE 13.1 The psychosocial components of the quality-of-life experience during palliative care.

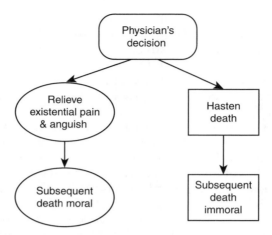

FIGURE 13.2 The rule of double effect.

INTENSIVE CARE AND TERMINAL ILLNESS

In addition to palliative care, an older adult will most likely find himself or herself in an intensive care unit as part of his or her terminal care. Intensive care units in hospitals are the site where 20% of deaths occur during the older person's stay or shortly thereafter (Angus et al., 2004). Similar to palliative care, an intensive care unit may prolong life, may hasten death, or death may occur there. Unlike palliative care, an older adult's experience with pain and anguish is handled with little communication with the patient or family because of the accurate nature of intensive care treatment. Because of the immediacy of decisions, an older adult patient or family members may make decisions for procedures that would not be chosen in a palliative care setting, which facilitates more comprehensive communication (Curtis et al., 2004; Lorenz et al., 2008).

Advance directives (also see End-of-life Planning section earlier) are an effective means to avoid unnecessary intensive care procedures that may not extend life or are not wanted by the older adult patient (Merryn Gott et al., 2013; Sudore & Fried, 2010). Older adult patients can predetermine what procedures they do not want implemented with respect to the resultant quality-of-life changes. Procedures may be granted if there is a high probability of returning functioning at a level desired by the older adult, who is then transitioned to palliative care, or the older adult may be spared from intensive care treatment. They also spare family members from the distress experienced when there is no advanced directive and there is poor or little communication with the treating physician (Tilden, Tolle, Garland, & Nelson, 1995).

A dimension of terminal illness that needs to be considered by the social worker is the *bereavement effect*. In this phenomenon, the spouse/partner of the terminally ill patient has an increased risk of worsening morbidity and an increased risk of mortality (Lillard & Waite, 1995; Martikainen & Valkonen, 1996; Schulz & Beach, 1999). Increased mortality in the spouse/partner is also been described as *caregiver burden* (Dunkin & Anderson-Hanley, 1998). The bereavement effect may be more complex and serious when the spouse/partner has co-occurring psychological problems, or the terminal disease of an older adult may induce psychological problems in the spouse/partner (Li, Laursen, Precht, Olsen, & Mortensen, 2005). The bereavement effect may also be considered when an older adult has dementia. The spouse/partner in effect loses the older adult before the older adult's body is dead. In addition, the bereavement effect may be exacerbated by other psychosocial factors such as poverty, race, and lack of a formal education.

EUTHANASIA

Euthanasia, or *hastened death*, is seen by some as an alternative to palliative care (Cole, 1993; Seale & Addington-Hall, 1994). This type of euthanasia is considered to be *active euthanasia* (Wooddell & Kaplan, 1998). An argument for physician-assisted suicide (PAS) is that it is a rational alternative when palliative care no longer relieves suffering and anguish (Quill, Lee, & Nunn, 2000). A physician considering this option must assess the older patient's competence and must determine whether the procedure is legal. In most cases, physician-assisted suicide is not legal. Therefore, physicians, mental health professionals, and allied medical professionals who believe that euthanasia is a viable alternative to palliative care need to advocate for policy changes in order for older adults to have this option. In Oregon, physician-assisted suicide was made legal in 1994 by the passage of the Death with Dignity Act. Leman found that since 1997, 292 people elected PAS, in contrast to 85,755 who declined to have PAS. Interestingly, even though PAS is legal in Oregon, nurses' and social workers' attitudes were found to be more favorable to passive euthanasia than active euthanasia (PAS). In contrast to this study, Caroll found an increasing public trend to support active euthanasia the United States (2006).

There are criticisms of advocating for physician-assisted suicide. One is that an older person's will to live may fluctuate over time and therefore the desire for a hastened death may be momentary and not a sustained wish (Chochinov, Tataryn, Clinch, & Dudgran, 1999). Another is that most religions do not support active euthanasia. Their teachings support *passive euthanasia*, which allows withdrawing or withholding life support when an older adult is in the process of dying. The approval of passive euthanasia over active euthanasia is seen, for example, in Christianity (Engelhardt & Smith Iltis, 2005), Judaism (Kinzbrunner, 2004), Islam (Hussein, 2004), and Buddhism (Keown, 2005). The basic premise of these religions is their view that dying is a natural process that one should not interfere with. A disturbing turn of events occurred in Arizona, where the Arizona Students' Rights bill was recently passed (Cordaro, 2012). This bill prevents counseling, social work, and psychology programs from requiring their students to learn to work with patients whose behaviors are incompatible with the student's religious beliefs. This law is in conflict with the codes of ethics of these professions, which insist on client-centered care. Caroll (2006) finds that religion is negatively correlated to euthanasia acceptance, which suggests that this law might emanate from conservative religious lobbies.

In 2011 the Netherlands allowed a woman suffering from advanced Alzheimer's disease to be euthanized. This is an unusual precedent for the Netherlands. Before this euthanasia, the Netherlands only allowed euthanasia of a patient who was suffering with intractable pain and who was able to give authorization in *full control of his or her mental faculties*. This included patients in early stages of dementia ("First euthanasia in Netherlands of severe Alzheimer's patient performed," 2011). The patient in 2011 had late-stage Alzheimer's disease and was not in full control of her mental faculties.

There are many reasons an older adult may desire a hastened death. Older adults who are terminally ill and socially isolated have a high probability of desiring a hastened death (Chochinov et al., 1999; A. Street & Kissen, 1999–2000). Older adults who have witnessed other terminally ill older adults suffering may make a conscious choice to not allow themselves to be subjected to suffering and agony (Kissane, 1998; A. Street & Kissen, 1999–2000). Many older adults whose physicians poorly communicate the need for palliative care cause the older adults to feel hopeless and fear a *bad death*. This instigates an impulsive desire for a hastened death or to institute unnecessary acute emergency interventions rather than a comfortable death process afforded by palliative care (Steinhauser et al., 2000; A. Street & Kissen, 1999–2000; Vittica et al., 2010; Whitehead et al., 2011).

PLACE OF DEATH

Currently there is an emphasis on aging in place and dying in place. In general, older adults prefer, if they have a choice, to die at home (Detering et al., 2010; Higginson & Sen-Gupta, 2000; Meeussen et al., 2009; Steinhauser et al., 2000; Wood, Storey, & Clark, 2007). However, a past prejudice held that many older adults and their families, physicians, and social workers preferred a hospital or nursing home death (Steinhauser, et al., 2000). In addition, the choice of place of death is not static; it is a choice process that changes over time according to changing medical and psychological variables (Munday, Petrova, & Dale, 2009).

Ironically, of the patients preferring to die at home, few actually do die at home (Gallo, Baker, & Bradley, 2001; Tiernann, O'Connor, O'Siorain, & Kearney, 2002). Place of death may also have gender predictors. Older women tend not to die at home, married older men tend to die at home, married older women tend not to die at home, and poor older men and poor older women tend not to die at home (Grande, Addington-Hall, & Todd, 1998; Hunt, Fazekas, Luke, & Roder, 2001). In addition, older women who are not married prefer to die in a hospice setting (Robinson, Morris, Luck, & Pruitt, 2002; Tiernann et al., 2002).

A psychological aspect of death that an older adult is concerned with, in addition to place of death, is whether he or she will die in his or her sleep or die suddenly, making the death experience an individual phenomenon (Clarke & Seymour, 2010). Contrarily, death might be witnessed by family, spouse/partner, friends, and other significant figures in the older adult's life. This communal death gives opportunities of farewell communications, facilitating closure for both the older adult and loved ones (2010).

END-OF-LIFE PSYCHOTHERAPY

Unfortunately, older adults are often robbed of the opportunity to discuss their anticipated death by family members, caregivers, spouse/partners, friends, and the various physicians they come in contact with for treatment of chronic and acute illnesses (Clarke & Seymour, 2010; Lloyd-Williams et al., 2007). This avoidance of talking about death leads older adults to disengage and retreat into a psychological isolation that facilitates loneliness and depression. Problem-solving psychotherapy and cognitive behavioral psychotherapy are useful in the dying adult suffering from depression (Alexopolous, Raue, & Arean, 2003; Kraus, Kunik, & Stanley, 2007). This requires a social worker to understand the process of grief and loss and to be able to communicate this understanding to the family members who are grieving (Pomeroy & Garcia, 2011). Paradoxically, older adults do not perceive death in the negative and fearful way their significant others do, and yet they suffer because their significant others' fear and negativity are projected onto the older adult's anticipated death.

It is important for a social worker to recognize that an older adult nearing death, in order to accept the inevitable, goes through various stages of preparation for death. End-of-life psychotherapy is a valuable clinical resource that is helpful for the older patient and his or her family, caretakers, and palliative care professionals (Holland, 2002; Katz & Johnson, 2006; Shuster, Breitbart, & Chochinov, 1999). Preparation for death for the older adult can be focused on in psychotherapy sessions using cognitive behavioral therapy, narrative therapy, and reminiscence therapy techniques (see Chapter 3, Intervention Theories Informing the Clinician Treating Older Adults; Kraus et al., 2007; Naakashima & Canda, 2005). The older adult needs to find meaning in his or her life experiences, resolve conflicts of life experience, and allow a sense of closure to his or her life experiences. By using life-review techniques, the social worker enables the older adult to achieve empowerment over his or her life by the older adult's choice to rewrite his or her life narrative to achieve closure and initiate psychological preparation for subsequent death.

GRIEF COUNSELING

For those coping with the loss of an older adult or anticipating a loss of an older adult, a social worker must understand that the grieving person may be in an acute state of disbelief and psychic numbing (Giddons & Giddons, 2000). In addition, the grieving person may experience symptoms that mimic those of depression. These include sleep disturbance, loss of appetite, unintended weight loss, and a long period of sadness. This is not considered a pathological depression, it is considered a normal state of bereavement (Wordon, 2008). However, a controversial decision was made by the American Psychiatric Association to remove this bereavement exclusion from the *Diagnostic and Statistical Manual of Mental Disorders*, fifth edition (*DSM-5*; American Psychiatric Association, 2013; Begley, 2013). Begley feels that removal of the bereavement exclusion will lead to more depression diagnoses and increased use of psychotropic medications that, if given time, would prove to be unnecessary. Nevertheless, even though these symptoms may be considered a normal aspect of bereavement by some social workers, a social worker must differentiate this constellation of symptoms from a major depressive episode and rule out any co-occurring depression or pre-existing depression in which bereavement is co-occurring (Zisook, 2000). In addition, a social worker needs to be familiar with the different theories of grief processes that articulate the experience of a grieving person during normal bereavement. Implementation of this knowledge to the grieving person enables him or her to experience normal bereavement, lessening the probability of a subsequent depression or the misdiagnosis of a depression.

Kübler-Ross (1969) in a classic book described five stages of grief a person undergoes as a reaction to dying (Figure 13.3). These stages are denial, anger, bargaining, depression, and acceptance. A common misconception is that these stages are linear and that a successful grief process occurs on the completion of each stage. Contemporary thought is that these stages are not sequential; they may occur in any order, and some stages may not be experienced at all (Leming & Dickinson, 2007; Neimeyer, 2000). Walter and McCoyd (2009) indicate that Kübler-Ross's stages of grief "are now widely applied to all types of losses, despite their development from an anticipated loss of self after critical illness" (p. 8).

Another nonlinear dynamic of grief is called the *dual process model of coping with bereavement* (Stroebe & Schut, 1999, 2001; Stroebe, Schut, & Stroebe, 2005). This model consists of two processes: *loss orientation* and *restoration orientation*. These processes are not separate and distinct; they are dynamic processes that interact with each other to facilitate bereavement and guide the grieving person through the grief process (Figure 13.4).

Loss orientation causes the grieving person within the grieving period to experience conflicting feelings of relief and painful feelings of loss and yearning for the deceased older adult. Feelings of relief may encompass an absence of the pain and anguish experienced during the dying process by the grieving person or the grieving person no longer witnessing the pain and anguish of the dying older adult. *Yearning* is the grieving person feeling an emotional bond with the dead older adult despite the fact that he or she is physically unavailable. The grieving person may exhibit object loss symptoms such as mimicking the way the dead older adult talked or sitting in the dead older adult's chair and talking with him or her. *Restoration orientation* is the process of the grieving person re-establishing his or her role in family, vocational, and social spheres.

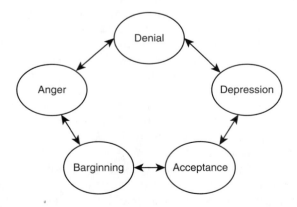

FIGURE 13.3 The five stages of grief described by Kübler-Ross.

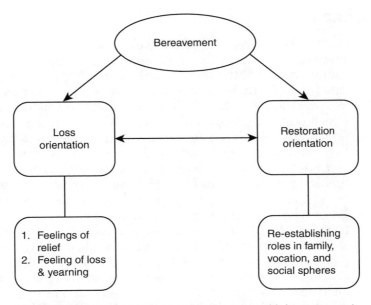

FIGURE 13.4 Dual-process model of coping with bereavement.

Grieving persons also have dynamic styles for expressing grief. Martin and Doka (2000) explain these styles are on a continuum: intuitive, instrumental, and intuitive–instrumental (Figure 13.5). An *intuitive griever* expresses grief at an emotional level by vocalizing his or her grief, crying, or depressed affect (slumping posture, flat facial expression, etc.). An *instrumental griever* tends to join a self-help bereavement group, attend individual or group psychotherapy, or seek religious counseling. An *intuitive–instrumental griever* will spend time thinking of past experiences with the dead older adult, engaging in activities that he or she enjoyed with the dead older adult like listening to music previously shared with the older adult or any other activity or experience linked to the dead older adult.

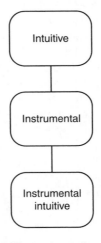

FIGURE 13.5 Three dynamic styles of grief.

THE CASE OF YAEL

Yael* is an 89-year-old Jewish woman who is a Holocaust survivor. She presented for counseling at the in-house psychotherapy center in her continuing care facility. She reported feeling angry and depressed. She indicated that she had not slept well since her husband died 6 weeks before her presentation. She also indicated that she was unable to concentrate, which prevented her from reading. She felt that this was another loss for her because she always found reading a pleasurable activity. She indicated that she and her husband would spend many hours reading together, and now "I don't have Nathan, I lost my desire and ability to read. Why this, after all, Nathan and I are Holocaust survivors, why more suffering?"

After three individual psychotherapy sessions with her social worker, Yael was able to communicate to her social worker that she felt very conflicted. Yael indicated that Nathan had had stage-four intestinal cancer. He was in severe pain for approximately 5 months, during which he was treated with chemotherapy, in several cycles, each cycle lasting many days. Nathan's oncologist indicated that the prognosis was very poor and that medical treatment might only give him a few months or so; if he elected not to be treated, then he would probably die in 2 months. The oncologist offered palliative care as an option to the chemotherapy and explained that he would be kept comfortable and that his pain would be managed. In essence, he would achieve a good death.

Yael indicated that Nathan said that he was a survivor and that he did not want to leave Yael, that he would fight the cancer and beat it. Nathan elected to undergo the chemotherapy treatment. Yael witnessed Nathan suffering excruciating pain, becoming very sick from the chemotherapy, and progressively becoming more frail and skeletal. Yael told her social worker that she had often wished Nathan would die so that he would not have to suffer, so that his agony would end. Yael indicated that she also felt guilty for thinking that Nathan should die. Perhaps, she thought, her thoughts contributed to Nathan's death.

Yael said that when Nathan died, she felt an immediate sense of relief. She said that she now feels that she is a horrible person because she felt relieved when Nathan died. "Yes, he was no longer suffering, but now he is no longer." Yael told her social worker that she yearns for Nathan every day, misses him, and wherever she goes something reminds her of Nathan. She does not want to see friends because it was always "Yael and Nathan" when they were with friends. They were the couple who never separated. Now it is "Yael, no Nathan," which she said is unbearable.

The social worker recognized that Yael was suffering from a loss-orientation conflict. Over the next several weeks, the social worker helped Yael understand the conflicting feelings that she was experiencing and this conflict was a normal aspect of grieving that many people experience. To reinforce the insight Yael was gaining in individual psychotherapy, the social worker encouraged Yael to join a bereavement support group she was running twice a month at the continuing care center. After 2 weeks, Yael agreed to attend the support group while continuing her individual counseling.

---

*Names and other identifying information have been changed to preserve confidentiality.

In conjunction with Yael's individual counseling, the social worker incorporated problem-solving strategies to enable Yael to achieve a state of restoration orientation by helping Yael reconnect with activities that she previously enjoyed. The primary objective was to increase Yael's socialization to lessen her isolation, which was facilitating her depressed reaction to Nathan's death. The social worker suggested that Yael join a reading group at the center that met once a week and discussed books that the group was reading. Yael was reluctant but was now fully engaged in her therapy and trusted her social worker's advice. Consequently, she joined the group. After several group meetings, Yael told her social worker that she'd met some new friends who knew her as Yael without the association of Yael and Nathan. In addition, Yael indicated that she had begun reading on her own and was able to recapture the pleasure that reading used to give her. Yael still yearned for Nathan, but the pain of his loss was lessening, and the real painful moments only seemed to happen for a brief time, no more than once per week.

Yael continued to make positive progress. She reported that she was able to sleep most nights without any problem even though she would always wake early. However, her early awakening was a normal event before Nathan's death. Yael felt that she was now able to eat three meals a day in the common dining room where, in addition, she started to enjoy socializing. She no longer ate in her room, which had a small kitchenette. The social worker observed that Yael's prior weight loss was no longer visibly apparent.

SUMMARY

Dying and death are normal aspects of life but phenomena that most people avoid thinking about. It is imperative for social workers to become familiar with various aspects of dying and death that give older people concern. These include end-of-life palliative care, terminal illness, intensive hospital care, euthanasia, and where they may die.

A social worker is also involved with psychotherapeutic interventions with an older adult who is experiencing the dying process. Particular attention is directed to helping the older adult find meaning in his or her life experiences, resolve conflicts of life experience, and allow a sense of closure to his or her life experiences. This is accomplished by using cognitive behavioral techniques, existential insight, reminiscence therapy, and narrative therapy techniques. In addition, social workers must learn the various theories of grief to guide appropriate grief counseling interventions for those significant others who lose an older adult. These theories include Kübler-Ross's five stages of grief, the dual-process model of coping with grieving, and the dynamic stages of grieving that a person experiences.

DISCUSSION TOPICS

1. Discuss any experiences you have had with a loved one dying.
2. If you sought counseling while grieving a loved one, discuss your experience.
3. Discuss your experience in fieldwork or a job counseling an older adult who was dying.
4. Discuss your experience in fieldwork or a job counseling an older adult who was grieving a loved one.

References

Abbey, R., & Hyde, S. (2009). No country for older people? Age and the digital divide. *Journal of Information Communication Ethics Society, 22*(4), 225–242.

Abel, J., Rich, A., & Griffin, T. (2009). End-of-life care in hospital: A descriptive study of all inpatient deaths in 1 year. *Palliative Medicine, 23,* 616–622.

Abendroth, M., & Graven, L. J. (2013). Integrating care of older adults into the nursing curriculum: A case exemplar project. *Journal of Nursing Education, 52*(9), 529–530.

Abolfathi Momtaz, Y., Hamid, T. A., & Ibrahim, R. (2013). Theories and measures of elder abuse. *Psychogeriatrics, 13*(3), 182–188.

Abrams, R. C., Alexopoulos, G. S., Spielman, L. A., Klausner, E., & Kakuma, T. (2001). Personality disorder symptoms predict declines in global functioning and quality of life in elderly depressed patients. *American Journal of Geriatric Psychiatry, 9*(1), 67–71.

Abrams, R. C., Lachs, M., McAvay, G., Keohane, D. J., & Bruce, M. L. (2002). Predictors of self-neglect in community-dwelling elders. *American Journal of Psychiatry, 159*(10), 1724–1730.

Abrams, R. C., Marzuk, P. M., Tardiff, K., & Leon, A. C. (2005). Preference for fall from height as a method of suicide by elderly residents of New York City. *American Journal of Public Health, 95*(6), 1000–1002.

Acierno, R., Hernandez, M. A., Arnstadter, A. B., Resnick, H. S., Steve, K., Muzzy, W., et al. (2010). Prevalence and correlates of emotional, physical, sexual, and financial abuse and potential neglect in the United States: The National Elder Mistreatment Study. *American Journal of Public Health, 100*(2), 292–297.

Adams, B. (2003). Keeping it up. *Advocate* (902), 38–41.

Addis, S., Davies, M., Greene, G., Macbride-Stewart, S., & Shepherd, M. (2009). The health, social care and housing needs of lesbian, gay, bisexual and transgender older people: A review of the literature. *Health Social Care Community, 17*(6), 647–658.

Affleck, G., Tennen, H., Pfeiffer, C., & Fifield, J. (1987). Appraisals of control and predictability in adapting to a chronic disease. *Journal of Personality and Social Psychology, 53,* 273–279.

Agich, G. J. (2003). *Dependence and autonomy in old age: An ethical framework for long-term care* (2nd ed.). New York, NY: Cambridge University Press.

Agusi, A., Pages, E., Cuxart, A., Ballarn, E., Vidal, X., Teixidor, J., et al. (2012). Exposure to medicines among patients admitted for hip fracture and the case-fatality rate at 1 year: a longitudinal study. *European Journal of Clinical Pharmacology, 68*(11), 1525–1531.

Ai, A. L., Hopp, F., & Shearer, M. (2006). Getting affairs in order: Influences of social support and religious coping on end-of-life planning among open-heart surgery patients. *Journal of Social Work in End-of-Life & Palliative Care, 2*(1), 71–94.

Ai, A. L., Tice, T. N., Petersen, C., & Huang, B. (2005). Prayers, spiritual support, and positive attitudes in coping with the September 11 national crisis. *Journal of Personality, 73,* 763–792.

Aita, K., Takahashi, M., Miyata, H., Kai, I., & Finucane, T. E. (2007). Physicians' attitudes about artificial feeding in older patients with severe cognitive impairment in Japan: A qualitative study. *BMC Geriatrics, 7*(22), 1471–1480.

Alagiakrishnan, K., Lim, D., Brahim, A., Wong, A., Wood, A., Senthilselvan, A., et al. (2005). Sexually inappropriate behavior in demented elderly people. *Postgraduate Medical Journal, 81*(957), 463–466.

Alegria, M., Canino, G., Rios, R., Vera, M., Calderon, J., Rusch, D., et al. (2002). Inequalities in use of specialty mental health services among Latinos, African Americans, and non-Latino whites. *Psychiatric Services, 53*(12), 1547–1555.

Alemagno, S. A., Niles, S. A., & Treiber, E. A. (2004). Using computers to reduce medication misuse of community-based seniors: Results of a pilot intervention program. *Geriatric Nursing, 25,* 281–285.

Alexopoulos, G. S., Buckwalter, K. C., Olin, J., Martinez, R., Wainscott, C., & Krishman, K. R. (2002). Comorbidity of late-life depression: An opportunity for research in mechanisms and treatment. *Biological Psychiatry, 52,* 543–558.

Alexopoulos, G. S., Raue, P., & Arean, P. A. (2003). Problem-solving therapy versus supportive therapy in geriatric major depression with executive dysfunction. *American Journal of Geriatric Psychiatry, 11*(1), 46–52.

Alkhalil, C., Tanvir, F., Alkhalil, B., & Lowenthal, D. T. (2004). Treatment of sexual disinhibition in dementia: Case reports and review of the literature. *American Journal of Therapy, 11*(3), 231–235.

Allen, D. (2005). A rainbow in retirement. *Advocate* (952), 19–20.

Alpay, L. L., Toussaint, P. J., Ezendam, N. P. M., Rovekamp, T. A., Graafmans, W. C., & Westendorp, R. G. (2004). Easing internet access of health information for elderly users. *Health Infomatics Journal, 10*(3), 185–194.

Althof, S. E., Assalian, P., Chevret-Messon, M., Leiblum, S. R., Simonelli, C., & Wylie, K. (2005). Psycholgical and interpersonal dimensions of sexual function and dysfunction. *Journal of Sexual Medicine, 2,* 793–800.

Altman, C. (1999). Gay and lesbian seniors: Unique challenges of coming out in later life. *SIECUS Report, 27*(3), 14–17.

Altman, D., Aggleton, P., Williams, M., Kong, T., Reddy, V., Harrad, D., et al. (2012). Men who have sex with men: Stigma and discrimination. *Lancet, 380*(9839), 439–445.

Altman, R. D., Hochberg, M. C., Moskowitz, R. W., & Schnitzer, T. J. (2000). Recommendations for the medical management of osteoarthritis of the hip and knee: 2000 update. American College of Rheumatology subcommittee on osteoarthritis guidelines. *Arthritis & Rheumatism, 43*(9), 1905–1915.

Altman, S. H., & Shactman, D. I. (2002). *Policies for an aging society.* Baltimore, MD: Johns Hopkins Universtiy Press.

Alvarez-Galvez, J., & Salvador-Carulla, L. (2013). Perceived discrimination and self-rated health in Europe: Evidence from the European Social Survey (2010). *PLoS One, 8*(9), 1–10.

Alvidrez, J., & Arean, P. A. (2002). Physician willingness to refer older depressed patients for psychotherapy. *International Journal of Psychiatry in Medicine, 32*(1), 21–35.

American community survey 2005 questionnaire. (2005). Retrieved December 24, 2007, from http://www.census.gov/acs/www/downloads/squotes.pdf

American Heart Association. (2009). Heart disease and stroke statistics—2009 update. American Heart Association. Retrieved from www.americanheart.org/downloadable/heart/1240250946756LS-1982%20Heart%20and%20Stroke%20Update.042009.pdf

American Psychiatric Association. (1952). *Diagnostic and statistical manual of mental disorders.* Washington, DC: Author.

American Psychiatric Association. (1968). *Diagnostic and statistical manual of mental disorders* (2nd ed.). Washington, DC: Author.

American Psychiatric Association. (1980a). *Diagnostic and statistical manual of mental disorders* (3rd ed.). Washington, DC: Author.

American Psychiatric Association. (1980b). *Diagnostic criteria for the DSM-III.* Washington, DC: Author.

American Psychiatric Association. *Diagnostic and statistical manual of mental disorders* (4th ed., text rev.). Washington, DC: Author.

American Psychiatric Association. (2013). *Diagnostic and statistical manual of mental disorders* (5th ed.). Washington, DC: Author.

Anderson, H., Ward, C., Eardley, A., Gomm, S. A., Connolly, M., Coppinger, T., et al. (2001). The concerns of patients under palliative care and a heart failure clinic are not being met. *Palliative Medicine, 15,* 279–286.

Andreasen, N. C. (2007). DSM and the death of phenomenology in America: An example of unintended consequences. *Schizophrenia Bulletin, 33*(1), 108–112.

Andreoli, R. (2004). Angels for gay inmates. *Advocate* (915), 30.

Andrews, G., Henderson, S., & Hall, W. (2001). Prevalence, comorbidity, disability, and service utilisation: Overview of the Australian national mental health survey. *British Journal of Psychiatry, 178*, 145–153.

Anetzberger, G. J., Ishler, K. J., Mostade, J., & Blair, M. (2004). Gray and gay: A community dialogue on the issues and concerns of older gays and lesbians. *Journal of Gay and Lesbian Social Services, 17*, 23–45.

Angel, J. L., Angel, R. J., Aranda, M. P., & Miles, T. P. (2004). Can the family still cope? Social support and health determinants of nursing home use in the older Mexican-origin population. *Journal of Aging and Health, 16*, 338–354.

Angus, D. C., Barnato, A. E., Linde-Zwirble, W. T., Weissfeld, L. A., Watson, R. S., Rickert, T., et al. (2004). Use of intensive care at the end of life in the United States: An epidemiologic study. *Critical Care Medicine, 32*, 638–643.

Anonymous. (2004). Bush defends war on Iraq, edges toward gay wedding ban. *Christian Century, 121*(3), 14.

Anonymous. (2011). *The health of lesbian, gay, bisexual and transgender people: Building a foundation for better understanding*. Washington, DC: National Academies Press.

Anonymous. (2012). *Alcohol and seniors: Lesbian, gay, bisexual, and transgender (LGBT) older adults*. Retrieved from www.asaging.org/lfain

Anshel, M. H. (2013). A cognitive-behavioral approach for promoting exercise behavior: The disconnected values model. *Journal of Sport Behavior, 36*(2), 107–129.

Anti-Ageism Task Force (Ed.). (2006). *Ageism in America*. New York, NY: International Longevity Center - USA.

Appelt, C. J., Burant, C. J., Siminoff, L. A., Kwoh, C. K., & Ibrahim, S. A. (2007). Arthritis-specific health beliefs related to aging among older male patients with knee and/or hip osteoarthritis. *Journals of Gerontology, 62A*(2), 184–190.

Arber, S., Vandrevala, T., Daly, T., & Hampson, S. (2008). Understanding gender differences in older people's attitudes towards life-prolonging medical technologies. *Journal of Aging Studies, 22*(4), 366–375.

Arean, P., Hegel, M., Vannoy, S., Fan, M.-Y., & Unuzter, J. (2008). Effectiveness of problem-solving therapy for older, primary care patients with depression: Results from the IMPACT project. *The Gerontologist, 48*(3), 311–323.

Arean, P. A. (2004). Psychosocial treatments for depression in the elderly. *Primary Psychiatry, 11*(5), 48–53.

Arean, P. A., & Alvidrez, J. (2001). The prevalence of psychiatric disorders and subsyndromal mental illness in low-income, medically ill elderly. *International Journal of Psychiatry in Medicine, 31*(1), 9–24.

Aserr, L., Milillo, D., Long, S., & Horne-Moyer, H. (2004). The relationship between social desirability and death anxiety in elders. *The Gerontologist, 44*(1), 135.

Astin, J., Pelletier, K. R., Marie, A., & Haskell, W. (2000). Complementary and alternative medicine use among elderly persons: One-year analysis of a blue shield Medicare supplement. *Journal of Gerontology: Medical Sciences, 55a*(1), M4–M9.

Atchley, R. C. (1997). *Social forces and aging: An introduction to social gerontology* (8th ed.). Belmont, CA: Wadsworth.

Aubert, D., Beck, C., Kowanowski, A., Whall, A., & Richardes, K. (2001). Need-driven dementia-compromised behavior: An alternative view of disruptive behavior. *Amereican Journal of Alzheimer's Diesease, 11*(6), 10–19.

Avis, N. E. (2000). Sexual function and aging in men and women: Community and population-based studies. *Journal of Gender-Specific Medicine, 3*, 37–41.

Ayta, I. A., McKinlay, J. B., & Krane, R. J. (1999). The likely worldwide increase in erectile dysfunction between 1995 and 2025 and some possible policy consequences. *British Journal of Urology International, 84*, 50–56.

Azermai, M., Bourgeois, J., Somers, A., & Petrovic, M. (2013). Inappropriate use of psychotropic drugs in older individuals: Implications for practice. *Aging Health, 9*(3), 255–264.

Bacon, C. G., Mittleman, M. A., Kawachi, I., & Giovannucci, E. (2003). Sexual function in men older than 50 years of age: Results from the health professionals follow-up study. *Annals of Internal Medicine, 139*, 161–168.

Bakalar, N. (2011, August 9). Risks: Heart risks may hasten mental delcine. *New York Times*. Retrieved from http://www.nytimes.com/2011/08/09/health/research/09risks.html?ref=todayspaper

Bakker, R. (2003). Sensory loss, dementia, and environments. *Generations, 27*(1), 46–51.

Baldissera, V. D., Bueno, S. M., & Hoga, L. A. (2012). Improvement of older women's sexuality through emancipatory education. *Health Care for Women International, 33*(10), 956–972.

Ball, K., Berch, D. B., Helmers, K. F., Jobe, J. B., Leveck, M. D., Marsiske, M., et al. (2002). Effects of cognitive training interventions with older adults: A randomized controlled trial. *Journal of the American Medical Association, 288*(18), 2271–2281.

Bance, M. (2007). Hearing and aging. *Canadian Medical Association Journal, 176*(7), 925–927.

Barba, B. E., Tesh, A. S., & Courts, N. F. (2002). Promoting thriving in nursing homes: The Eden Alernative. *Journal of Gerontological Nursing, 28*(3), 7–13.

Barney, L. J., Grifiths, K. M., Jorm, A. F., & Christensen, H. (2006 January). Stigma about depression and its impact on help-seeking intentions. *Australian New Zealand Journal of Psychiatry, 1*, 51–54.

Barnow, S., & Linden, M. (2000). Epidemiology and psychiatric morbidity of suicidal ideation among the elderly. *Crisis, 21*(4), 171–180.

Barr, W., Leitner, M., & Thomas, J. (2004). Do older people who self-harm receive the hospital care they need? *Quality in Ageing, 5*(4), 10–19.

Barrett, A., Street, D., & Whiteford, S. (2004). What students see: Ageism in student drawings of the elderly. *The Gerontologist, 44*(1), 229.

Barry, R., Sallah, M., & Miller, C. M. (2011). Neglected to death. Part 1: Once pride of Florida; now scenes of neglect. *The Miami Herald*. Retrieved from http://www.miamiherald.com/2011/04/30/2194842/once-pride-of-florida-now-scenes.html

Bartels, S. J., Blow, F. C., Brockman, L. M., & Van Citters, A. D. (2005). *Substance abuse and mental health among older Americans: The state of knowledge and future directions*. Rockville, MD: Older American Substance Abuse and Mental Health Technical Assistance Center.

Bartels, S. J., Haley, W. E., & Dums, A. R. (2002). Implementing evidence-based practices in geriatric mental health. *Generations, 26*(1), 90–98.

Barth, J., Schumacher, M., & Herrmann-Lingen, C. (2004). Depression as a risk factor for mortality in patients with coronary heart disease: A meta-analysis. *Psychosomatic Medicine, 66*, 802–813.

Bass, S. A., & Ferraro, T. M. (2000). Gerontology education in transition: Considering disciplinary and paradigmatic evolution. *The Gerontologist, 40*, 97–106.

Basson, R. (2000). The female sexual response. A different model. *Journal of Sex and Marital Therapy, 26*, 51–65.

Battels, S. J., & Naslund, J. A. (2013). The underside of the silver tsunami—Older adults and mental health care. *New England Journal of Medicine, 368*(6), 493–496.

Bauer, M., McAuliffe, L., Nay, R., & Chenco, C. (2013). Sexuality in older adults: Effect of an education intervention on attitudes and beliefs of residential aged care staff. *Educational Gerontology, 39*(2), 82–91.

Baxter, S. K., Baird, W. O., Thompson, S., Bianchi, S. M., Walters, S. J., Lee, E., et al. (2013). The use of non-invasive ventilation at end of life in patients with motor neurone disease: A qualitative exploration of family career and health professional experiences. *Palliative Medicine, 27*(6), 516–523.

Bayer, J. K., & Peay, M. Y. (1997). Predicting intentions to seek help from professional mental health services. *Australian New Zealand Journal of Psychiatry, 31*, 504–513.

Bayer, R., & Spitzer, R. L. (1985). Neurosis, psychodynamics, and *DSM-III*: A history of the controversy. *Archives of General Psychiatry, 42*(2), 187–196.

Bayliss, K. (2000). Social work values, anti-discriminatory practice and working with older lesbian service users. *Social Work Education, 19*, 45–53.

Beauchamp, T. L., & Childress, J. F. (2009). *Principles of biomedical ethics* (6 ed.). New York, NY: Oxford University Press.

Beautrais, A. L. (2002). A case control study of suicide and attempted suicide in older adults. *Suicide & Life-Threatening Behavior, 32*(1), 1–9.

Beck, A. T. (1979). *Cognitive therapy and the emotional disorders*. New York, NY: Penguin Books.

Becker, E. (1973). *The denial of death*. New York, NY: Free Press.

Becker, G. (1980). *Growing old in silence*. Berkeley, CA: University of California Press.

Becker, G. (1994). The oldest-old: Autonomy in the face of frailty. *Journal of Personality and Social Psychology, 51*, 1173–1182.

Becker, G. (1997). *Disrupted lives*. Berkely, CA: University of California Press.

Beckman, N., Waern, M., Gustafson, D., & Skoog, I. (2008). Secular trends in self reported sexual activity and satisfaction in Swedish 70 year olds: Cross sectional survey of four populations, 1971–2001. *British Medical Journal, 337,* 279–285.

Beebe, L. H., & Mills, J. (2013). Sexuality and long-term care: Understanding and supporting the needs of older adults. *Issues in Mental Health Nursing, 34*(4), 298.

Beecham, J., Knapp, M., & Fernandez, J. L. (2008). *Age discrimination in mental health services*: SSRU Discussion Paper 2536.

Beekman, A. T., de Beurs, E., van Balkom, A. J. L. M., Deeg, D. J. H., van Dyck, R., & van Tilburg, W. (2000). Anxiety and depression in later life: Co-occurance and communality of risk factors. *American Journal of Psychiatry, 157,* 89–95.

Beeler, J. A., Rawls, T. W., Herdt, G., & Chohler, B. J. (1999). The needs of older lesbians and gay men in Chicago. *Journal of Gay and Lesbian Social Services, 90*(1), 31–49.

Beers, M. B., & Jones, T. V. (Eds.). (2004). *The Merck manual of health & aging.* New York, NY: Ballantine Books.

Beers, M. H., Porter, R. S., Jones, T. V., Kaplan, J. L., & Berkwits, M. (Eds.). (2006). *The Merck manual of diagnosis and therapy* (19th ed.). Whitehouse Station, NJ: Merck Research Laboratories.

Begle, A. M., Strachan, M., Cisler, J. M., Arnstadter, A. B., Hernandez, M. A., & Acierno, R. (2011). Elder mistreatment and emotional symptoms among older adults in a largely rural population: The South Carolina Elder Mistreatment study. *Journal of Interpersonal Violence, 26*(11), 2321–2332.

Begley, S. (2013, May 17). DSM-5: Psychiatrists' "bible" finally unveiled. *Huffington Post,* pp. 1–3.

Beiser, B. (1999). Pensioners or prisoners? *Nation, 268*(18), 28–30.

Belenky, M. F., Cindy, B. M., Goldberger, N. R., & Tarule, J. M. (1997). *Women's ways of knowing: The development of self, voice, and mind* (10th ed.). New York, NY: Basic Books.

Bell, C. L., Somogyi-Zalud, E., & Masaki, K. H. (2009). Methodological review: Measured and reported congruence between preferred and actual place of death. *Palliative Medicine, 23,* 482–490.

Belluck, P. (2011, July 5). In the "stroke belt," erosion of memory is more likely too. *The New York Times.* Retrieved from http://www.nytimes.com/2011/07/05/health/05stroke.html?ref=todayspaper

Benbow, S. M., & Reynolds, D. (2000). Challenging the stigma of Alzheimer's disease. *Hospital Medicine, 61*(3), 174–177.

Bendick, M., Brown, I. E., & Wall, K. (1999). No foot in the door: An experimental study of employment discrimination against older workers. *Journal of Aging & Social Policy, 10*(4), 5–32.

Bengtson, V. L., Rice, C. J., & Johnson, M. L. (1999). Are theories of aging important? Models and explanations in gerontology at the turn of the century. In V. L. Bengtson & K. W. Schaie (Eds.), *Handbook of theories of aging* (pp. 3–20). New York, NY: Springer Publishing Company.

Bennett, D. A. (2004). Mild cognitive impairment. *Clinical Geriatrics and Medicine, 20,* 15–25.

Bennett, K. J. (2000). The psychosocial cost of sensory deprivation. *Geriatric Medicine, 3*(8), 22–24.

Benshoff, J. J., Harrawood, L. K., & Koch, D. S. (2003). Substance abuse and the elderly: Unique issues and concerns. *Journal of Rehabilitation, 69*(2), 43–48.

Bentancourt, J. (2004). Cultural competence: Marginal or mainstream movement? *New England Jornal of Medicine, 351,* 953–955.

Berger, R. M. (1977). An advocate model for intervention with homosexuals. *Social Work, 22,* 236–242.

Berger, R. M. (1996). *Gay and grey: The older homosexual man* (2nd ed.). Binghampton, NY: Haworth.

Berglund, A., & Erricsson, K. (2003). Different meaning of quality of life: A comparison between what elderly persons and geriatric staff believe is of importance. *International Journal of Nursing Practice, 9,* 112–119.

Bernier, F. (2002). Relationship of a pelvic floor rehabilitation program for urinary incontinence to Orems' self-care deficit theory of nursing Part 1. *Urologic Nursing, 22*(6), 378–390.

Bial, M., Gutheil, I. A., Hanson, M., & White-Ryan, L. (2012). Using personal narratives for curriculum development about substance abuse and older adults. *Journal of Teaching in Social Work, 32*(1), 121–131.

Biggs, S., Bernard, M., Kingston, P., & Nettleton, H. (2000). Lifestyles of belief: Narrative and culture in a retirement community. *Aging & Society, 20*(6), 649–672.

Biggs, S., Lowenstein, A., & Hendricks, J. (Eds.). (2003). *The need for theory: Critical approaches to social gerontology.* New York, NY: Baywood Publishing.

Bijl, R. V., & Ravelli, A. (2000). Psychiatric morbidity, service use, and need for care in the general population: Results of the Netherlands mental health survey and incidence study. *American Journal of Public Health, 90*, 602–607.

Bilwise, D. L., & Lee, K. A. (1993). Development of an agitated behavior rating scale for discrete temporal observations. *Journal of Nursing Measures, 1*, 115–124.

Bilwise, D. L., Rye, D. B., & Dihenia, B. (2002). Greater daytime sleepiness in subcortical stroke relative to Parkinson's disease and Alzheimer's disease. *Journal of Geriatric Psychiatry and Neurology, 15*(2), 61–67.

Birrer, R. B., & Vemuri, S. P. (2004). Depression in later life: A diagnostic and therapeutic challenge. *American Family Physician, 69*(10), 2375–2382.

Bisschop, M. I., Kriegsman, D. M., Deeg, D. J. H., Beekman, A. T., & van Tilburg, W. (2004). The longitudinal relation between chronic diseases and depression in older persons in the community: The Longitudinal Aging Study Amsterdam. *Journal of Clinical Epidemiology, 57*(2), 187–194.

Bitzer, J., Tshudin, S., & Adler, J. (2008). Sexual counseling in elderly couples. *Sexual counseling in elderly couples, 5*(9), 2027–2043.

Blackman, M. R., Sorkin, J. D., Munzer, T., Bellantoni, M. F., Busby-Whitehead, J., Stevens, T. E., et al. (2002). Growth hormone and sex steroid administration in healthy aged women and men: A randomized control trial. *Journal of the American Medical Association, 288*(18), 282–292.

Blazer, D. (2002). Self-efficacy and depression in later life: A primary prevention proposal. *Aging and Mental Health, 6*(4), 315–324.

Bleechem, M. (2002). *Elderly alcoholism: Intervention strategies.* Belmont, CA: Charles C Thomas.

Blow, F., & Schonfeld, L. (2004). Screening, brief intervention, and brief treatment of alcohol and medication problems in older adults: the Florida model. *The Gerontologist, 44*(1), 665.

Blow, F. C. (1998). *Use and abuse of psychoactive prescription drugs and over-the-counter medications, substance abuse among older adults. Treatment Improvement Protocol (TIP) series, No. 26.* Rockville, MD: U.S. Department of Health and Human Services, Center for Substance Abuse Treatment.

Blumel, J. E., Castel-Branco, C., Cancelo, M. J., Romero, H., Aprikian, D., Sarra, S. (2004). Impairment of sexual activity in middle-aged women in Chile. *Menopause, 11*(1), 78–81.

Bockting, W. O., Robinson, B. E., & Rosser, B. R. S. (1998). Transgender HIV prevention: A qualitative needs assessment. *AIDS Care, 10*(4), 505–525.

Bodner, E., & Lazar, A. (2009). On the origins of ageism among older and younger adults: A review. *International Psychogeriatrics, 21*, 1–12.

Boeckxstaens, P., Deregt, M., Vandesype, P., Williams, S., Brusselle, G., & De Sutter, A. (2012). Chronic obstructive pulmonary disease and comorbities through the eyes of the patient. *Chronic Respiratory Disease, 9*(3), 183–191.

Boeri, M. W. (2004). "Hell, I'm an addict, but I ain't no junkie": An ethnographic analysis of aging heroin users. *Human Organization, 63*(2), 236–245.

Bohlmeijer, E. T., Westerhof, G. J., & Emmerik-De Jong, M. (2008). The effects of integrative reminiscence on meaning in life: Results of a quasi-experimental study. *Aging and Mental Health, 12*, 639–646.

Bonnie, R. J., & Wallace, R. B. (Eds.). (2003). *Elder mistreatment: Abuse, neglect and exploitation in aging America.* Washington, DC: National Academic Press.

Bora, E., Harrison, B. J., Yucel, M., & Pantelis, C. (2013). Cognitive impairment in euthymic major depressive disorder: A meta-analysis. *Psychological Medicine, 43*, 2017–2026.

Borden, W. (1992). Narrative perspectives in psychosocial intervention following adverse life events. *Social Work, 37*, 125–141.

Borell, K., & Ghazanfareeon Karlsson, S. (2003). Reconceptualizing intimacy and ageing: Living apart together. In S. Arber, K. Davidson, & J. Ginn (Eds.), *Gender and aging: Changing roles and relationships.* Philadelphia, PA: Open University Press.

Bortz, W. M. (2002). A conceptual framework of fraility: A review. *Journal of Gerontology: Medical Sciences, 57A*, M283–M288.

Bouman, W. P. (2008). Sexuality in later life. In J. R. Oppenheimer & C. Dening (Eds.), *Oxford textbook of old age psychiatry* (Illustrated ed.). New York, NY: Oxford University Press.

Bowen, S., Witkiewitz, K., Chawla, N., & Grow, M. S. (2011). Integrating mindfulness meditation and cognitive behavioral traditions for the longterm treatment of addictive behaviors. *JCOM, 18*(10), 473–479.

Bowers, H., Clark, C., Crosby, G., Easterbrook, L., Macadam, A., MacDonald, R., et al. (2009). *Older people's vision for long-term care.* York, UK: Joseph Rowntree Foundation.

Bowes, A., Avan, G., & Macintosh, S. B. (2012). Cultural diversity and the mistreatment of older people in black and minority ethnic communities: Some implications for service provision. *Journal of Elder Abuse & Neglect, 24*(3), 251–274.

Bradley, D. (2000). The gay guru: Counterculture icon Ram Dass talks about being gay and getting older. *In the Family, 6*(1), 24–26.

Bradsher, J. E., Estes, C., & Stuart, M. H. (1995). Adult day care: A fragmented system of policy and funding streams. *Journal of Aging & Social Policy, 7*(1), 17–38.

Bradway, C., Dahlberg, B., & Barg, F. K. (2010). How women conceptualize urinary incontinence: A cultural model. *Journal of Women's Health, 19*(8), 1533–1541.

Brandl, B., & Raymond, J. A. (2012). Policy implications of recognizing that caregiver stress is not the primary cause of elder abuse. *Generations, 36*(3), 32–39.

Braun, S. R., Gregor, B., & Tran, U. S. (2013). Comparing bona fide psychotherapies of depression in adults with two meta-analytical approaches. *PLoS One, 8*(6), 1–14.

Breitbart, W., Rosenfelf, B., Pessin, H., Kaim, M., Funesti-Esch, J., Gallietta, M., et al. (2000). Depression, hopelessness, and desire for hastened death in terminally ill patients with cancer. *Journal of the American Medical Association, 284*, 2907–2911.

Brennan, L., & Moos, R. H. (1996). Late-life drinking behavior. *Alcohol Health and Research World, 20*(3), 197–205.

Brennan, M., & Silverstone, B. (2000). Developmental perspectives of aging and vision loss. In B. Silverstone, M. A. Lang, B. Rosenthal, & E. Faye (Eds.), *The Lighthouse handbook on vision impairment and rehabilitation* (Vol. 1, pp. 409–430). New York, NY: Oxford University Press.

Brennen, M., Horowitz, A., & Su, Y. (2005). Dual sensory loss and its impact on everyday competence. *The Gerontologist, 45*, 337–346.

Brezinka, V., Dusseldorp, E., & Maes, S. (1998). Gender differences in psychosocial profile at entry into cardiac rehabilitation. *Journal of Cardiopulmonary Rehabilitation, 18*(445–449).

Brierley, F., Guthrie, E., Busby, C., Marion-Francis, F., Byrne, J., & Burns, A. (2003). Psychodynamic interpersonal therapy for early Alzheimer's disease. *British Journal of Psychotherapy, 19*, 435–446.

Briggs, W. P., Magnus, V. A., Lassiter, P., Patterson, A., & Smith, L. (2011). Substance use, misuse, and abuse among older adults: Implications for clinical mental health counselors. *Journal of Mental Health Counseling, 33*(2), 112–127.

Brintnall-Peterson, M. (2012). *Caregiving is different for everyone.* Madison, WI: University of Wisconsin (Extension).

Broe, G. A., Jorm, A. F., Creasy, H., Bennett, H., Cullen, J., Edelbrock, D., et al. (1999). Career distress in the general population: Results from the Sydney Older Persons Study. *Age and Ageing, 38*, 307–311.

Brooks, C. L. (2011). Considering elderly competence when consenting to treatment. *Holistic Nursing Practice, 16*, 1678–1686.

Broom, A., & Cavenaugh, J. (2010). Masculinity, moralities, and being cared for: An exploration of experiences of living and dying in hospice. *Social Science & Medicine 71*(5), 869–876.

Brotman, S., Ryan, B., Collins, S., Chamberland, L., Cormier, R., Julien, D., et al. (2007). Coming out to care: Caregivers of gay and lesbian seniors in Canada. *The Gerontologist, 47*, 490–503.

Brotman, S., Ryan, B., & Cormier, R. (2003). The health and social service needs of gay and lesbian elders and their families in Canada. *The Gerontologist, 43*(2), 192–202.

Brown, A. F., Mangione, C. M., & Sarkisian, S. D. (2003). California Health Care Foundation/American Geriatrics Society panel on improving care for elders with diabetes: Guidelines for improving the care of the older person with diabetes mellitus. *Journal of the American Geriatric Society, 51(Supplement Guidelines)*, S5265–5280.

Brown, S. L., Lee, G. R., & Bulanda, J. R. (2006). Cohabitation among older adults: A national portrait. *Journal of Gerontology: Social Sciences, 61B*(2), 971–979.

Brown, T. N., Sellers, S. L., Brown, K. T., & Jackson, J. S. (1999). Race, ethnicity, and culture in the sociology of mental health. In J. C. Aneshensel & J. C. Phelan (Eds.), *Handbook of sociology of mental health* (pp. 167–182). New York, NY: Kluwer Publishing House Academic/Plenum Publishers.

Brownel, P., & Berman, J. (2004). Homicides of older women in New York City. In A. R. Roberts & K. R. Yeager (Eds.), *Evidence-based practice manual* (pp. 771–778). New York, NY: Oxford University Press.

Brownell, P., & Berman, J. (2004). Homicides of older women in New York City. In A. R. Roberts & K. R. Yeager (Eds.), *Evidence-based practice manual* (pp. 771–778). New York, NY: Oxford University Press.

Brownell, P., Berman, J., Salamone, A., & Welty, A. (2002). Elder abuse and the mentally ill abuser. In M. Landsberg, L. K. Rock, W. Berg, & A. Smiley (Eds.), *Serving mentally ill offenders: Challenges and opportunities for mental health professionals* (pp. 193–214). New York, NY: Springer Publishing Company.

Brownridge, D. A. (2006). Partner violence against women with disabilities: Prevalence, risk, and explanations. *Violence Against Women, 12*(9), 805–822.

Bryon, E., Dierckx de Casterle, C. B., & Gastmans, C. (2011). "Because we see them naked"—Nurses' experience in caring for hospitalized patients with dementia: Considering artificial nutrition or hydration (ANH). *Bioethics, 6*, 285–295.

Buchannan, D. (2012). Nursing students: Our future gerontological nurses. *Perspectives, 35*(3), 18–19.

Bucholz, K. K., & Robins, L. N. (1987). Who talks to a doctor about existing depressive illness? *Journal of Affective Disorders, 12*, 241–250.

Buettner, L. L., Fitzsimmons, S., & Atav, A. S. (2006). Predicting outcomes of therapeutic recreation interventions for older adults with dementia and behavioral symptoms. *Therapeutic Recreation Journal, 40*(1), 33.

Buettner, L. L., & Martin, S. L. (1995). *Therapeutic recreation in the nursing home.* State College, PA: Venture Publishing.

Buiting, H. M., Clayton, J. M., Butrow, P. N., van Delden, J. J., & van der Heide, A. (2011). Artificial nutrition and hydration for patients with advanced dementia: Perspectives from medical practitioners in the Netherlands and Australia. *Palliative Medicine, 25*, 83–91.

Burdge, B. J. (2007). Bending gender, ending gender: Theoretical foundations for social work practice with the transgender community. *Social Work, 52*(3), 243–250.

Burg, M. M., & Abrams, D. (2001). Depression in chronic medical illness: The case of coronary heart disease. *Journal of Clinical Psychology, 57*, 1323–1337.

Burgess, A. W., & Morgenbesser, L. I. (2005). Sexual violence and seniors. *Brief Treatment and Crisis Intervention, 5*(2), 193.

Burgess, A. W., Dowdel, E. B., & Prentky, R. A. (2000). Sexual abuse of nursing home residents. *Journal of Psychosocial Nursing & Mental Health Services, 38*(6), 8–10.

Burke, B. L. (2011). What can motivational interviewing do for you? *Cognitive and Behavioral Practice, 18*, 78–81.

Burke, B. L., Martens, A., & Fauchner, E. H. (2010). Two decades of terror management theory: A meta-analysis of mortality salience research. *Personality and Social Psychology Review, 14*, 155–195.

Burke, B. L., Vassilev, G., Kantchelov, A., & Zweben, A. (2002). Motivational interviewing with couples. In W. R. Miller & R. Robles (Eds.), *Motivational interviewing* (2nd ed., pp. 347–361). New York, NY: Guilford Press.

Burnett, J., Achenbaum, W. A., Hayes, L., Flores, D. V., Hochschild, A. E., Kao, D., et al. (2012). Increasing surveillance and prevention efforts for elder self-neglect in clinical settings. *Aging Health, 8*(6), 647–655.

Burns, A. (2000). Might olfactory dysfunction be a marker of early Alzheimer's disease? *Lancet, 355*(9198), 84–85.

Burns, P., Jones, S. C., Iverson, D., & Caputi, P. (2012). Riding the wave or paddling in the shallows? Understanding older Australians' use of the internet. *Health Promotion Journal of Australia, 23*(2), 145–148.

Burston, D. (1996). *The wings of madness: The life and work of R.D. Laing.* Cambridge, MA: Harvard University Press.

Butler, R. N. (1963). The life review: An interpretation of reminiscence in the aged. *Psychiatry, 119*, 721–728.

Butler, R. N. (1969). Ageism: Another form of bigotry. *Gerontologist, 9*, 243–246.

Butler, R. N. (1975). *Why survive? Being old in America.* New York, NY: Harper and Row.

Butler, R. N., & Lewis, M. I. (1983). *Aging and mental health: Positive psychosocial approaches* (3rd ed.). St. Louis: C.V. Mosby.

Byck, R. (Ed.). (1974). *Cocaine papers: Sigmund Freud.* New York, NY: Stonehill Publishing Company.

Cacioppo, J. T., Hawkley, L. C., Crawford, E., Ernst, J. M., Burleson, M. H., Kowalewski, R. B., et al. (2002). Loneliness and health: Potential problems. *Psychosomatic Medicine, 64*, 407–417.

Cahill, S. (2002). Long term care issues affecting gay, lesbian, bisexual, and transgender elders. *Geriatric Care Management Journal, 12*, 4–8.

Cahill, S. (2007). The Coming GLBT Senior Boom. *Gay & Lesbian Review Worldwide, 14*(1), 19–25.

Cahill, S., South, K., & Spade, J. (2000). *Outing age: Policy issues affecting gay, lesbian, bisexual and transgender elders.* New York: The Policy Institute of the Gay and Lesbian Task Force.

Cahill, S., & Valadez, R. (2013). Growing older with HIV/AIDS: New public health challenges. *American Journal of Public Health, 103*(3), E7–E15.

Calasanti, T., & Kiecolt, K. J. (2007). Diversity among late-life couples. *Generations, 31*(3), 10–17.

Callahan, D. (1987). *Setting limits: Medical goals in an aging society.* New York, NY: Simon and Schuster.

Campbell, A. I. (2003). *How policies make citizens: Senior political activism and the American Welfare State.* Princeton, NJ: Princeton University Press.

Cantor, M., Brennan, M., & Shippy, A. (2004). *Caregiving among lesbian gay, bisexual, and transgender New Yorkers.* New York, NY: National Gay and Lesbian Task Force Policy Institute.

Carkhuff, R. R. (2009). *The art of helping in the twenty-first century* (9th ed.). Amherst, MA: Human Resource Development Press.

Carp, F. M. (2000). *Elder abuse in the family: An interdisciplinary model for research.* New York, NY: Springer Publishing Company.

Carr, D., & Friedman, M. A. (2005). Is obesity stigmatizing? Body weight, perceived discrimination, and psychological well-being in the United States. *Journal of Health and Social Behavior, 46*(3), 244–259.

Carr, D., & Khodyakov, D. (2007). End-of-life health care planning among young-old adults: An assessment of psychosocial influences. *Journal of Gerontology: Social Sciences, 62B*(2), 135–141.

Carr, D. B., Gray, S., Baty, J., & Morris, J. C. (2000). The value of informant vs. individual's complaints of memory impairment in early dementia. *Neurology, 55,* 1724–1726.

Carr, D. B., Meuser, T. M., & Morris, J. C. (2006). Driving retirement: The role of the physician. *Canadian Medical Association. Journal, 175*(6), 601–602.

Carroll, J. (Producer). (2006). *Public continues to support right-to-die for terminally ill patients.* Retrieved from http://www.gallup.com/poll/23356/Public-Continues-Support-Right-to-Die-Terminally-Ill-Patients.aspx

Casteel, C., Martin, S. L., Smith, J. B., Gurka, K. K., & Kupper, L. L. (2008). National study of physical and sexual assault among women with disabilities. *Injury Prevention, 14*(2), 87–90.

Cavallini, E., Pagnin, A., & Vecchi, T. (2003). Aging and everyday memory: The beneficial effect of memory training. *Archives of Gerontology and Geriatrics, 37*(3), 241–257.

Cavelti, M., Kvrgic, S., Beck, E.-M., Rusch, N., & Vauth, R. (2012). Self-stigma and its relationship with insight, demoralization, and clinical outcome among people with schizophrenia spectrum disorders. *Comprehensive Psychiatry, 53*(5), 468–479.

Centers for Disease Control and Prevention, National Center for Injury Prevention and control. (2006). *Web-based injury statistics query and reporting system (WISQARS).* Retrieved October 23, 2009, from www.cdc.gov/ncipc/wisqars

Centers for Disease Control and Prevention (CDC). (2010). *HIV surveillance report, 2008.* Alanta, GA: Author.

Centers for Disease Control and Prevention (CDC). (2011). *Fact sheet: General information and national estimates on diabetes in the United States 2011.* Atlanta, GA: Author.

Cervilla, J. P., Prince, M., & Rabe-Hesketh, S. (2004). Vascular disease risk factors as determinant of incident depressive symptoms: A prospective community-based study. *Psychological Medicine, 4,* 635–641.

Chan, D., Kasper, J. D., Black, B. S., & Rabins, P. V. (2003). Prevalence and correlates of behavioral and psychiatric symptoms in community-dwelling elders with dememtia or mild cognitive impairment: The Memory and Medical Care Study. *International Journal of Geriatric Psychiatry, 18,* 174–192.

Chan, J. M., Stampfer, M. J., Giovanucci, E., Gann, P. H., Ma, J., Wilkinson, P., et al. (1998). Plasma insulin-like growth factor 1 and prostate cancer risk: A prospective study. *Science, 279*(5350), 563–566.

Chappell, N. L., McDonald, L., & Stone, M. (2010). *Aging in contemporary Canada.* Toronto, Canada: Prentice Hall.

Cheavens, J., & Lynch, T. (2004). Reporting of suicidal ideation in older and younger adults with and without psychiatric diagnoses. *The Gerontologist, 44*(1), 411–412.

Chesney, M. A., & Smith, A. W. (1999). Critical delays in HIV testing and care: The potential role of stigma. *American Behavioral Scientist, 47*(7), 1162–1174.

Cheston, R. (1996). Stories and metaphors: Talking about the past in a psychotherapy group for people with dementia. *Aging and Society, 16,* 579–602.

Chi, I., Yip, P. S., Chiu, H. F., Chou, K. L., Chan, K. S., & Kwan, C. W. (2005). Prevalence of depression and its correlates in Hong Kong's Chinese older adults. *American Journal of Geriatric Psychiatry, 13*(5), 409–416.

Childs, H. W., Hayslip, B., Radika, L. M., & Reinberg, J. A. (2000). Young and middle-aged adults' perceptions of elder abuse. *The Gerontologist, 40*(1), 75–85.

Chiu, H. F., Yip, P. S., Chi, I., Chan, K. S., Tsoh, J., & Kwan, C. W. (2004). Elderly suicide in Hong Kong: A case-controlled psychological autopsy study. *Acta Psychiatrica Scandinavica, 109*, 299–305.

Chochinov, H. M., Tataryn, D., Clinch, J., & Dudgran, D. (1999). Will to live in the terminally ill. *Lancet, 354*, 816–819.

Choi, N., Ransom, S., & Wyllie, R. (2008). Depression in older nursing home residents: The influence of nursing home environmental stressors, coping, and acceptance of group and individual therapy. *Aging and Mental Health, 12*(5), 536–547.

Cicirelli, V. G. (2002). Fear of death in older adults: Predictions from terror management theory. *Journal of Gerontology: Psychological Sciences, 57B*, P358–P366.

Clark, A. J. (2010). Empathy: An integral model in the counseling process. *Journal of Counseling & Development, 88*, 348–356.

Clark, J. (2006). Chronic pain prevalence and analgesic prescribing in a general population. *Journal of Pain Symptom Management, 23*, 131–137.

Clark, S. (2011). Integration of supportive psychotherapy with case management for older adults with borderline personality disorder. *Journal of Gerontological Social Work, 54*(6), 627.

Clarke, D., & Seymour, J. (2010). "At the foot of a very long ladder." Discussing the end of life with older adults and informed caregivers. *Journal of Pain and Symptom Management, 40*(6), 857–869.

Clayton, S. L. (1999). Friends for folks. *Corrections Today, 61*(3), 87.

Clegg, A., Young, J., Iliffe, S., Rikkert, M. O., & Rockwood, K. (2013). Frailty in elderly people. *Lancet, 381*(9868), 752–762.

Clements-Nolle, K., Marx, R., Guzman, R., & Katz, M. (2001). HIV prevalence, risk behaviors, health care use, and mental health status of transgender persons: Implications for public health interventions. *American Journal of Public Health, 91*(6), 915–921.

Cluse-Tolar, T., Lambert, E. G., Ventura, L. A., & Pasupuleti, S. (2004). The views of social work students toward gay and lesbian persons: Are they different from other undergraduate students? *Journal of Gay & Lesbian Social Services, 17*(3), 59.

Cohen, S. R. (1992). Quality of life assessment in terminal illness: Defining and measuring subjective well-being in the dying. *Journal of Palliative Care, 8*, 40–45.

Cohen, S. R., Mount, B. M., Tomas, J. J. N., & Mount, L. F. (1996). Existential well-being is an important determinant of quality of life. Evidence from the McGill quality of life questionnaire. *Cancer, 77*, 576–586.

Cole, M. G., & Dendukuri, N. (2003). Risk factors for depression among elderly community subjects: A systematic review and meta-analysis. *American Journal of Psychiatry, 160*(6), 1147–1156.

Cole, R. (1993). Communicating with people who request euthanasia. *Palliative Medicine, 7*, 139–143.

Cole, S. W., Kemeny, M. E., Taylor, S. E., & Visscher, B. R. (1996). Elevated physical health risk among gay men who conceal their homosexual identity. *Health Psychology, 15*, 243–251.

Coleman, E., & Boult, C. (2003). Improving the quality of transitional care for persons with complex care needs. *Journal of the American Geriatric Society, 51*, 556–557.

Coles, L. S. (2004). Demography of human supercentenarians. *Journals of Gerontology, 59A*(6), 579–586.

Collingwood, P., Emond, R., & Woodward, R. (2008). The theory circle: A tool for learning and practice. *Social Work Education, 27*(1), 70–83.

Collins, D. R., & Bird, R. (2007). The penitentiary visit—A new role for geriatricians? *Age and Ageing, 36*(1), 11.

Colliver, J. D., Compton, W. M., Gfroerer, J. C., & Condon, T. (2006). Projecting drug use among aging baby boomers in 2020. *Annals of Epidemiology, 16*, 257–265.

Compton, M. T., Esterberg, M. L., McGee, R., Kotwicki, R. J., & Oliva, J. R. (2006). Crisis intervention team training: Changes in knowledge, attitudes, and stigma related to schizophrenia. *Psychiatric Services, 57*(8), 1199–1202.

Congdon, N. G., Friedman, D. S., & Lietman, T. (2003). Important causes of visual impairment in the world today. *Journal of the American Medical Association, 290*, 2057–2060.

Conn, D. K., Clark, D., & van Reekum, R. (2000). Depression in holocaust survivors: Profile and treatment outcome in a geriatric day hospital program. *International Journal of Geriatric Psychiatry, 15*, 331–337.

Connidis, I. A. (2001). *Family ties and aging.* Thousand Oaks, CA: Sage.

Connidis, I. A. (2006). Intimate relationships: Learning from later life experience. In T. Calasanti & K. Slevin (Eds.), *Age matters.* New York, NY: Routledge.

Conrad, P. (2005). The shifting engines of medicalization. *Journal of Health and Social Behavior, 46*(1), 3–14.

Convey, H. C. (1989). Perceptions and attitudes toward sexuality of the elderly during the Middle Ages. *The Gerontologist, 29*, 416–417.

Conway, B. N., May, M. E., & Blot, W. J. (2012). Mortality among low-income African Americans and Whites with diabetes. *Diabetes Care, 35*(11), 2293–2299.

Cook-Daniels, L., & Munson, M. (2010). Sexual violence, elder abuse, and sexuality of transgender adults, age 50+: Results of three surveys. *Journal of GLBT Family Studies, 6*(2), 142–177.

Cooper, B. (1988). *Over the hill: Reflections on ageism between women.* Freedom, CA: Crossing Press.

Cooper, L. (2012). Combined motivational interviewing and cognitive-behavioral therapy with older adult drug and alcohol abusers. *Health & Social Work, 37*(3), 173–179.

Cooper, M. (2003). *Existential therapies.* London, UK: Sage.

Cooper, R. A. (1994). A case study in the use of race and ethnicity in public health surveillance. *Public Health Report, 109*, 46–51.

Cordaro, M. (2012). Pet loss and disenfranchised grief: Implications for mental health counseling practice. *Journal of Mental Health Counseling, 34*(4), 283–294.

Corkem, S. M., Parks, S. B., & Morgan, M. I. (2013). Embracing the future: What can accounting graduates expect? *American Journal of Business Education, 6*(5), 531–537.

Corona, G., Lee, D. M., Forti, G., O'Connor, D. B., Maggi, M., O'Neil, T. W., et al. (2010). Age-related changes in general and sexual health in middle-aged and older men: Results from the European Male Ageing Study (EMAS). *Journal of Sexual Medicine, 7*, 1362–1380.

Corrigan, P. W. (2007). How clinical diagnosis might exacerbate the stigma of mental illness. *Social Work, 52*(1), 31–39.

Corrigan, P. W., Edwards, A. B., Greene, A., Diwan, S. L., & Penn, D. L. (2001). Prejudice, social distance, and familiarity with mental illness. *Schizophrenia Bulletin, 27*, 219–225.

Corrigan, P. W., Greene, A., Lundin, R., Kubiak, M. A., & Penn, D. L. (2001). Familiarity with and social distance from people who have serious mental illness. *Psychiatric Services, 52*, 953–958.

Corrigan, P. W., Watson, A. C., & Barr, L. (2006). The self-stigma of mental illness: Implications for self-esteem and self-efficacy. *Journal of Social and Clinical Psychology, 25*(8), 875–884.

Corrigan, P. W., Watson, A. C., & Miller, F. E. (2006). Blame, shame, and contamination: The impact of mental illness and drug dependence stigma on family members. *Journal of Family Psychology, 20*, 239–246.

Cortes, D., Deren, S., Andia, J., Colon, H., Robles, R., & Kang, S. (2003). The use of the Puerto Rican biculturality scale with Puerto Rican drug users in New York and Puerto Rico. *Journal of Psychoactive Drugs, 35*, 197–207.

Council of Social Work Gero-Ed Center. (2013). Retrieved from http://www.cswe.org/CentersInitiatives/GeroEdCenter.aspx

Covinsky, K. E., Eng, C., Lui, L., Sands, L. P., & Yaffe, K. (2003). The last 2 years of life: Functional trajectories of frail older people. *Journal of the American Geriatrics Society, 51*, 492–498.

Coyne, P. J., & Lyckholm,. L. J. (2010). Artifical nutrition for cognitively impaired individuals: Strategies to promote appropriate care. *Journal of Hospice & Palliative Nursing, 12*, 263–267.

Crawley, E. (2005). Institutional thoughtlessness in prisons and its impacts on the day-to-day prison lives of elderly men. *Journal of Contemporary Criminal Justice, 21*(4), 350.

Crisp, C., & McCave, E. L. (2007). Gay affirmative practice: A model for social work practice with gay, lesbian, and bisexual youth. *Child and Adolescent Social Work Journal, 24*, 403–421.

Cronin, A., & King, A. (2010). Power, inequality and identification: Exploring diversity and intersectionality amongst older LGB adults. *Sociology, 44*(5), 876–892.

Crowther, M. R., & Zeiss, A. M. (2003). Aging and mental health. In J. S. Mio & G. Y. Iwamasa (Eds.), *Culturally diverse mental health: The challenge of research and resistance* (pp. 309–322). New York, NY: Brunner-Routledge.

Crystal, S., Sambamoorthi, U., Walkup, J., & Akincigil, A. (2003). Diagnosis and treatment of depression in the elderly Medicare population: Predictors, disparities, and trends. *Journal of the American Geriatrics Society, 51*, 1718–1728.

Csikai, E. L., & Rozensky, C. (1997). Social work idealism and students' perceived reasons for entering social work. *Journal of Social Work Education, 13*(44–57).

Cuijpers, P., Berking, M., Andersson, G., Quigley, L., Kleiboer, A., & Dobson, K. S. (2013). A meta-analysis of cognitive-behavioural therapy for adult depression, alone and in comparison with other treatments. *Canadian Journal of Psychiatry, 58*(7), 376–385.

Culberson, J. W., & Ziska, M. (2008). Prescription drug misuse/abuse in the elderly. *Geriatrics, 63*, 22–28.

Cumming, R. G., & Le Couteur, D. G. (2003). Benzodiazepines and risk of hip fractures in older people: A review of the evidence. *CNS Drugs, 17*(11), 825–837.

Cummings, J. W., & Cooper, R. L. (2011). The addicted geriatric patient. In E. O. Bryson & E. A. M. Frost (Eds.), *Perioperative addiction: Clinical management of the addicted patient* (pp. 239–252). New York, NY: Springer.

Cummings, S. M., Chapin, R., Dobbs, D., & Hayes, J. (2004). Assisted living facilities' response to residents' mental health needs: A study in two states. *Journal of Mental Health and Aging, 10*, 151–162.

Cummings, S. R., & Melton, L. J. (2002). Epidemiology and outcomes of osteoporotic fractures. *Lancet, 359*, 1761–1777.

Curtis, J. R., Engelberg, R. A., Nielsen, E. L., Au, D. H., & Patrick, D. L. (2004). Patient–physician communication about end-of-life care for patients with severe COPD. *European Respiratory Journal, 24*(2), 200–205.

Dalby, P. (2006). Is there a process of spiritual change or development associated with aging? A critical review of research. *Aging and Mental Health, 10*, 4–12.

Dannefer, D. (1988). Differential gerontology and the stratified life course: Conceptual and methodological issues. In G. L. Maddox & M. P. Lawton (Eds.), *Annual review of gerontology and geriatrics* (Vol. 8, pp. 3–36). New York, NY: Springer Publishing Company.

Darton, R., Baumker, T., Callaghan, L., Holder, J., Netten, A. N. N., & Towers, A.-M. (2011). The characteristics of residents in extra care housing and care homes in England. *Health and Social Care in the Community, 20*(1), 87–96.

Dass, R. (2000). *Embracing aging, changing, and dying.* New York: Riverhead Books.

Daveson, B. A., Bausewein, C., Murtagh, F. E. M., Calanzani, N., Higginson, I. J., Harding, R., et al. (2013). To be involved or not to be involved: A survey of public preferences for self-involvement in decision-making involving mental capacity (competency) within Europe. *Palliative Medicine, 27*(5), 418–427.

Davies, A. S., Greene, G., Macbridge-Stewart, S., & Sheperd, M. (2009). The health, social care and housing needs of lesbian, gay, bisexual, and transgender older people: A review of the literature. *Health Social Care Community, November 17*(6), 647–658.

Davis, L. E., & Gelsomino, J. (1994). An assessment of practitioner cross-racial treatment experiences. *Social Work, 39*(1), 116–123.

Davis, M. (2012). Naked at our age: Talking out loud about senior sex. *American Journal of Sexuality Education, 7*(2), 176–180.

de Vries, B. (2005). Home at the end of the rainbow. *Generations, 29*(4), 64–69.

Decker, B. (2004). Age of surprises: Therapy in the end zone. *In the Family, 9*(3), 16–25.

Dehart, S. S., & Hoffmann, N.G. (1997). Screening and diagnoses: Alcohol use disorders in older adults. In A. M. Gurnack (Ed.), *Older adults' misuse of alcohol, medicines, and other drugs: Research and practice issues* (pp. 25–53). New York, NY: Springer Publishing Company.

Deisch, P., Soukup, S. M., Adams, P., & Wild, M. C. (2000). Guided imagery: Replication study using coronary artery bypass graft patients. *Nursing Clinics of North America, 35*(2), 417–425.

Dennis, M., Beach, M., Evans, A., Winston, A., & Friedman, T. (1997). An examination of the accident and emergency management of deliberate self-harm. *Journal of Accident and Emergency Medicine, 14*, 311–315.

Detering, K. M., Hancock, A. D., Reade, M. C., & Silvester, W. (2010). The impact of advance care planning on end of life care in elderly patients: Randomised controlled trial. *British Medical Journal (Clinical Research Education), 340*, 1345–1354.

Detlefsen, E. G. (2004). Where am I to go? Use of the internet for consumer health information by two vulnerable communities. *Library Trends, 53*(2), 283.

Devanand, D. P., Turret, N., & Moody, B. J. (2000). Personality disorders in elderly patients with dysthymic disorder. *American Journal of Geriatric Psychiatry, 8*(3), 188–195.

Devine, E. C., Bevsek, S. A., Brubakken, K., Johnson, B. P., Ryan, P., & Sliefert, M. K. (1999). AHCPR clinical practice guideline on surgical pain management: Adoption and outcomes. *Research in Nursing & Health, 22*, 19–130.

Di Napoli, E. A., Breland, G. L., & Allen, R. S. (2013). Staff knowledge and perceptions of sexuality and dementia of older adults in nursing homes. *Journal of Aging & Health, 25*(7), 1087–1105.

Diefenbach, G. J., Hopko, D. R., Felgon, S., Stanley, M., Novy, D. M., Beck, J. G., et al. (April 2003). "Minor GAD": Characteristics of subsyndromal GAD in older adults. *Behavior Research and Therapy, 41*(4), 481–487.

Dienemann, J., Glass, N., & Hyman, R. (2005). Survivor preferences for response to IPV disclosure. *Clinical Nursing Research.*

DiGiuseppe, R., & Linscott, J. (1993). Philosophical differences among cognitive-behavioral therapists: Rationalism, constructivism, or both? *Journal of Cognitive Psychotherapy, 7*, 117–130.

Dignity and nutrition for older people. (2011). Care Quality Commission. Retrieved from http://www.cqc.org.uk/public/reports-surveys-and-reviews/themes-inspections/dignity-and-nutrition-older-people

Ditto, P. H., Hawkins, N. A., & Pizzaro, D. A. (2006). Imagining the end-of-life: On the psychology of advance decision making. *Motivation and Emotion, 27*, 481–502.

Dobbs, D., Hayes, J., Chapin, R., & Oslund, P. (2006). The relationship between psychiatric disorders and the ability to age in place in assisted living. *American Journal of Geriatric Psychiatry, 14*(7), 613–620.

Dohrenwend, B. P. (2000). The role of adversity and stress in psychopathology: Some evidence and its implications for theory and research. *Journal of Health Social Behavior, 41*(1), 1–19.

Doka, K. J. (2002). *Disenfranchised grief: New directions, challenges, and strategies for practice*. Champaign, IL: Research Press.

Donahue, P., & McDonald, L. (2005). Gay and lesbian aging: Current perspectives and future directions for social work practice and research. *Families in Society, 86*(3), 359–366.

Dong, X., & Simon, M. (2013). Association between reported elder abuse and rates of admission to skilled nursing facilities: Findings from a longitudinal population-based cohort study. *Gerontology, 59*(5), 464–472.

Dong, X., Simon, M., & Evans, D. (2013). Elder self-neglect is associated with increased risk for elder abuse in a community-dwelling population: Findings from the Chicago Health and Aging Project. *Journal of Aging & Health, 25*(1), 80–96.

Dong, X., Simon, M., Mendes de Leon, C. F., Fulmer, T., Beck, T., Herbert, L., et al. (2009). Elder self-neglect and abuse and mortality risk in a community-dwelling population. *Journal of the American Medical Association, 302*(5), 517–526.

Dong, X., Simon, M. A., Fulmer, T., Mendes de Leon, C. F., Herbert, L. E., Beck, T., et al. (2011). A prospective population-based study of differences in elder self-neglect and mortality between black and white older adults. *Journals of Gerontology Series A: Biological Sciences and Medical Sciences, 66*(6), 695–740.

Dong, X., Simon, M., Wilson, R. S., & Mendes de Leon, C. F. (2010). Decline in cognitive function and risk of elder self-neglect: Finding from the Chicago Health Aging Project. *Journal of the American Geriatrics Society, 58*(12), 2292–2299.

Doukas, D. J., & Hardwig, J. (2003). Family covenant in planning end of life care: Obligations and promises of patients, families, and physicians. *Journal of the American Geriatrics Society, 51*(8), 1155–1158.

Dovidio, J. F., Major, B., & Fan, X. (2000). Stigma: Introduction and overview. In T. F. Heatherton, R. E. Kleck, M. R. Hebl, & J. G. Hull (Eds.), *The social psychology of stigma* (pp. 1–30). New York, NY: Guilford Press.

Dreher, H. (1988). Mind-body interventions for surgery: Evidence and exigency. *Advances in Mind-Body Medicine, 14*, 207–222.

Drummond, T. (1999). Cellblock seniors. *Time, 153*(24), 60.

Druss, B. G., Bradford, D. W., Rosenheck, R. A., Radford, M. J., & Krumholz, H. M. (2000). Mental disorders and use of cardiovascular procedures after myocardial infarction. *Journal of the American Medical Association, 283*, 506–511.

Dubinsky, R. M., Stein, A. C., & Lyons, K. (2000). Practice parameter: Risk of driving and Alzheimer's disease (an evidenced-based review). Report of the Quality Standards Subcommittee of the American Academy of Neurology. *Neurology, 54*, 2205–2211.

Duffy, M. (Ed.). (1999). *Handbook of counseling and psychotherapy with older adults*. New York, NY: Wiley.

Dufrene, C. (2012). Health care partnerships: A literature review of interdisciplinary education. *Journal of Nursing Education, 51*, 212–216.

Dulaney, D. D., & Kelly, J. (1982). Improving services to gay and lesbian clients. *Social Work, 27*, 178–183.

Dunkin, J. J., & Anderson-Hanley, C. (1998). Dementia caregiver burden: A review of the literature and guidelines for assessment and intervention. *Neurology, 51*(Suppl. 1), S53–S60.

Dybicz, P. (2012). The ethic of care: Recapturing social work's first voice. *Social Work, 57*(3), 271–280.

Dyer, C. B. (2005). Neglect assessment in elderly persons. *Journals of Gerontology, 60A*(8), 1000.

Dyer, C. B., Goodwin, J. S., Pickens-Pace, S., Burnett, J., & Kelly, P. A. (2007). Self-neglect among the elderly: A model based on more than 500 patients seen by a geriatric medicine team. *American Journal of Public Health, 97*(9), 1671.

Dyer, C. B., Pavlik, V. N., Murphy, K. P., & Hyman, D. J. (2000). The high prevalence of depression and dementia in elder abuse or neglect. *Journal of the American Geriatrics Society, 48*(2), 205–208.

Eckert, J., Carter, P., Morgan, L., Frankowski, A., & Roth, E. (2009). *Inside assisted living: The search for home*. Baltimore, MD: Johns Hopkins University Press.

Edelman, P., Guihan, M., Bryant, F., & Munroe, D. (2006). Measuring resident and family member determinants of satisfaction with assisted living. *The Gerontologist, 46*(5), 599–608.

Edelstein, B., & Kalish, K. (1999). Clinical assessment of older adults. In J. C. Cavanaugh & S. Whitbourne (Eds.), *Gerontology: An inter-disciplinary perspective* (pp. 269–304). New York, NY: Oxford University Press.

Effing, T. W., Williams, M. T., & Frith, P. A. (2013). Health literacy: How much is lost in translation? *Chronic Respiratory Disease, 10*(2), 61–63.

Egan, G. (2010). *The skilled helper: A problem management and opportunity-development approach to helping* (9th ed.). Belmont, CA: Brooks Cole.

Egdell, V. (2012). Development of support networks in informal dementia care: Guided, organic, and chance routes through support. *Canadian Journal on Aging, 31*(4), 445–455.

El-Hai, J. (2005). *The lobotomist: A maverick medical genius and his tragic quest to rid the world of mental illness*. Hoboken, NJ: Wiley.

Eller, L. (1999). Guided imagery interventions for symptom management. In J. J. Fitzpatrick (Ed.), *Annual review of nursing research* (Vol. 17, pp. 57–83). New York, NY: Springer Publishing Company.

Emlet, C. A. (2006). "You're awfully old to have this disease": Experiences of stigma and ageism in adults 50 years and older living with HIV/AIDS. *The Gerontologist, 46*(6), 781–790.

Emlet, C. A. (2007). Experiences of stigma in older adults living with HIV/AIDS: A mixed-method analysis. *AIDS Patient Care and STDs, 21*, 740–752.

Engelhardt, H. T., & Smith Iltis, A. (2005). End-of-life: The traditional Christian view. *Lancet, 366*, 1045–1049.

Eposito, K., Giugliano, F., Di Palo, C., Giugliano, G., Marfella, R., D'Andrea, F., et al. (2004). Effect of lifestyle changes on erectile dysfunction in obese men: A randomized controlled trial. *Journal of the American Medical Association, 291*(24), 2978–2984.

Epstein, E. E., Fischer-Elber, K., & Al-Otaiba, Z. (2007). Women, aging, and alcohol use disorders. *Journal of Women and Aging, 19*, 31–48.

Eriksen, K. A., Sundfor, B., Karlsson, B., Raholm, M.-B., & Arman, M. (2012). Recognition as a valued human being: Perspectives of mental health service users. *Nursing Ethics, 19*(3), 357–368.

Erikson, E. H. (1982). *The life cycle completed: A review*. New York, NY: Norton.

Erikson, E. H., & Erikson, J. M. (1997). *The life cycle completed: Extended version with new chapters on the ninth state of development*. New York, NY: Norton.

Erikson, E. H., Erikson, J. M., & Kivnick, H. Q. (1986). *Vital involvement in old age*. New York, NY: W.W. Norton.

Erikson, M. A., Krout, J. A., Ewen, H., & Robison, J. (2006). Should I stay or should I go? Moving plans for older adults. *Journal of Housing for the Elderly, 20*(3), 5–22.

Erlangsen, A., Bille-Brahe, U., & Jeune, B. (2003). Differences in suicide between the old and the oldest. *Journals of Gerontology, 58B*(5), S314–S322.

Erlangsen, A., Jeune, B., Bille-Brahe, U., & Vaupel, J. W. (2004). Loss of partner and suicide risks among old: A population-based register study. *Age and Ageing, 33*(4), 378–383.

Estes, C. L. (1979). *The aging enterprise.* San Francisco, CA: Jossey-Bass.

Evans, O., Singleton, N., Meltzer, H., Stewart, R., & Prince, M. (2003). *The mental health of older people.* London, UK: Office for National Statistics.

Evans, S. (2009). *Community and aging. Maintaining quality of life in housing with care settings.* Bristol, UK: Policy Press.

Evans-Lacko, S., Brohan, E., Mojtabai, R., & Thornicroft, G. (2012). Association between public views of mental illness and self-stigma among individuals with mental illness in 14 European countries. *Psychological Medicine, 42*(8), 1741–1752.

Fain, M. (2003). Should older drivers have to prove that they are able to drive? *Archives of Internal Medicine, 163,* 2126–2128.

Fannin, A. (2006). Gay and grey: Lifting the lid on sexuality and ageing. *Working with Older People, 10*(4), 31–34.

Farrall, S., Jackson, J., & Gray, E. (2009). *Social order and the fear of crime in contemporary times.* Oxford, UK: Oxford University Press.

Fassberg, M. M., van Orden, K. A., Duberstein, P., Erlangsen, A., Lapierre, S., Bodner, E., et al. (2012). A systematic review of social factors and suicidal behavior in older adulthood. *International Journal of Environmental Research and Public Health, 9*(3), 722–745.

Fava, G., & Ruini, C. (2003). Development and characteristics of a well-being enhancing psychotherapeutic strategy: Well-being therapy. *Journal of Behavior Therapy and Experimental Psychiatry, 34,* 45–63.

Fazel, S., Hope, T., O'Donnell, I., Piper, M., & Jacoby, R. (2001). Health of elderly male prisoners: Worse than the general population, worse than younger prisoners. *Age and Ageing, 30*(5), 403–407.

Fazel, S., McMillan, J., & O'Donnell, I. (2002). Dementia in prison: Ethical and legal implications. *Journal of Medical Ethics, 28*(3), 156–159.

Feldman, B. N., & Freedenthal, S. (2006). Social work education in suicide intervention and prevention: An unmet need? *Suicide & Life-Threatening Behavior, 36*(4), 467.

Feldman, D. B., & Crandall, C. S. (2007). Dimensions of mental illness stigma: What about mental illness causes social rejection? *Journal of Social and Clinical Psychology, 26*(2), 137–154.

Ferrie, J. E., Head, J., Shipley, M. D., Vahtera, J., Marmot, M. G., & Kivimaki, M. (2006). Injustice at work and incidence of psychiatric morbidity: The Whitehall II study. *Occupational Environmental Medicine, 63,* 443–450.

Fessman, N., & Lester, D. (2000). Loneliness and depression among elderly nursing home patients. *International Journal of Aging and Human Development, 51*(2), 137–141.

Finlaysoon, R. E., & Davis, L. J. (2004). Prescription drug dependence in the elderly population: Demographic and clinical features of 100 inpatients. *Mayo Clinic Proceedings, 69*(12), 1137–1145.

First euthanasia in Netherlands of severe Alzheimer's patient performed. (2011, November 9). *News, Science & Health, World.* Retrieved from http://news.nationalpost.com/2011/11/09first-euthanasia-in-netherlands-of-severe-alzheimers-patient/

Fitzgerald, J. (2012, November 5). Overnight dementia "camp" allows caregivers rest. *Huffington Post.* Retrieved from file:///Volumes/NO%20NAME/Overnight%20Dementia%20'Camp'%20Allows%20Caregivers%20Rest.webarchive

Fitzgerald, R. (2008). *Fear of crime and the neighbourhood context in Canadian cities.* Ottawa, Ontario, Canada: Canadian Centre for Justice Statistics.

Flatt, J. D., & Hughes, T. F. (2013). Participation in social activities in later life: Does enjoyment have important implications for cognitive health? *Aging Health, 9*(2), 149–158.

Foley, D. J., Heimovitz, H. K., Guralnik, J. M., & Brock, D. B. (2002). Driving life expectancy of persons aged 70 years and older in the United States. *American Journal of Public Health, 92,* 1284–1289.

Force, A.-A. T. (2006). *Ageism in America.* New York: International Longevity Center.

Forsgard, M., Westman, B., & Jansson, L. (2002). Professional carers' struggle to be confirmed. Narratives within the care of the elderly and disabled. *Scandinavian Journal of Caring Science, 16*(1), 12–18.

Fortner, B. V., Neimeyer, R. A., & Rybarczyk, B. (2000). Correlates of death anxiety in older adults: A comprehensive review. In A. Tomer (Ed.), *Death attitudes and the older adult: Theories, concepts, and applications*. Philadelphia, PA: Taylor & Francis.

Fournier, S. M. (2000). Social expectations for sexuality among the elderly. *Dissertation Abstracts International, 60*(12A), 4610.

Frances, A. (2012, January). Two fallacies invalidate the *DSM-5* field trials. *Psychiatric Times*, 1–2.

Frank, A. W. (2012). Practicing dialogical narrative analysis. In J. A. Holstein & J. F. Gubrium (Eds.), *Varieties of narrative analysis*. London, UK: Sage.

Frank, J. (2001). How long can I stay? The dilemma of aging in place in assisted living. *Journal of Housing for the Elderly, 15*(1/2), 5–30.

Frankl, V. E. (1992). *Man's search for meaning* (4th ed.). Boston, MA: Beacon.

Franklin, L., Ternestedt, B., & Nordenfelt, L. (2006). Views on dignity of elderly nursing home residents. *Nursing Ethics, 13*(2), 130–146.

Fraser, H. C., Kuter, J. S., & Pfeifer, M. P. (2001). Senior medical students' perceptions of the adequacy of education on end-of-life issues. *Journal of Palliative Medicine, 4*(3), 337–343.

Fredrisken-Goldsen, K., Kim, H.-J., Emlet, C. A., Muraco, A., Erosheva, E. A., Hoy-Ellis, C. P., et al. (2011). *The aging and health report: Disparities and resilience among lesbian, gay, bisexual, and transgender older adults*. Seattle, WA: Institute for Multigenerational Health.

Freeman, L. (1972). *The story of Anna O.* New York: Walker and Company.

Freud, S. (1953). On psychotherapy. In J. Strachey (Ed. and trans.), *The standard edition of the complete psychological works of Sigmund Freud* (Vol. 6, pp. 249–263). London, UK: Hogarth Press.

Fried, I. P., & Guarlnik, J. M. (1997). Disability in older adults: Evidence regarding significance, etiology, and risk. *Journal of the American Geriatrics Society, 45*, 92–100.

Friedan, B. (1963). *The feminine mystique*. New York, NY: W.W. Norton.

Friedan, B. (1993). *The fountain of age*. New York, NY: Simon & Schuster.

Friedman, J. H. (2013). Neurological stigma. *Medicine and Health Rhode Island, 96*(8), 7–8.

Fries, J. F. (1990). Medical perspective upon successful aging. In P. B. Baltes & M. M. Baltes (Eds.), *Successful aging: Perspectives from the behavioral sciences* (pp. 35–49). Cambridge, UK: Cambridge University Press.

Fritsch, T. (2005). HIV/AIDS and the older adult: An exploratory study of the age-related differences in access to medical and social services. *Journal of Applied Gerontology, 24*(1), 35.

Frosch, D. (2011, October 29). Hard times for gay retirement havens. *New York Times*. Retrieved from http://www.nytimes.com/2011/10/29/us/gay-retirement-communities-struggling-in-the-recession.html?ref=todayspaper

Fuher, R., Dufouil, C., & Dartigues, J. F. (2003). Exploring sex differences in the relationship between depressive symptoms and dementia incidence: Prospective results from the PAQUID Study. *Journal of the American Geriatrics Society, 51*(1055–1063).

Fulmer, T., Guadagno, L., Bitondo-Dyer, C., & Connolly, M. T. (2004). Progress in elder abuse screening and assessment instruments. *Journal of American Geriatircs Society, 52*, 297–304.

Furlan, A. D., Sandoval, J. A., & Mallis-Gagnon, A. (2006). Opioids for chronic noncancer pain: A meta-analysis of effectiveness and side effects. *CAMJ, 174*, 1589–1594.

Gallagher, D. E., & Thompson, L. W. (1996). Applying cognitive-behavior therapy to the psychological problems of late life. In S. H. Zarit & B. G. Knight (Eds.), *A guide to psychotherapy and aging* (pp. 61–82). Washington, DC: American Psychological Association.

Gallagher-Thompson, D., Brooks, J. O., & Bilwise, D. (1992). The relations among caregiver stress, "sundowning" symptoms, and cognitive decline in Alzheimer's disease. *Journal of the American Geriatrics Society, 40*, 807–810.

Gallo, W. T., Baker, M. J., & Bradley, E. H. (2001). Factors associated with home versus institutional death among cancer patients in Connecticut. *Journal of the American Geriatrics Society, 49*, 771–777.

Gask, L. (2013). Educating family physicians to recognize and manage depression: Where are we now? *Canadian Journal of Psychiatry, 58*(8), 449–455.

Gatz, M., & Smyer, M. A. (2001). Mental health and aging at the outset of the 21st century. In J. E. Birren & K. W. Schaie (Eds.), *Handbook of the psychology of aging* (5th ed.). San Diego, CA: Academic Press.

Gatz, M., Fiske, A., Fox, L. S., Kaskie, B., Kasi-Godley, J., McCallum, T., et al. (1998). Empirically-validated psychological treatments for older adults. *Journal of Mental Health and Aging, 4*, 9–46.

Gaugler, J. E., Jarrott, S. E., Zarit, S., Stephens, M. A., Townsend, A., & Greene, R. (2003). Respite for dementia caregivers: The effects of adult day service use on caregiving hours and care demands. *International Psychogeriatrics, 15*(1), 37–58.

Germer, C. K., Siegel, R. D., & Fulton, P. R. (Eds.). (2013). *Mindfulness and psychotherapy* (2nd ed.). New York, NY: Guilford Press.

Gfoerer, J. C., Penne, M. A., Pemberton, M. R., & Folson, J., R.E. (2008). The aging baby boom cohort and future prevalence of substance abuse. In Substance Abuse and Mental Health Services Administration, Office of Applied Studies: *Substance use by older adults: Estimates of future impact on the treatment system.* (OAS Analytic Series #A-21, DHHS Publication No. [SMA] 03–3763). Rockville, MD: Substance Abuse and Mental Health Administration.

Ghaemi, S. N. (2007). Feeling and time: The phenomenology of mood disorders, depressive realism, and existential psychotherapy. *Schizophrenia Bulletin, 33*(1), 120–130.

Ghaemi, S. N., Lenox, M. S., & Baldessarini, R. J. (2001). Effectiveness and safety of long-term antidepressant treatment in bipolar disorder. *Journal of Clinical Psychiatry, 62*, 565–569.

Ghazanfareeon Karlsson, S., & Borell, K. (2005). A home of their own: Women's boundary work in LAT relationships. *Journal of Aging Studies, 19*(1), 73–84.

Gibbons, S. B. (2011). Understanding empathy as a complex construct: A review of the literature. *Clinical Social Work Journal, 39*(3), 243–252.

Giddons, S., & Giddons, O. (2000). *Coping with grieving and loss.* New York, NY: Rosen Publishing Group.

Gidman, J. (2013). Listening to stories: Valuing knowledge from patient experience. *Nurse Education in Practice, 13*(3), 192–196.

Gilleard, C., & Higgs, P. (2008). Internet use and the digital divide in the English longitudinal study of ageing. *European Journal of Ageing, 5*(3), 233–239.

Glasgow, R., Orleans, C., Wagner, R., Curry, S., & Solberg, L. (2001). Does the chronic care model serve also as a template for improving prevention? *Millbank Quarterly, 79*, 579–612.

Glasner, S. V. (2004). Motivation and addiction: The role of incentive processes in understanding and treating addictive disorders. In W. M. Cox & E. Klinger (Eds.), *Handbook of motivational counseling: Concepts, approaches, and assessment* (pp. 29–47). Hoboken, NJ: John Wiley.

Glipin, D. R., & Murphy, P. J. (2008). *Crisis management in a complex world.* New York, NY: Oxford University Press.

Goffman, E. (1963). *Stigma: Notes on the management of spoiled identity.* Englewood Cliffs, NJ: Prentice Hall.

Golan, I., Ligumsky, M., & Brezis, M. (2007). Percutaneous endoscopic gastrostomy in hospitalized incompetent geriatric patients: Poorly informed, constrained and paradoxical decisions. *Israeli Medical Association Journal, 9*, 839–842.

Goldberg, S., Sickler, J., & Dibble, S. L. (2005). Lesbians over sixty: The consistency of findings from twenty years of survey data. *Journal of Lesbian Studies, 9*(1/2), 195.

Gomberg, E. (1995). Older women and alcohol: Use and abuse. In M. Galanter (Ed.), *Recent developments in alcohol: Alcoholism and women* (Vol. 12, pp. 61–79). New York, NY: Plenum Press.

Gomez, J., Miranda, R., & Polanco, L. (2011). Acculturative stress, perceived discrimination, and vulnerability to suicide attempts among emerging adults. *Journal of Youth and Adolescence, 40*(11), 1465–1476.

Goodstein, R. K. (1985). Common clinical problems in the elderly: Camouflaged by ageism and atypical presentation. *Psychiatric Annals, 15*, 299–312.

Gott, M., Frey, R., Robinson, J., Boyd, M., O'Callaghan, A., Richards, N., et al. (2013). The nature of, and reasons for, "inappropriate" hospitalizations among patients with palliative care needs: A qualitative exploration of the views of generalist palliative care providers. *Palliative Medicine, 27*(8), 747–756.

Gott, M., Small, N., Barnes, S., Payne, S., & Seamark, D. (2008). Older people's views of a good death in heart failure: Implications for palliative care provision. *Social Science and Medicine, 97*(7), 1113–1121.

Grace, J. B., Walker, M. P., & McKeith, J. G. (2000). A comparison of sleep profiles in patients with dementia with Lewy bodies and Alzheimer's disease. *Journal of Geriatric Psychiatry 15*(11), 1028–1033.

Grace, S. L., Abbey, S. E., Irvine, J., Shnek, Z. M., & Stewart, D. E. (2004). Prospective examination of anxiety persistence and its relationship to cardiac symptoms and recurrent cardiac events. *Psychotherapy and Psychosomatics, 73*, 344–352.

Grande, G. E., Addington-Hall, J. M., & Todd, C. J. (1998). Place of death and access to home care services: Are certain patient groups at a disadvantage? *Social Science and Medicine, 47*, 565–579.

Grant, J. E., Donahue, C. B., & Odlaug, B. I. (2011). *Treatments that work: Treating impulse control disorders: A cognitive-behavioral therapy program therapist guide.* Oxford, UK: Oxford University Press.

Grant, J. E., Schreiber, L., & Odiaug, B. L. (2013). Phenomenology and treatment of behavioral addictions. *Canadian Journal of Psychiatry, 58*(5), 252–259.

Grant, J. M., Mottel, L. A., Tanis, J., Harrison, J., Herman, J. L., & Kwisling, M. (2011). *Injustice at every turn. A report of the national transgender discrimination survey.* Washington, DC: National Center for Transgender Equality and National Gay and Lesbian Task Force.

Gray-Little, B., & Hafdahl, A. R. (2000). Factors influencing racial comparisons of self-esteem: A quantitative review. *Psychological Bulletin, 126,* 26–54.

Greenberg, J., & Arndt, J. (2011). Terror management theory. In P. Kruglanski, A. M. Van Lange, & E. T. Higgins (Eds.), *Handbook of theories of social psychology* (Vol. 1, pp. 339–415). New York, NY: Sage.

Greenberg, J., Pyszczynski, T., & Solomon, S. (1986). The cause and consequences of a need for self-esteem: A terror management theory. In R. F. Baumeister (Ed.), *Public self and private self* (pp. 189–212). New York, NY: Springer-Verlag.

Greenberg, J., Pyszczynski, T., Solomon, S., Rosenblatt, A., Veeder, M., Kirkland, S., et al. (1990). Evidence for terror management theory II. The effects of mortality salience on reactions to those who threaten or bolster the cultural worldview. *Journal of Personality and Social Psychology, 58,* 308–318.

Greene, A., Aranda, S., Tieman, J. J., Fazekas, B., & Currow, D. C. (2012). Can assessing caregiver needs and activating community networks improve caregiver-defined outcomes? A single-blind, quasi-experimental pilot study: Community facilitator pilot. *Palliative Medicine, 26*(7), 917–923.

Greene, R. R. (2002). *Resiliency theory: An integrated framework for practice research.* Washington, DC: NASW Press.

Greene, R. R. (2010). A study of Holocaust survivors: Implications for curriculum. *Journal of Social Work Education, 46*(2), 293–303.

Greene, S. (2003). *The psychological development of girls and women: Rethinking change in time.* Hove, UK: Routledge.

Grek, A. (2007). Clinical management of suicidality in the elderly: An opportunity for involvement in the lives of older patients. *Canadian Journal of Psychiatry, 52*(6), 47S–57S.

Grossman, A. H., D'Augelli, A. R., & Hersberger, S. L. (2000). Social support networks of lesbian, gay and bisexual adults 60 years of age and older. *Journal of Gerontology: Psychological Sciences, 55B*(3), P171–P179.

Grov, C., Golub, S. A., Parsons, J. T., Brennan, M., & Karpiak, S. E. (2010). Loneliness and HIV-related stigma explain depression among older HIV-positive adults. *AIDS Care, 22,* 630–639.

Gruber-Bakdini, A. L., Boustani, M., Sloane, P., & Zimmerman, S. (2004). Behavioral symptoms in residential care/assisted living facilities: Prevalence, risk factors, and medical management. *Journal of the American Geriatrics Society, 52*(10), 1610–1617.

Grundy, E., & Sloggett, A. (2003). Health inequalities in the older population: The role of person capital, social resources and socio-economic circumstances. *Social Science and Medicine, 56,* 935–947.

Guay, D. R. (2008). Inappropriate sexual behaviours in cognitively impaired older individuals. *American Journal of Geriatric Pharmacotherapy, 6*(5), 269–288.

Guerriere, D. N., Zagorski, B., & Coyte, P. C. (2013). Family caregiver satisfaction with home-based nursing and physician care over the palliative care trajectory: Results from a longitudinal survey questionnaire. *Palliative Medicine, 27*(7), 632–638.

Haas, A., Eliason, M., Mays, V., Mathy, R., Cochran, S., D'Augelli, A., et al. (2011). Suicide and suicide risk in lesbian, gay, bisexual, and transgender populations: Review and recommendations. *Journal of Homosexuality, 58,* 10–51.

Hack, T. F., McClement, S., Chochinov, H. M., Cann, B. J., Hassard, T. H., Kristjanson, L. J., et al. (2010). Learning from dying cancer patients during their final days: Life reflections gleaned from dignity therapy. *Palliative Medicine, 24,* 715–723.

Hagestad, G. O., & Dannefer, D. (2001). Concepts and theories of aging: Beyond microfication in social science approaches. In R. H. Binstock & L. K. George (Eds.), *Handbook on aging and social sciences* (5th ed., pp. 3–21). San Diego, CA: Academic Press.

Haggstrom, E., Mamhidir, A. G., & Kihlgren, A. (2010). Caregivers' strong commitment to their relationship with older people. *International Journal of Nursing Practice, 16*(2), 99–105.

Haight, B. K., & Webster, J. D. (Eds.). (1995). *The art and science of reminiscing: Theory, research, methods, and applications.* Bristol, PA: Taylor & Francis.

Hain, D. J., & Sandy, D. (2013). Partners in care: Patient empowerment through shared decision-making. *Nephrology Nursing Journal, 40*(2), 153–157.

Hajjar, R. R., & Kamel, H. K. (2003). Sexuality in the nursing home, part 1: Attitudes and barriers to sexual expression. *Journal of the American Medical Directors Association, 4*(3), 152–156.

Haldeman, D. C. (2007). The village people: Identity and development in the gay male community. In K. J. Bieschke, R. M. Perez, & A. DeBord (Eds.), *Handbook of counseling and psychotherapy with lesbian, gay, bisexual, and transgender clients* (2nd ed., pp. 71–89). Washington, DC: American Psychological Association.

Halding, A. G., Heggdal, K., & Wahl, A. (2011). Experiences of self-blame and stigmatization for self-infliction among individual living with COPD. *Scandinavian Journal of Caring Science, 25*(1), 100–107.

Halding, A. G., Wahl, A., & Heggdal, K. (2010). "Belonging." Patients' experiences of social relationships during pulmonary rehabilitation. *Disability Rehabilitation, 32*(15), 1272–1280.

Hall, H. I., Song, R., Rhodes, P., & Janssen, R. S. (2008). Estimation of HIV incidence in the United States. *Journal of the American Medical Association, 300*, 520–529.

Halpert, B. P., & Zimmerman, M. K. (1986). The health status of the "old-old": A reconsideration. *Social Science and Medicine, 22*, 893–899.

Han, B., Gfroerer, J. C., Colliver, J. D., & Penne, M. A. (2009). Substance use disorder among older adults in the United States in 2020. *Addiction, 104*, 88–96.

Hanchate, A., Kronman, A. C., Young-Xu, Y., Ash, A. S., & Emanuel, E. (2009). Racial and ethnic differences in end of life costs: Why do minorities cost more than whites? *Archives of Internal Medicine, 169*(5), 493–501.

Hanson, L. C., Henderson, M., & Rodgeman, E. (1999). Where will we die? A national study of nursing home death (Letter to the editor). *Journal of General Internal Medicine, 14*.

Hardman, A. E., & Stensel, D. J. (2009). *Physical activity and health: The evidence explained.* New York, NY: Routledge.

Harris, M., Mayo, A., Balas, M. C., Aaron, C. S., & Buron, B. (2013). Trends and opportunities in gero-psychiatric nursing: Enhancing practice through specialization and interprofessional education. *Journal of Nursing Education, 52*(6), 317–322.

Harper Ice, G. (2002). Daily life in a nursing home. Has it changed in 25 years? *Journal of Aging Studies, 16*, 345–359.

Harris, K. M., & Edlund, M. J. (2005). Use of mental health care and substance abuse treatment among adults with co-occurring disorders. *Psychiatric Services, 56*, 954–959.

Harrison, J. (2001). "It's none of my business." Gay and lesbian invisibility in aged care. *Australian Occupational Therapy Journal, 48*, 142–145.

Harwood, D., Hawton, K., Hope, T., & Jacoby, R. (2001). Psychiatric disorder and personality factors associated with suicide in older people: A descriptive and case-control study. *International Journal of Geriatric Psychiatry, 16*, 155–165.

Harwood, D., & Jacoby, R. (2000). Suicide behavior amongst the elderly. In K. Hawton & K. Van Heering (Eds.), *The international handbook of suicide and attempted suicide.* Chichester, UK: John Wiley & Sons.

Hassouneh-Phillips, D. S., & McNeff, E. (2004). Understanding care-related abuse and neglect in the lives of women with SCI. *Spinal Chord Injury Nursing, 21*(2), 75–81.

Hatzimouratidis, K., & Hatzichristou, D. G. (2005). A comparative review of the options for treatment of erectile dysfunction: Which treatment for which patient? *Drugs, 65*(12), 1621–1650.

Haugan, G., & Moksnes, U. K. (2013). Meaning-in-life in nursing home patients: A validation study of the Purpose-in-Life test. *Journal of Nursing Measurement, 21*(2), 296–319.

Havens, L. L. (2004). The best kept secret: How to form an effective alliance. *Harvard Review of Psychiatry, 12*, 56–62.

Hawthorne, G. (2006). Measuring social isolation in older adults: Development and initial validation of the friendship scale. *Social Indicators Research, 77*(3), 521–548.

Hawton, K., & Fagg, J. (1990). Deliberate self-poisoning and self-injury in older people. *International Journal of Geriatric Psychiatry, 5*, 367–373.

Hawton, K., Zahl, D., & Weatherall, R. (2003). Suicide following deliberate self-harm: Long-term follow-up of patients who presented to a general hospital. *British Journal of Psychiatry, 182,* 537–542.

Hayes, R. D., & Debbersteub, L. (2006). Aging issues. In I. Goldstein, C. M. Meston, S. R. Davis, & A. M. Traish (Eds.), *Womens' sexual function and dysfunction.* Abingdon, UK: Taylor & Francis.

Hays, J. C., Landerman, L. R., George, L. K., Flint, E. P., Koenig, H. G., Land, K. C., et al. (1998). Social correlates of the dimensions of depression in the elderly. *Journal of Gerontology: Psychological Sciences, 53B,* P31–P39.

Healy, D. (2002). *The creation of psychopharmacology.* Cambridge, MA: Harvard University Press.

Heaphy, B., Yip, A. K. T., & Thompson, D. (2004). Ageing in a non-heterosexual context. *Ageing and Society, 24,* 881–902.

Hebblethwaite, S. (2013). "I think that it could work but . . .": Tensions between the theory and practice of person-centred and relationship-centred care. *Therapeutic Recreation Journal, 47*(1), 13–34.

Helgeson, V. S. (1992). Moderators of the relation between perceived control and adjustment of chronic illness. *Journal of Personality and Social Psychology, 63,* 656–666.

Henderson, L. A. (2008). Age differences in multiple drug use: National admissions to publicly funded substance abuse treatment. In *Substance use by older adults: Estimates of future impact on the treatment system.* (OAS Analytic Series #A-21, DHHS Publication No. [SMA] 03–3763). Rockville, MD: Substance Abuse and Mental Health Services Administration.

Henry, K. (2009). Internal medicine/primary care reminder: What are the standards for care for HIV-positive patients age 50 years and older? *Current HIV/AIDS Reports, 6,* 153–161.

Herek, G. M. (1998). *Stigma and sexual orientation: Understanding prejudice against lesbians, gay men, and bisexuals.* Thousand Oaks, CA: Sage.

Higgins, A., Barker, P., & Begley, C. M. (2004). Hypersexuality and dementia: Dealing with inappropriate sexual expression. *British Journal of Nursing, 13*(22), 1330–1334.

Higgins, A. B., & Follette, V. M. (2002). Frequency and impact of interpersonal trauma in older women. *Journal of Clinical Geropsychiatry, 8*(3), 215–226.

Higginson, I. J., & Sen-Gupta, G. J. (2000). Place of care in advanced cancer: A qualitative systematic literature review of patient preferences. *Journal of Palliative Medicine, 3,* 287–300.

Hill, S., Dziedzic, K., & Ong, B. N. (2010). The functional and psychological impact of hand osteoarthritis. *Chronic Illness, 6*(2), 101–110.

Hinshaw, S. P., & Cicchetti, D. (2000). Stigma and mental disorder: Conceptions of illness, public attitudes, personal disclosure, and social policy. *Development and Psychopathology, 12*(4), 555–598.

Ho, M. Y., Cheung, F. M., & Cheung, S. F. (2010). The role of meaning in life and optimism in promoting well-being. *Personality and Individual Differences, 48,* 658–663.

Holland, J. C. (2002). History of psycho-oncology: Overcoming attitudinal and conceptual barriers. *Psychosomatic Medicine, 64*(2), 206–221.

Holt-Lunstad, J., Smith, T. B., & Layton, J. B. (2010). Social relationships and mortailty risk: A meta-analytic review. *PLoS Medicine, 7*(7), 1–19.

Hooyman, N. R., & Kiyak, H. A. (2010). *Social gerontology: A multidisciplinary perspective.* Boston, MA: Pearson Allyn & Bacon.

Hovath, A. O., & Bedu, R. P. (2002). The alliance. In J. C. Nocross (Ed.), *Psychotherapy relationships that work* (pp. 37–70). New York, NY: Oxford University Press.

Hudson, M. F., Beasley, C. M., Benedict, R. H., Carlson, J. R., Craig, B. F., Herman, C., et al. (2000). Elder abuse: Some Caucasian-American views. *Journal of Elder Abuse & Neglect, 12*(1), 89–114.

Huffman, G. B. (2002). Evaluating and treating unintentional weight loss in the elderly. *American Family Physician, 65*(4), 640–650.

Hughes, M. (2007a). Imagined futures and communities: Older lesbian and gay people's narratives on health and aged care. *Journal of Gay and Lesbian Social Services, 20,* 167–186.

Hughes, M. (2007b). Older lesbians and gays accessing health and aged care services. *Australian Social Work, 60,* 197–209.

Hughes, M., & Thomas, M. E. (1998). The continuing significance of race revisited: A study of race, class, and quality of life in America, 1972–1996. *American Journal of Sociology, 63,* 785–795.

Hunt, M. D., Feldt, A., Marans, R. W., Pastalan, L., & Vakalo, K. (1984). *Retirement communities: An American original.* New York, NY: Haworth Press.

Hunt, R. W., Fazekas, B. S., Luke, C. G., & Roder, D. M. (2001). Where patients with cancer die in South Australia, 1990–1999: A population-based review. *Medical Journal of Australia, 175,* 526–529.

Husaini, B. A., Sherkat, D. E., Levine, R., Bragg, R., Holzer, C., Anderson, K., et al. (2002). Race, gender, and health care service utilization and costs among Medicare elderly with psychiatric diagnoses. *Journal of Aging and Health, 14*(1), 79–95.

Hussein, R. G. (2004). Philosophical and ethical issues: An Islamic perspective. *Journal of Advanced Nursing, 46,* 251–283.

Huston, M., & Schwartz, P. (1995). The relationship of lesbians and of gay men. In J. T. Wood & S. Duck (Eds.), *Understudied relationships: Off the beaten track.* Thousand Oaks, CA: Sage.

Huybrechts, K. F., Ishak, K. J., & Caro, J. J. (2006). Assessment of compliance with osteoporosis and its consequences in a managed care population. *Bone, 38,* 922–928.

Hybels, C. F., Blazer, D. G., & Pieper, C. F. (2001). Toward a threshold for subthreshold depression: An analysis of correlates of depression by severity of symptoms using data from an elderly community sample. *The Gerontologist, 41*(3), 357–365.

Inagaki, T., Horiguchi, J., Tsubouchi, K., Miyaoka, T., Uegaki, J., & Seno, H. (2002). Late onset anorexia nervosa: Two case reports. *International Journal of Psychiatry in Medicine, 32*(1), 91–95.

Insel, K., Morrow, D., Brewer, B., & Figueredo, A. (2006). Executive function, working memory, and medication adherence among older adults. *Journal of Gerontology: Biomedical Sciences, 61*(B), 102–107.

Interprofessional Education Collaborative. (2011). *Core competencies for interprofessional collaborative practice: Report of an expert panel.* Washington, DC: Interprofessional Education Collaborative.

Ivers, N., Dhalla, I. A., & Allan, G. M. (2012). Opioids for osteoarthritis pain: Benefits and risks. *Canadian Family Physician, 58*(12), e708.

Iwarsson, S., & Stahl, A. (2003). Accessibility, usability, and universal design—Positioning and definition of concepts describing person-environment relationships. *Disability and Rehabilitation, 25,* 57–66.

Jackson, K. F., & Samuels, G. M. (2011). Multiracial competence in social work: Recommendations for culturally attuned work with multiracial people. *Social Work, 56*(3), 235–245.

Jacobi, F., Wittchen, H. U., & Holting, C. (2004). Prevalence, co-morbidity, and correlates of mental disorders in the general population: Results from the German health interview and examination survey (GHS). *Psychological Medicine, 34,* 597–611.

Jacobs, R. J., & Kane, M. N. (2010). HIV-related stigma in midlife and older women. *Social Work in Health Care, 49,* 68–89.

James, D. J., & Glaze, L. E. (2006). *Mental health problems of prison and jail inmates. Bureau of Justice Statistics Special Report.* Washington, DC: U.S. Department of Justice, Office of Justice Programs, Bureau of Justice Statistics.

James, J. W., & Haley, W. E. (1995). Age and health bias in practicing clinical psychologists. *Psychology and Aging, 10,* 610–616.

Janssens, H., & Vanderschueren, D. M. (2000). Endocrinological aspects of aging in men: Is hormone replacement of benefit? *European Journal of Obstetrics and Gynecological Reproductive Biology, 92,* 7–12.

Jellinger, K. A. (2013). Ask the expert: How should vascular dementia be managed? *Neurodegenerative Disease Management, 3*(2), 109–113.

Jensen, C. J., Lukow, H. R., & Heck, A. L. (2012). Identifying barriers to care for older adults with substance use disorders and cognitive impairments. *Alcoholism Treatment Quarterly, 30*(2), 211–223.

Jessup, M. A., & Dibble, S. L. (2012). Unmet mental health and substance abuse treatment needs of sexual minority elders. *Journal of Homosexuality, 59*(5), 656–674.

Johnson, J., Weissman, M. M., & Klerman, G. I. (1992). Service utilization and social morbidity associated with depressive symptoms in the community. *Journal of the American Medical Association, 267,* 1478–1483.

Johnson, M. J., Jackson, N. C., Arnette, J. K., & Koffman, S. D. (2005). Gay and lesbian perceptions of discrimination in retirement care facilities. *Journal of Homosexuality, 49*(2), 83–85.

Jones, C. (2011). Person-centered care: The heart of culture change. *Journal of Gerontological Nursing, 37*(6), 18–23.

Joo, J. H., Morales, K. H., de Vries, H. F., & Gallo, J. J. (2010). Disparity in use of psychotherapy offered in primary care between older African-American and White adults: Results from a practice-based depression intervention trial. *Journal of the American Geriatrics Society, 58*(1), 154–160.

Jopling, K. (2007). Older people deserve just equal treatment. *Working With Older People, 11*(2), 24–27.

Judd, L. L., Akiskal, H. S., Schettler, P. J., Endicott, J., Maser, J., & Solomon, D. A. (2002). The long-term natural history of the weekly symptomatic status of bipolar I disorder. *Archives of General Psychiatry, 59*, 530–537.

Judge, K. S., Camp, C. J., & Orsulic-Jeras, S. (2010). Use of Montessori-based activities for clients with dementia in adult day care: Effects on engagement. *American Journal of Alzheimer's Disease & Other Dementias, 25*, 657–665.

Jungers, C. M., & Slagel, L. (2009). Crisis model for older adults: Special considerations for an aging population. *Adultspan Journal, 8*(2), 92–101.

Justice, A. (2010). HIV and aging: Time for a new paradigm. *Current HIV/AIDS Reports, 7*, 69–76.

Kagawa-Singer, M., Wellisch, D., & Durvasula, R. (1997). Aging, chronic conditions, and physical disabilities in Asian and Pacific Islander Americans. In K. S. Markides & M. Miranda (Eds.), *Minorities, aging, and health* (pp. 149–180). Thousand Oaks, CA: Sage.

Kalish, R. (1979). The new ageism and the failure models: A polemic. *The Gerontologist, 19*, 398–402.

Kalra, G., Subramanyam, A., & Pinto, C. (2011). Sexuality: Desire, activity and intimacy in the elderly. *Indian Journal of Psychiatry, 53*(4), 300–306.

Kane, M. N. (2008). Imagining recovery, resilience and vulnerability at 75: Perceptions of social work students. *Educational Gerontology, 34*(1), 30–50.

Kane, M. N., & Green, D. (2009a). Perceptions of elders' substance abuse and resilience. *Gerontology & Geriatrics Education, 30*(2), 164–183.

Kane, M. N., & Green, D. (2009b). Substance abuse by elders and self-enhancement bias. *Educational Gerontology, 35*, 95–120.

Kaplan, M. S., Adamel, M. E., & Rhoades, J. A. (1998). Prevention of elder suicide: Physicians' assessment of firearm availability. *American Journal of Preventative Medicine, 15*(1), 60–64.

Kasl-Godley, I., & Gatz, M. (2000). Psychosocial interventions for individuals with dementia: An integration of theory, therapy, and a clinical understanding of dementia. *Clinical Psychology Review, 20*, 755–782.

Katz, A. (2013). Sexuality in nursing care facilities. *American Journal of Nursing, 113*(3), 53–56.

Katz, J., Joiner, T. E., Jr., & Kwon, P. (2002). Membership in a devalued social group and emotional well-being: Developing a model of personal self-esteem, collective self-esteem, and group socialization. *Sex Roles, 47*(9/10), 419–431.

Katz, R. S., & Johnson, T. G. (Eds.). (2006). *When professionals weep. Emotional and countertransference responses in end of life care*. New York, NY: Routledge.

Kaufman, R., Segal-Engelchin, D., & Huss, E. (2012). Transitions in first-year students' initial practice orientations. *Journal of Social Work Education, 48*(2), 337–359.

Kaufman, S. (2005). *And a time to die: How American hospitals shape the end of life*. London, UK: University of Chicago Press.

Kayser-Jones, J. (2002). The experience of dying: An ethnographic nursing home study. *The Gerontologist, 42*(Special Issue 3), 11–19.

Kein, W. C., & Jess, C. (2002). One last pleasure? Alcohol use among elderly people in nursing homes. *Health & Social Work, 27*, 193–203.

Kenagy, G. P. (2005). Transgender health: Findings from two needs assessment studies in Philadelphia. *Health & Social Work, 30*(1), 19–26.

Kennamer, J. D., Honnold, J., Bradford, J., & Hendricks, M. (2000). Differences in disclosure of sexuality among African American and White gay/bisexual men: Implications for HIV/AIDS preventions. *AIDS Education and Prevention, 12*, 519–531.

Kennedy, D., Sylvia, E., Banni-Issa, W., Khater, W., & Forbes-Thompson, S. (2005). Beyond the rhythm and routine: Adjusting to life in assisted living. *Journal of Gerontological Nursing, 3*(1), 17–23.

Kenyon, G. M. (1996). Ethical issues in aging and biography. *Ageing and Society, 16*(6), 659–675.

Kenyon, G. M., Clark, P., & de Vries, B. (Eds.). (2001). *Narrative gerontology: Theory, research, and practice*. New York: Springer Publishing Company.

Keown, D. (2005). End of life: The Buddhist view. *Lancet, 366*, 952–955.

Keshen, A. (2006). A new look at existential psychotherapy. *American Journal of Psychotherapy, 60*(3), 285–298.

Kessler, R., Berglund, P., Demler, O., Jin, R., Koretz, D., Merikangas, K. R., et al. (2003). The epidemiology of major depressive disorder: Results from the National Comorbidity Survey Replication (NCS-R). *Journal of the American Medical Association, 289*(23), 3095–3105.

Kim, P., Louis, C., & Muralee, S. (2005). Sundowning syndrome in the older patient. *Clinical Geriatrics and Medicine, 13*(4), 32–36.

Kimmel, D., Rose, T., & David, S. (2006). *Lesbian, gay, bisexual and transgender aging: Research and clinical perspectives.* New York, NY: Columbia University Press.

King, L., Hicks, J., Krull, J., & Del Gaiso, A. (2006). Positive affect and the experience of meaning of life. *Journal of Personality and Social Psychology, 90*(1), 179–196.

Kingston, P., Bernard, M., Biggs, S., & Nettleton, H. (2001). Assessing the health impact of age-specific housing. *Health & Social Care in the Community, 9*(4), 228–234.

Kinzbrunner, B. M. (2004). Jewish medical ethics and end-of-life care. *Journal of Palliative Medicine, 7*, 558–573.

Kissane, D. W. (1998). Models of psychological response to suffering. *Progress in Palliative Care, 6*, 197–204.

Kissane, D. W., & Clarke, D. M. (2001). Demoralization syndrome—A relevant psychiatric diagnosis for palliative care. *Journal of Palliative Care, 17*, 12–21.

Klasuner, E. J., Clarkin, J., Spielman, L. A., Pupo, C., Abrams, R. C., & Alexopoulos, G. S. (1998). Late-life depression and functional disability: The role of goal-focused group psychotherapy. *International Journal of Geriatric Psychiatry, 13*(10), 707–716.

Kleftaras, G., & Psarra, E. (2012). Meaning in life, psychological well-being and depressive symptomatology: A comparative study. *Psychology, 3*, 337–345.

Klein, B. E., Klein, R., & Lee, K. E. (2002). Incidence of age-related cataract over a 10–year interval: The Beaver Dam Eye Study. *Ophthalmology, 109*, 2052–2057.

Kling, K. C., Ryff, C., Love, G., & Essex, M. (2003). The role of the gerontological social worker in assisted living. *Journal of Gerontological Social Work, 54*, 494–510.

Knight, B. G. (1999). The scientific basis for psychotherapeutic interventions with older adults. An overview. *Journal of Clinical Psychology: In Session, 55*, 927–934.

Knight, B. G. (2004). Grief work with older adults: *Psychotherapy with older adults* (3rd ed., pp. 139–159). Thousand Oaks, CA: Sage.

Knight, B. G., & Satre, D. D. (1999). Cognitive behavioral psychotherapy with older adults. *Clinical Psychology: Science and Practice, 6*(2), 188–203.

Knight, B. G., Teri, L., Wohford, P., & Santos, J. (Eds.). (1995). *Mental health services for older adults: Implications for training and practice in geropsychology.* Washington, DC: American Psychological Association.

Knight, T., & Ricciardelli, L. A. (2003). Successful aging: Perceptions of adults aged between 70 and 101 years. *International Journal of Aging and Human Development, 56*, 223–245.

Knox, S., & Hill, C. (2003). Therapist self-disclosure: Research-based suggestions for practitioners. *Journal of Clinical Psychology, 59*, 529–539.

Koch, D. S., & Benshoff, J. J. (2002). Rehabilitation professionals' familiarity with and utilization of Alcoholics Anonymous. *Journal of Applied Rehabilitation Counseling, 33*(3), 35–40.

Koch, T. (2000). *Age speaks for itself: Silent voices of the elderly.* Westport, CT: Praeger.

Kochman, A. (1997). Gay and lesbian elderly: Historical overview and implications for social work practice. *Journal of Gay and Lesbian Social Services, 6*, 1–10.

Koenig, H. G., McCullough, M. E., & Larson, D. B. (2001). *Handbook of religion and health.* New York: Oxford University Press.

Kohm, S. (2009). Spatial dimensions of fear in a high-crime community: Fear of crime or fear of disorder? *Canadian Journal of Criminology and Criminal Justice, 51*(1), 1–30.

Komiti, A., Judd, F., & Jackson, H. (2006). The influence of stigma and attitudes on seeking help from a GP for mental health problems. *Social Psychiatry and Psychiatric Epidemiology, 41*(9), 738–745.

Korfage, I. J., Plujim, S., Roobol, M., Dohle, G. R., Schroder, F. H., & Essink-Bot, M. L. (2009). Erectile dysfunction and mental health in a general population of older men. *Journal of Sexual Medicine, 6*, 505–512.

Korte, J., Bohlmeijer, E. T., Cappeliez, P., Smit, F., & Westerhof, G. J. (2012). Life review therapy for older adults with moderate depressive symptomatology: A pragmatic randomized controlled trial. *Psychological Medicine, 42*(6), 1163–1173.

Krach, C. A. (1999). *Projected number of U.S. centenarians (2000–2050).* Washington, DC: U.S. Census Bureau.

Kraener, K. L., Conigliaro, J., & Saitz, R. (1999). Managing alcohol withdrawal in the elderly. *Drugs Aging, 14*(6), 409–425.

Krantz, D. S., Sheps, D. S., Carney, R. M., & Natelson, B. H. (2000). Effects of mental stress in patients with coronary artery disease: Evidence and clinical implications. *Journal of the American Medical Association, 283*, 1800–1802.

Kraus, C. A., Kunik, M. E., & Stanley, M. A. (2007). Use of cognitive behavioral therapy in late life psychiatric disorders. *Geriatrics, 62*(6), 21–26.

Kravitz, R. L., Epstein, R. M., Feldman, M. D., Francz, C. E., Azari, R., Wilkes, M. S., et al. (2005). Influence of patients' requests for direct-to-consumer advertised antidepressants: A randomized controlled trial. *Journal of the American Medical Association, 293*, 1995–2002.

Krishna, M., Jauhari, A., Lepping, P., Turner, J., Crossley, D., & Krishnamoorthy, A. (2011). Is group psychotherapy effective in older adults with depression? A systematic review. *International Journal of Geriatric Psychiatry, 26*(4), 331.

Krishnan, K. R., Hays, J. C., & Blazer, D. G. (1997). MRI-defined vascular depression. *American Journal of Psychiatry, 154*, 497–500.

Krout, J. A., Moen, P., Holmes, H. H., Oggins, J., & Bowen, N. (2002). Reasons for relocation to a continuing care retirement community. *Journal of Applied Gerontology, 21*(2), 236–256.

Kübler-Ross, E. (1969). *On death and dying.* New York, NY: Scribner.

Kübler-Ross, E., & Kessler, D. (2005). *On grief and grieving.* New York, NY: Scribner.

Kuhn, D. (2003). New horizons: Early diagnosis of Alzheimer's means new implications for care. *Contemporary Long-Term Care, 26*, 25–27.

Kulik, I. (2002). Marital equality and the quality of long-term marriage in later life. *Ageing & Society, 22*(4), 459–481.

Kuo, W. H., Gallo, J. J., & Tien, A. Y. (2001). Incidence of suicide and attempts in adults: The 13–year follow-up of a community sample in Baltimore, Maryland. *Psychological Medicine, 31*, 1181–1191.

Kwak, J., & Haley, W. E. (2005). Current research findings on end of life decision making among racially or ethnically diverse groups. *The Gerontologist, 45*(5), 634–641.

Kwak, J., Tang, M., & Woo, J. (2001). The management of demented people with feeding problem. *International Journal of Geriatric Psychiatry, 16*, 337–338.

Lachman, M. E. (2000). Promoting a sense of control over memory aging. In L. Backman, R. D. Hill, & A. Stigsdotter-Neely (Eds.), *Cognitive rehabilitation in old age* (pp. 106–120). New York, NY: Oxford University Press.

Lachs, M. S., Bachman, R., Williams, C. S., Kossack, A., Bove, C., & O'Leary, J. (2004). Older adults as crime victims, perpetrators, witnesses, and complainants: A population study of police interactions. *Journal of Elder Abuse & Neglect, 16*, 25–40.

Lachs, M. S., & Berman, J. (2011). *New York State elder abuse prevalence study. Self-reported prevalence and documented case surveys: Final report.* New York, NY: Lifespan of Greater Rochester, Inc., Weill Cornell University, & New York City Department of Aging.

Lachs, M. S., Williams, C. S., O'Brien, S., & Pillemer, K. A. (2002). Adult protective service use and nursing home placement. *The Gerontologist, 42*, 734–739.

Laing, R. D. (1960). *The divided self.* London: Tavistock.

Lane, D., Carrol, D., & Lip, G. Y. H. (2003). Anxiety, depression, and prognosis after myocardial infarction: Is there a causal association? *Journal of the American College of Cardiology, 42*, 1808–1810.

Laskin, R. S. (1999). Total knee replacement in patients older than 85 years. *Clinical Orthopaedics and Related Research, 367*, 43–49.

LaTorre, R. A., & Kear, K. (1977). Attitudes toward sex in the elderly. *Archives of Sexual Behavior, 6*, 203–213.

Lau, E., & Kosberg, J. I. (1978). *Abuse of the elderly by informal care providers.* Paper presented at the Annual Meeting of the Gerontological Society of America, Dallas, Texas.

Laumann, E. O., Paik, A., Glasser, D. B., Kang, J. H., Wang, T., Levinson, B., et al. (2006). A cross-national study of subjective sexual well-being among older women and men: Findings from the global study of sexual attitudes and behaviors. *Archives of Sexual Behavior, 35*, 145–161.

Laumann, E. O., Paik, A., & Rosen, R. C. (1999). Sexual dysfunction in the United States. *Journal of the American Medical Association, 281*, 537–544.

Lavretsky, H. (2012). The role of family caregivers and inappropriate medication use in the community-dwelling older adults with dementia. *Aging Health, 8*(5), 457–460.

Lawner, P. (1981). Reflections on the "unknown" in psychotherapy. *Psychotherapy Theory, Research, and Practice, 18*, 306–312.

Lawton, M. P., & Nahemow, L. (1973). Ecology and the aging process. In C. Eisdorfer & M. P. Lawton (Eds.), *The psychology of adult development and aging* (pp. 619–674). Washington, DC: American Psychological Association.

Lazarou, J., Pomeranz, B. H., & Corey, P. N. (1998). Incidence of adverse drug reactions in hospitalized patients: A meta-analysis of prospective studies. *Journal of the American Medical Association, 279,* 1200–1205.

Lee, B., Hatzenbuehler, M. L., Phelan, J. C., & Link, B. G. (2013). The role of stigma in health disparities. *American Journal of Public Health, 103*(8), E4–E5.

Lee, J., & Bean, F. D. (2004). America's changing color lines: Immigration, race/ethnicity, and multicultural identification. *Annual Review of Sociology, 30,* 221–242.

Lee, K. M., Volans, P. J., & Gregory, N. (2003). Attitudes towards psychotherapy with older adults among trainee clinical psychologists. *Aging & Mental Health, 7,* 133–141.

Lee, S., Lee, M. T., Chiu, M. Y., & Kleinman, A. (2005). Experience of social stigma by people with schizophrenia in Hong Kong. *British Journal of Psychiatry, 186,* 153–157.

Leming, M. R., & Dickinson, G. E. (2007). *Understanding death, dying, and bereavement* (6th ed.). New York, NY: Wadsworth.

Lent, R. W. (2004). Toward a unifying theoretical and practical perspective on well-being and psychosocial adjustment. *Journal of Counseling Psychology, 51*(4), 482–509.

Lerner, R., M., (2006). Developmental science, developmental systems, and contemporary theories of human development. In W. Damon & R. M. Lerner (Eds.), *Theoretical models of human development. Handbook of child psychology* (6th ed., Vol. 1, pp. 1–17). New York, NY: Wiley.

Leszcz, M. (2002). Group therapy for depression. *International Journal of Group Psychotherapy, 52,* 451–457.

Levin, S. M., & Kruger, J. (Eds.). (2000). *Substance abuse among older adults: A guide for social service providers.* Rockville, MD: Substance Abuse and Mental Health Services Administration.

Levinson, D. J. (1986). A conception of adult development. *American Psychologist, 41,* 3–13.

Levinson, D. J., Darrow, C. M., Klein, E. B., Levinson, M.H., & McKee, B. (1978). The season's of a man's life. New York, NY: Knopf.

Levy, B. R., Slade, M. D., & Gill, T. M. (2006). Hearing decline predicted by elders' stereotypes. *The Journals of Gerontology, 61B*(2), P82–P87.

Levy, J. A., Ory, M. G., & Crystal, S. (2003). HIV/AIDS interventions for midlife and older adults: Current status and challenges. *Journal of Acquired Immune Deficiency Syndrome, 33*(Suppl. 2), S59–S67.

Lewis, H. J., Hems, D. J., Bosanquet, K. N., & Overend, K. J. (2013). Is enough being done to treat depression in the elderly? *Aging Health, 9*(3), 243–245.

Li, J., Laursen, T. M., Precht, D. H., Olsen, J., & Mortensen, P. B. (2005). Hospitalization for mental illness among patients after the death of a child. *New England Journal of Medicine, 352,* 1190–1196.

Li, S. (2004). "Symbiotic niceness": Constructing a therapeutic relationship in psychosocial palliative care. *Social Science & Medicine, 58,* 2571–2583.

Ligon, J. (2013). When older adult substance abuse affects others: What helps and what doesn't? *Journal of Social Work Practice in Addictions, 13*(2), 223–226.

Lillard, L. A., & Waite, L. J. (1995). Til death do us part: Marital disruption and mortality. *American Journal of Sociology, 100,* 1131–1156.

Lim, J., & Zebrack, B. (2004). Caring for family members with chronic physical illness: A critical review of caregiver literature. *Health and Quality of Life Outcomes*(2), 50–59.

Limb, G. E., & Organista, K. C. (2006). Change between entry and graduation in MSW student views on social work's traditional mission, career motivations, and practice preferences: Caucasian, student of color, and American Indian group comparisons. *Journal of Social Work Education, 42*(269–290).

Lin, E. H., Katon, W., & Korff, M. (2004). Relationship of depression and diabetes self-care, medication adherence, and preventative care. *Diabetes Care, 27,* 2154–2160.

Linn, B. S., & Linn, M. W. (1980). Objective and self-assessed health in the old and very old. *Social Science and Medicine, 14A,* 311–315.

Lindau, S. T., Leitsch, S. A., Lundberg, K. L., & Jerome, J. (2006). Older women's attitudes, behavior, and communication about sex and HIV: A community-based study. *Journal of Womens Health (Larchmont), 15*(6), 747–753.

Lindau, S. T., Schumm, L. P., & Laumann, E. O. (2007). A study of sexuality and health among older adults in the United States. *New England Journal of Medicine, 357*(8), 762–774.

Lindau, S. T., Schumm, L. P., Laumann, E. O., Levinson, W., O'Muircheartaigh, C. A., & Waite, L. J. (2007). A study of sexuality and health among older adults in the United States. *New England Journal of Medicine, 357,* 762–774.

Lindrooth, R. C., Hoerger, T. J., & Norton, E. C. (2000). Expectations among the elderly about nursing home entry. *Health Services Research, 35*(5 Part 2), 1181–1202.

Lingaraju, R., & Ashburn, M. A. (2013). Pain management in the elderly. *Aging Health, 9*(3), 265–274.

Link, B. G. (1987). Understanding labeling effects in the area of mental disorders: An assessment of the effects of expectations of rejection. *American Sociological Review, 52*(96–112).

Link, B. G., & Phelan, J. C. (2001). Conceptualizing stigma. *Annual Review of Sociology, 27,* 363–385.

Linley, L., Prejean, J., An, Q., Chen, M., & Hall, H. I. (2012). Racial/ethnic disparities in HIV diagnoses among persons aged 50 years and older in 37 US States, 2005–2008. *American Journal of Public Health, 102*(8), 1527–1534.

Linnebur, S. A., O'Connell, M. D., & Wessell, A. M. (2005). Pharmacy practice, research, education, and advocacy for older adults. *Pharacotherapy, 25,* 1404–1405.

Liorente, M. D., Oslin, D. W., & Malphurs, J. (2006). Substance use disorders in the elderly. In M. E. Agonin & G. J. Maletta (Eds.), *Principles and practice of geriatric practice* (pp. 471–488). Philadelphia: Lippincot Williams & Williams.

Lipsitz, L. A. (2002). Dynamics of stability: The physiological basis of functional health and frailty. *Journal of Gerontology: Biological Sciences, 2002*(57A), B115–B125.

Li-Tzy, W., & Blazer, D. G. (2011). Illicit and nonmedical drug use among older adults: A review. *Journal of Aging & Health, 23*(3), 504–524.

Liu, C.-J., Brost, M. A., Horton, V. E., Kenyon, S. B., & Mears, K. E. (2013). Occupational therapy interventions to improve performance of daily activities at home for older adults with low vision: A systematic review. *American Journal of Occupational Therapy, 67*(3), 279–287.

Lloyd-Williams, M., Kennedy, V., Sixsmith, A., & Sixsmith, J. (2007). The end of life: A qualitative study of the perceptions of people over the age of 80 on issues surrounding death and dying. *Journal of Pain and Symptom Management, 34*(1), 60–66.

Lo, R. S., Woo, J., Zhoc, K. C., Li, C. Y., Yeo, W., Johnson, P., et al. (2002). Quality of life of palliative care patients in the last two weeks of life. *Journal of Pain Management, 24*(4), 388–397.

Lochlainn, M. N., & Kenny, R. A. (2013). Sexual activity and aging. *Journal of American Medical Directors Association, 14*(8), 565–572.

Loeb, D. F., Lee, R. S., Binswanger, I. A., Ellison, M. C., & Aagaard, E. M. (2011). Patient, resident physician, and visit factors associated with documentation of sexual history in the outpatient setting. *Journal of General Internal Medicine, 26*(8), 887–893.

Logie, C., & Gadalla, T. M. (2009). Meta-analysis of health and demographic correlates of stigma towards people living with HIV. *AIDS Care, 21,* 742–753.

London, C., Scriven, A., & Lalani, N. (2006). Sir Winston Churchill: Greatest Briton used as an anti-stigma icon. *Journal of the Royal Society for the Promotion of Health, 126*(4), 163–164.

Long, R. G., Boyette, L. W., & Griffin-Shirley, N. (1996). Older persons and community travel: The effect of visual impairment. *Journal of Visual Impairment & Blindness, 90,* 303–313.

Longino, C. F., Jr. (2005). Exploring the connections: Theory and research. *Journal of Gerontology: Social Sciences, 60B,* S172.

Longino, C. F., Perzynski, A. T., & Stoller, E. P. (2002). Pandora's briefcase: Unpacking the retirement migration decision. *Research on Aging, 24*(1), 29–49.

Longo, L., & Johnson, B. (2000). Benzodiazepines: Side effects, abuse, risk, and alternatives. Addiction part 1. *American Family Physician, 61,* 2120–2130.

Lopez, M. A., & Mermelstein, R. J. (1995). A cognitive-behavioral program to improve geriatric rehabilitation outcome. *The Gerontologist, 35,* 696–700.

Lorenz, K. A., Lynn, J., Dy, S. M., Shugarman, L. R., Wilkinson, A., Mularski, R. A., et al. (2008). Evidence for improving palliative care at the end of life: A systematic review. *American Internal Medicine, 148*(2), 147–159.

Louie, G. H., & Ward, M. M. (2011). Socioeconomic and ethnic differences in disease burden and disparities in physical function in older adults. *American Journal of Public Health, 101*(7), 1322–1329.

Lu, F. P., Lin, K. P., & Kuo, H. K. (2009). Diabetes and the risk of multi-system aging phenotypes: A systematic review and meta-analysis. *PLoS One, 4,* 4144.

Luborsky, M. R. (1993). The romance with personal meaning in gerontology: Cultural aspects of life themes. *The Gerontologist, 33*(4), 445–452.

Luszczynska, A., Guttierrez-Dona, B., & Schwarzer, R. (2005). General self-efficacy in various domains of human functioning: Evidence from five countries. *International Journal of Psychology, 40*(2), 80–89.

Lyketsos, C. G., & Olin, J. (2002). Depression in Alzheimer's disease: Overview and treatment. *Biological Psychiatry, 52,* 242–252.

Maddox, G. L. (1987). Aging differently. *The Gerontologist, 27,* 557–564.

Maidment, J. (2006). The quiet remedy: A dialogue on reshaping professional relationships. *Journal of Contemporary Social Sciences, 87*(1), 115–121.

Mak, W. W., & Wu, C. F. (2006). Cognitive insight and causal attribution in the development of self-stigma among individuals with schizophrenia. *Psychiatric Services, 57*(12), 1800–1802.

Makino, K. M., & Porsteinson, A. P. (2011). Memantine: A treatment for Alzheimer's disease with a new formulation. *Aging Health, 7*(3), 349–362.

Mallon, R. (2006). "Race": Normative, not metaphysical or semantic. *Ethics, 116*(3), 525–623.

Malone, D. (1951). Jefferson and the rights of man. In D. M. Oshinsky, *Polio: An American Story* (pp. 32). New York, NY: Oxford University Press.

Manning, P. K. (1980). Goffman's framing order: Style as structure. In J. Ditton (Ed.), *The view from Goffman* (p. 267). New York, NY: St. Martin's Press.

Manzer, J. (2003). Medical students lack sex abuse info. *Medical Post, 39*(2), 2.

Marienfeld, C. B., Tek, E., Diaz, E., Schottenfeld, R., & Chawarski, M. (2012). Psychiatrist decision-making towards prescribing benzodiazepines: The dilemma with substance abusers. *Psychiatric Quarterly, 83*(4), 521–529.

Maris, R. W., & Berman, A. L. (2000). *Comprehensive textbook of suicidology.* New York, NY: Guilford Press.

Markovitz, P. (2004). Recent trends in the pharmacotherapy of personality disorders. *Journal of Personality Disorders, 18*(1), 90–101.

Marlatt, G. A., Bowen, S., & Chawla, N. (2010). *Mindfulness-based relapse prevention for addictive behaviors: A clinician's guide.* New York, NY: Guilford Press.

Marlatt, G. A., & Donovan, D. M. (2005). *Relapse prevention: Maintenance strategies in the treatment of addictive behaviors.* New York, NY: Guilford Press.

Mars, G. M., Kempen, G. I., Mesters, I., Proot, I. M., & Van Eijk, J. T. (2008). Characteristics of social participation as defined by older adults with a chronic physical illness. *Disability Rehabilitation, 30*(17), 1298–1308.

Marshall, B. L. (2010). Sexual medicine, sexual bodies, and the pharmaceutical imagination. *Sociology of Health and Illness, 32*(2), 211–224.

Martikainen, P., & Valkonen, T. (1996). Mortality after the death of a spouse: Rates and causes of death in a large Finnish cohort. *American Journal of Public Health, 86,* 1087–1093.

Martin, S. L., Ray, N., Sotres-Alverez, D., Kupper, L. L., Moracco, K. E., Dickens, P. A., et al. (2006). Physical and sexual assault of women with disabilities. *Violence Against Women, 12*(9), 823–837.

Martin, T., & Doka, K. (2000). *Men don't cry … women do: Transcending gender stereotypes of grief.* Philadelphia, PA: Brunner/Mazel.

Marx, A. (2002a). Illicit drug use grows among the elderly. *Christian Science Monitor, 94*(85), 3.

Marx, A. (2002b). Illicit drug use grows among the elderly. *Christian Science Monitor, 94*(85), 166–184.

Maslow, A. H. (1968). *Toward a psychology of being* (2nd ed.). New York, NY: Van Nostrand.

McCann, I. (2003). *Age discrimination in employment legislation in the United States experience.* Washington, DC: AARP Foundation Litigation.

McCann, J. J., Herbert, L. E., Li, Y., Wolinsky, F. D., Gilley, D. W., Aggarwal, N. T., et al. (2005). The effect of adult day care services on time to nursing placement in older adults with Alzheimer's disease. *The Gerontologist, 45*(6), 754–763.

McCarthy, V., L. (2011). A new look at successful aging: Exploring a mid-range nursing theory among older adults in a low-income retirement community. *Journal of Theory Construction & Testing, 15,* 17–21.

McCarthy, V. L., Ling, J., & Carini, R. M. (2013). The role of self-transcendence: A missing variable in the pursuit of successful aging? *Research in Gerontological Nursing, 6*(3), 178–186.

McCombs, J. S., Thiebaud, P., McLaughlin-Milley, C., & Shi, J. (2004). Compliance with drug therapies for the treatment and prevention of osteoporosis. *Maturitas, 48,* 271–287.

McCormick, B. (2001). Autonomy and the relationship between nurses and older people. *Aging and Society, 21*(4), 417–446.

McCurry, J. (2004). Japanese leprosy patients continue to fight social stigma. *Lancet, 363*(9408), 544.

McCusker, J., Cole, M. G., Dufoull, C., Dendukuri, N., Latimer, E., Windholz, S., et al. (2005). The prevalence and correlates of major depression in older medical inpatients. *Journal of the American Geriatrics Society, 53*(8), 1344–1353.

McDougall, G. J. (2000). Memory improvement in assisted living elders. *Issues in Mental Health Nursing, 21*(2), 217–233.

McGuire, T. G., Wells, K. B., Bruce, M. L., Miranda, J., Scheffler, R., Durham, M., et al. (2002). Burden of illness. *Mental Health Services Research, 4*(4), 179–185.

McKenzie, K., Serfaty, M., & Crawford, M. (2003). Suicide in ethnic minority groups. *British Journal of Psychiatry, 183,* 100–101.

McKinley, E. D., Garrett, J. M., Evans, A. T., & Danis, M. (1996). Differences in end-of-life decision making among black and white ambulatory cancer patients. *Journal of General Internal Medicine, 11*(11), 651–656.

McKinnes-Dittrich, K. (2005). *Social work with elders: A biopsychosocial approach to assessment and intervention* (2nd ed.). Boston: Allyn & Bacon.

McKinney, E. A., Harel, Z., & Williams, M. (1990). Introduction. In Z. Harel, E. A. McKinney & M. Williams (Eds.), *Black aged: Understanding diversity and service needs* (pp. 19–32). Newbury Park, CA: Sage.

McNeil, R. D. (2001). Bob Dylan and the baby boom generation: The times are a-changin' again. *Activities, Adaptation & Aging, 25*(3–4), 45–58.

McQuaide, S., & Ehrenreich, J. H. (1997). Assessing client strengths. *Families in Society, 78*(2), 201–212.

Meadows, G., Burgess, P., & Bobevski, I. (2002). Perceived need for mental health care: Influences of diagnosis, demography, and disability. *American Journal of Public Health, 87,* 1136–1143.

Mechanic, D. (2003). Is the prevalence of mental disorders a good measure of the need for services? *Health Affairs, 22*(5), 8–20.

Meeussen, K., Van de Block, L., Bossuyt, N., Bilsen, J., Echteld, M., Van Casteren, V., et al. (2009). GP's awareness of patients' preference for place of death. *British Medical Journal, 56*(665–670).

Melton, A., & Schulunberg, S. E. (2008). On the measurement of meaning: Logotherapy's empirical contributions to humanistic psychology. *Humanistic Psychologist, 36,* 31–44.

Mendes de Leon, C. F., DiLillo, V., Czaijkowski, S., Norten, J., Schaefer, J., Catellier, D., et al. (2001). Psychosocial characteristics after acute myocardial infarction: The ENRICHD pilot study. *Journal of Cardiopulmonary Rehabilitation, 21,* 353–362.

Menec, V. H., & Chipperfield, J. G. (1997). The interactive effect of perceived control and functional status on health and mortality among young-old and old-old adults. *Journals of Gerontology, 52B*(3), P118–P126.

Menninger, J. A. (2002). Assessment and treatment of alcoholism and substance-related disorders in the elderly. *Bulletin of the Menninger Clinic, 66,* 166–184.

Meston, C. M., & Frohlich, P. F. (2000). The neurobiology of sexual function. *Archives of General Psychiatry, 57*(11), 1012–1030.

MetLife Mature Market Institute. (2011). *The MetLife study of elder financial abuse: Crimes of occasion, desperation, and predation against America's elders.* New York, NY: Author.

Meyer, I. H. (1995). Minority stress and mental health in gay men. *Journal of Health and Social Behavior, 36,* 38–56.

Meyer, I. H. (2001). Why lesbian, gay, bisexual, and transgender public health? *American Journal of Public Health, 91,* 856.859.

Meyer, I. H. (2003). Prejudice, social stress, and mental health in lesbian, gay, and bisexual populations: Conceptual issues and research evidence. *Psychological Bulletin, 129*(5), 674–697.

Midtgaard, J., Rossell, K., Christensen, J. F., Uth, J., Adamsen, L., & Rorth, M. (2012). Demonstration and manifestation of self-determination and illness resistance: A qualitative study of long-term maintenance of physical activity in posttreatment cancer survivors. *Supportive Care in Cancer, 20*(9), 1999–2008.

Miech, R. A., Eaton, W. W., & Brennan, K. (2005). Mental health disparities across education and sex: A prospective analysis examining how they persist over the life course. *Journals of Gerontology: Pscyhological Sciences and Social Sciences, 60B*(Special Issue II), 93–98.

Millender, E. (2011). Using stories to bridge cultural disparaties, one culture at a time. *Journal of Continuing Education in Nursing, 42*(1), 37–42.

Miller, E. A., & Weissert, W. G. (2000). Predicting elderly people's risk for nursing home placement, hospitalization, functional impairment, and mortality: A synthesis. *Medical Care Research & Review, 57*(3), 259–297.

Miller, I. V. (1996). Ethical and liability issues concerning invisible rationing. *Professional Psychology: Research and Practice, 27*, 583–587.

Miller, W. R., & Rollnick, S. (2002). *Motivational interviewing* (2nd ed.). New York, NY: Gillford Press.

Miller, W. R., Forcehimes, A. A., & Zweben, A. (2011). *Treating addiction: A guide for professionals.* New York: Guilford Press.

Milne, A. (2010). The "D" word: Reflections on the relationship between stigma, discrimination and dementia. *Journal of Mental Health, 19*(3), 227–233.

Minicuci, N., Maggi, S., Pavan, M., Enzi, G., & Crepaldi, G. (2002). Prevalence rate and correlates of depressive symptoms in older individuals: The Veneto study. *Journal of Gerontology: Medical Sciences, 57A*, M155–M161.

Minicuci, N., Maggi, S., Pavan, M., Enzi, G., & Crepaldi, G. (2002). Prevalence rate and correlates of depressive symptoms in older individuals: The Veneto study. *Journal of Gerontology: Medical Sciences, 57A*, M155–M161.

Miranda, J., Bernal, G., Lau, A., Kohn, L., Hwang, W. C., & LaFromboise, T. (2005). State of the science on psychosocial interventions for ethnic minorities. *Annual Review of Psychology, 1*, 113–142.

Miranda, J., & Cooper, L. A. (2004). Disparities in care for depression among primary care patients. *Journal of General Internal Medicine, 19*, 120–126.

Mitchell, A. J., Ferguson, D. W., Gill, J., Paul, J., & Symonds, P. (2013). Depression and anxiety in long-term cancer survivors compared with spouses and healthy controls: A systematic review and meta-analysis. *Lancet Oncology, 14*(8), 721–732.

Mitchell, S. L., Teno, J. M., Kiely, D. K., Shaffer, M. L., Jones, R. N., Prigerson, H. G., et al. (2009). The clinical course of advanced dementia. *New England Journal of Medicine, 361*(16), 1529–1538.

Mojtabai, R. (2007). Americans' attitudes toward mental health treatment seeking: 1990–2003. *Psychiatric Services, 58*(5), 642–651.

Mojtabai, R., & Olfson, M. (2008). National trends in psychotherapy by office-based psychiatrists. *Archives of General Psychiatry, 65*(8), 962–970.

Mojtabai, R., Olfson, M., & Mechanic, D. (2002). Percieved need and help-seeking in adults with mood, anxiety, or substance use disorders. *Archives of General Psychiatry, 59*, 77–84.

Mollica, R., & Johnson-Lamarche, H. (2005). *State residential care and assisted living policy: 2004.* Research Triangle Park, NC: RTI International.

Montague, D. K., Jarow, J. P., Broderick, G. A., Dmochowski, R. R., Heaton, J. P., Lue, T. F., et al. (2005). Chapter 1: The management of erectile dysfunction: An AUA update. *Journal of Urology, 174*(1), 230–239.

Moorman, S., Carr, D., Hammes, B. J., & Kirchhoff, K. T. (2012). Evaluating the Respecting Choices Advanced Care Planning Program: An indirect assessment. *Death Studies, 36*(4), 301–323.

Moos, R., Brennan, P., Schutte, K., & Moos, B. (2004). High-risk alcohol comsumption and late-life use problems. *American Journal of Public Health, 94*, 1985–1991.

Morano, C. L., & Bravo, M. (2002). A psychoeducational model for Hispanic Alzheimer's disease care-givers. *The Gerontologist, 42*, 122–126.

Morgan, M. L., & Brosi, M. W. (2007). Prescription drug abuse among older adults: A family ecological case study. *Journal of Applied Gerontology, 26*, 419–432.

Morgan, M. L., Brosi, W. A., & Brosi, M. W. (2011). Restorying older adults' narratives about self and substance abuse. *American Journal of Family Therapy, 39*, 444–455.

Morris, J. C., Price, J. L., McKeel, D. W., Higdon, R., & Buckles, V. D. (2004). The neurobiology of non-demented aging. *Neurobiology of Aging, 25*(S2), 137.

Moyers, T. B., & Houck, J. (2011). Combining motivational interviewing with cognitive-behavioral treat-ments for substance abuse: Lessons from the COMBINE research project. *Cognitive and Behavioral Practice, 18*, 38–45.

Munday, D., Petrova, M., & Dale, J. (2009). Exploring preferences for place of death with terminally ill patients: Qualitative study of experiences of general practitioners and community nurses in England. *British Medical Journal, 339*, B2391–B2400.

Munley, A. (1983). *The hospice alternative: A new context for death and dying.* New York: Basic Books.

Murphy, C., Cain, W. S., & Bartoshuk, L. M. (1977). Mutual action of taste and olfaction. *Sensory Processes, 1*, 204–211.

Myerhoff, B. (1978). *Number our days.* New York, NY: Dutton.

Naakashima, M., & Canda, E. R. (2005). Positive dying and resiliency in later life: A qualitative study. *Journal of Aging Studies, 19*(1), 109–125.

Nagi, S. Z. (1991). *Disability concepts revisited: Implications for prevention.* Washington, DC: National Academies Press.

Nahemow, L. (2000). The ecology theory of aging: Powell Lawton's legacy. In R. Rubenstein, M. Moss, & M. Kleban (Eds.), *The many dimensions of aging* (pp. 22–40). New York, NY: Springer Publishing Company.

Narrow, W. E., Regier, D. A., Norquist, G., Rae, D. S., Kennedy, C., & Arons, B. (2000). Mental health service use by Americans with severe mental illness. *Social Psychiatry and Psychiatric Epidemiology, 35,* 147–155.

National Council on Aging. (2012). *Top 6 policy issues affecting seniors in 2012.* Washington, DC: Author.

National Institute of Mental Health. (2007). *Older adults: Depression and suicide facts.* Retrieved October 3, 2009, from http://www.nimh.nih.gov/health/publications/older-adults-depression-and-suicide-facts-fact-sheet/index.shtml

Naylor, M. D., & Keating, S. A. (2008). Transitional care. *American Journal of Nursing, 108*(9), 58–63.

Neimeyer, R. A. (1993). An appraisal of the constructivist psychotherapies. *Journal of Consulting and Clinical Psychology, 61,* 221–234.

Neimeyer, R. A. (2000). *Lessons of loss: A guide to coping.* Memphis, TN: Center for the Study of Loss and Transition.

Nelson, D. (2002). Violence against elderly people: A neglected problem. *The Lancet, 360*(9339), 1094.

Ness, J., Ahmed, A., & Aronow, W. S. (2004). Demographics and payment characteristics of nursing home residents in the United States: A 23–year trend. *Journals of Gerontology Series A: A Biological Sciences & Medical Sciences, 59*(11), 1213–1217.

Neugarten, B. L. (1975). The future and the young-old. *The Gerontologist, 15*(1, Part 2), 4–9.

Neukrug, E. (2011). *Counseling theory and practice.* Belmont, CA: Brooks/Cole.

Nevins, A. (1932). Grover Cleveland: A study in courage. In D. M. Oshinsky, *Polio: An American Story* (p. 32). New York, NY: Oxford University Press.

Newton, N. A., & Jacobowitz, J. (1999). Transferential and countertransferential processes in therapy with older adults. In M. Duffy (Ed.), *Handbook of counseling and psychotherapy with older adults* (pp. 21–40). New York: Wiley.

Nicholas, L. H., Langa, K. M., Iwashyna, J., & Weir, D. R. (2011). Regional variation in the association between advance directives and end-of-life expenditures. *Journal of the American Medical Association, 306*(13), 144791453.

Nicholson, S. D. (1998). Anorexia nervosa in later life: An overview. *Hospital Medicine, 59,* 268–272.

Nickoletti, P., & Taussig, H. N. (2006). Outcome expectancies and risk behaviors in maltreated adolescents. *Journal of Research on Adolescence, 16*(2), 217–228.

Nilsson, U., Rawal, N., Unestahl, L. E., Zetterberg, C., & Unossoon, M. (2001). Improved recovery after music and therapeutic suggestions during general anesthesia: A double-blind randomized controlled trial. *Acta Anaesthesiologica Scandinavica, 45,* 812–817.

Noel, P. H., Williams, J. W., Jr., Unutzer, J., Worchel, J., Shuko, L., Cornell, J., et al. (2004). Depression and comorbid illness in elderly primary care patients: Impact on multiple domains of health status and well-being. *Annuals of Family Medicine, 2*(6), 555–562.

Nordin, S., Monsch, A. U., & Murphy, C. (1995). Unawareness of smell loss in normal aging and Alzheimer's disease: Discrepancy between self-reported and diagnosed smell sensitivity. *Journals of Gerontology, 50,* P187–P192.

Nouwen, A., Winkley, K., & Twisk, J. (2010). European Depression in Diabetes (EDID) Research Consortium Type 2 diabetes mellitus as a risk factor for the onset of depression: A systematic review and meta-analysis. *Diabetologia, 53*(2480–2486).

Novak, M., & Campbell, L. D. (2006). Self-identifying as a caregiver: Exploring the positioning process. *Journal of Aging Studies, 21*(2), 165–174.

O'Connell, H., Chin, A.-V., Cunningham, C., & Lawlor, B. (2003). Alcohol use disorders in elderly people: Redefining an age-old problem in old age. *British Medical Journal, 327,* 664–667.

Office on Aging, Department of Health and Human Services. (2010). *Projected future growth of the older population by race and Hispanic origin.* Washington, DC: Author.

Ojeda, V. D., & McGuire, T. G. (2006). Gender and racial/ethnic differences in use of outpatient mental health and substance use services by depressed adults. *Psychiatric Quarterly, 77*(3), 211–222.

Old Lesbians Organizing for Change. (2012). *Who we are*. Retrieved from http://www.oloc.org

Oldman, C. (2000). *Blurring the boundaries: A fresh look at housing and care provision for older people*. Brighton, UK: Joseph Rowntree Foundation & Pavilion Publishing.

Olfson, M., & Marcus, S. C. (2010). National trends in outpatient psychotherapy. *American Journal of Psychiatry, 167*(12), 1456–1463.

Olfson, M., Marcus, S. C., Druss, B. G., Elinson, L., Tanielian, T., & Pincus, H. A. (2002). National trends in the outpatient treatment of depression. *Journal of the American Medical Association, 287*(2), 203–209.

Oliver, D. P., & DeCostero, V. A. (2006). Health care needs of aging adults: Unprecedented opportunities for social work. *Health & Social Work, 31*, 243–245.

O'Neill, E. S. (2002). Illness representations and coping of women with chronic obstructive pulmonary disease: A pilot study. *Heart Lung, 31*(4), 295–302.

Onen, N. F., Shacham, E., Stamm, K. E., & Overton, E. T. (2010). Comparisons of sexual behaviors and STD prevalence among older and younger individuals with HIV infection. *AIDS Care, 22*(6), 711–717.

Onishi, J., Suzuki, Y., Umegaki, H., Endo, H., Kawamura, T., Imaizumi, M., et al. (2006). Behavioral, psychological and physical symptoms in group homes for older adults with dementia. *International Psychogeriatric Association, 18*(1), 75–86.

Oosterveld-Vlug, M. G., Pasman, H. R., Gennip, I. E., Willems, D. L., & Onwuteaka-Philipsen, B. D. (2013). Changes in the personal dignity of nursing home residents: A longitudinal qualitative interview study. *PLoS One, 8*(9), 1–8.

Oshinsky, D. M. (2005). *Polio: An American story*. New York, NY: Oxford University Press.

Ostman, M., & Kjellin, L. (2002). Stigma by association: Psychological factors in relatives of people with mental illness. *British Journal of Psychiatry, 181*, 494–498.

Oswalt, S. B., & Wyatt, T. J. (2011). Sexual orientation and differences in mental health, stress, and academic performance in a national sample of U.S. college students. *Journal of Homosexuality, 58*, 1255–1280.

Overton, W. F. (2006). Developmental psychology: Philosophy, concepts, methodology. In R. M. Lerner (Ed.), *Theoretical models of human development* (Vol. 4, pp. 18–88). New York: Wiley.

Owens, D., Dennis, M., Jones, S., Dove, A., & Dave, S. (1991). Self-poisoning patients discharged from accident and emergency: Risk factors and outcome. *Journal of the Royal College of Physicians, 25*, 218–222.

Page, C., Conner, T., Prokhorov, A., Fang, Y., & Post, L. (2009). The effect of care setting on elder abuse: Results from a Michigan survey. *Journal of Elder Abuse & Neglect, 21*(3), 239–252.

Palmer, J. A., Meterko, M., Zhao, S., Berkowitz, D., Mobley, E., & Hartman, C. W. (2013). Nursing home employee perceptions of culture groups. *Research in Gerontological Nursing, 6*(3), 152–160.

Palmore, E. (2001). The ageism survey: First findings. *The Gerontologist, 41*(5), 572–575.

Pang, M. C., Volicer, L., Chung, P. M., Chung, Y. M., Leung, W. K., & White, P. (2012). Comparing the ethical challenges of forgoing tube feeding in American and Hong Kong patients with advanced dementia. *Journal of Nutrition Health & Nursing, 11*, 495–501.

Parker, M. G., Thorslund, M., & Nordstrom, M. L. (1992). Predictors of mortality for the oldest old: A 4–year follow-up of community-based elderly in Sweden. *Archives of Gerontology and Geriatrics, 14*, 227–237.

Parr, J. M., Kavanagh, D. J., & Young, R. M. (2011). Acceptability of CBT via the internet for cessation benzodiazepine use. *Drug and Alcohol Review, 30*, 306–314.

Parr, J. M., Kavanagh, D. J., Young, R. M., Stubbs, B., & Bradizza, N. (2013). Impact of cognitive behaviour therapy via mail for cessation of benzodiazepine use: A series of case reports. *Behaviour Change, 30*(2), 74–83.

Patterson, T., & Jeste, D. (1999). The potential impact of the baby-boom generation on substance abuse among elderly persons. *Psychiatric Services, 50*, 1184–1188.

Patton, M. Q. (2002). *Qualitative research & evaluation methods* (3rd ed.). Thousand Oaks, CA: Sage Publications.

Payne, B., & Civokie, R. (1996). An empirical examination of the characteristics, consequences, and causes of elder abuse in nursing homes. *Journal of Elder Abuse & Neglect, 7*, 61–74.

Payne, B. K. (2005). *Crime and elder abuse* (2nd ed.). Springfield, IL: Charles C Thomas.

Payne, B. K., & Gainey, R. R. (2006). The criminal justice response to elder abuse in nursing homes: A routine activities perspective. *Western Criminology Review, 7*(3), 67–81.

Peace, S., Wahl, H. W., Oswald, F., & Mollenkopf, H. (2007). Environment and ageing: Space, time, and place. In P. Bond, F. Dittmann-Kohli, S. Peace, & G. Westerhof (Eds.), *Ageing in society: An introduction to social gerontology* (3rd ed., pp. 209–234). London, UK: Sage.

Peacock, J. R. (2000). Gay male adult development: Some stage issues of an older cohort. *Journal of Homosexuality, 40*, 13–29.

Peake, T. H. (1998). *Healthy aging, health treatment: The impact of telling stories*. Westport, CT: Praeger Publishers.

Pear, R. (2010). *Obama returns to end-of-life plan that caused stir*. Retrieved from http://www.nytimes .com/2010/12/26/us/politics/26death.html?r=2&nl=todaysheadlines&emc=a2

Peate, I. (2004). Sexuality and sexual health promotion for the older person. *British Journal of Nursing, 13*(4), 188–193.

Peltz, J. (2009, October 17). Advocates: NYC Astor case a win on financial abuse. *Associated Press*.

Pennington, H., Butler, R., & Eagger, S. (2000). The assessment of patients with alcohol disorders by an old age psychiatric service. *Aging & Mental Health, 4*, 182–185.

Perez, R. M., & Amadia, D. M. (2004). *Affirmative counseling and psychotherapy with lesbian, gay, and bisexual clients*. Reno, NV: Bent Tree Press.

Perkinson, M. A. (2013). Gerontology and geriatrics education: New models for a demographically transformed world. *Generations, 37*(1), 87–92.

Perkinson, M. A., Berg-Weger, M., Carr, D. B., Meuser, T. M., Palmer, J., & Buckles, V. D. (2005). Driving and dementia of the Alzheimer type: Beliefs and cessation strategies among stakeholders. *The Gerontologist, 45*, 675–685.

Peterson, D. M. (1988). Substance abuse, criminal behavior, and older people. *Generations, 12*(4), 63–67.

Peterson, P. G. (1999). *Gray dawn: How the coming age wave will transform America and the world*. New York, NY: Times Books.

Pfeiffer, E., Verwoerdt, A., & Davis, G. C. (1972). Sexual behavior in middle life. *American Journal of Psychiatry, 128*, 1262–1267.

Pfeiffer, E., Verwoerdt, A., & Wang, H. S. (1969). The natural history of sexual behavior in a biologically advantaged group of aged individuals. *Journal of Gerontology, 24*, 193–198.

Phelan, E. A., Anderson, L. A., LaCroix, A. Z., & Larson, E. B. (2004). Older adults' views of "successful aging" – how do they compare with researchers' definitions? *Journal of the American Geriatrics Society, 52*(2), 211–216.

Phelan, J. C., & Link, B. G. (1998). The growing belief that people with mental illness are violent: The role of the dangerousness criterion for civil commitment. *Social Psychiatry and Psychiatric Epidemiology, 33*, S7–S12.

Pinquart, M., & Soerensen, S. (2001). How effective are psychotherapeutic and other psychosocial interventions with older adults? *Journal of Mental Health and Aging, 7*, 207–243.

Pinquart, M., & Sorensen, S. (2001). Influences on loneliness in older adults: A meta-analysis. *Basic and Applied Social Psychology, 23*(4), 245–266.

Pinquart, M., & Sorensen, S. (2002). Preparation for death and preparation for care in older community-dwelling adults. *Omega: Journal of Death and Dying, 45*, 348–362.

Podnieks, E. (2003). *Focus group guidelines: A guideline for assessing perceptions on elder abuse among older people and primary health care workers*. Toronto, Canada: Ontario Network for the Prevention of Elder Abuse.

Pollak, C. P., Perlick, D., & Linsner, J. P. (1991). Sleep problems and institutionalization of the elderly. *Journal of Geriatric Psychiatry and Neurology, 4*, 204–210.

Pomeroy, E. C., & Garcia, R. B. (2011). Theories of grief and loss: An overview. In E. C. Pomeroy & R. B. Garcia (Eds.), *Children and loss: A practical handbook for professionals* (pp. 1–16). Chicago, IL: Lyceum Books.

Pomeroy, E. C., & Parrish, D. E. (2012). The new *DSM-5:* Where have we been and where are we going? *Social Work, 57*(3), 195–200.

Pompili, M., Mancinelli, I., & Tararelli, R. (2003). Stigma as a cause of suicide. *British Journal of Psychiatry, 183*, 173–174.

Porter, M., Russell, C., & Sullivan, G. (2004). Gay, old, and poor: Service delivery to aging gay men in inner city Sydney, Australia. *Journal of Gay & Lesbian Social Services, 16*(2), 43.

Potter, J. F. (2010). Aging in America: Essential considerations in shaping senior care policy. *Aging Health, 6*(3), 289–299.

Powell, J., & Wahidin, A. (2006). Rethinking criminology: The case of "aging" studies. In A. Wahidin & M. Cain (Eds.), *Aging, Crime, and Society* (pp. 17–34). Cullompton, UK: Willan.

Powers, L., Curry, M. A., Oschwald, M., Saxton, M., & Eccles, K. (2002). Barriers and strategies in addressing abuse: A survey of disabled women's experiences. *Journal of Rehabilitation, 68*(1), 4–13.

Powers, L., Renker, P., Robinson-Whelen, S., Oschwald, M., Hughes, R., Swank, P., et al. (2009). Interpersonal violence and women with disabilities: Analysis of safety promoting behaviors. *Violence Against Women, 15*(9), 1040–1069.

Pratt, R., Clare, L., & Aggarwal, N. (2005). The "Talking about Memory Coffee Group": A new model of support for people with early-stage dementia and their families. *Dementia, 4*, 143–148.

Prejean, J., Song, R., Hernandez, A., Ziebell, R., Green, T., Walker, F., et al. (2011). *Estimated HIV incidence in the United States, 2006–2009. PLoS One, 6*(8), e17502. Retrieved from http://www.plosone.org/article/info%3Adoi%2F10.1371%2Fjournal.pone.0017502

Preston, D. B., D'Augelli, A. R., Kassab, C. D., & Starks, M. T. (2007). The relationship of stigma to the sexual risk behavior of rural men who have sex with men. *AIDS Education and Prevention, 19*(3), 218–230.

Preston, S. H. (1994). Children and the elderly in the U.S. *Scientific American, 251*(6), 44–49.

Preville, M., Bosse, C., Vasiliadis, H.-M., Voyer, P., Laurier, C., Berbiche, D., et al. (2012). Correlates of potentially inappropriate prescriptions of benzodiazepines among older adults: Results from the ESA study. *Canadian Journal on Aging, 31*(3), 313–322.

Pride Senior Network. (2012). *Welcome!* Retrieved from http:www.pridesenior.org

Prince, D., & Butler, D. (2007). *Clarity final report: Aging in place in America.* Nashville, TN: Prince Market Research.

Pritchard, J. (2000). *The needs of older women: Services for victims of elder abuse and other abuse.* Bristol, UK: Policy Press.

Proctor, E., Morrow-Howel, N., Li, H., & Dore, P. (2000). Adequacy of home care and hospital readmission for elderly congestive heart failure patients. *Health & Social Work, 25*, 87–96.

Quam, J. K. (June/July 1993). Gay and lesbian aging. *SIECUS Report.* Retrieved from www.cyfc.umn.edu/diversity/gay/gayaging.html

Quill, T. E., Dresser, R., & Brock, D. W. (1997). The rule of double effect—A critic of its role in end-of-life decision making. *New England Journal of Medicine, 337*, 1768–1771.

Quill, T., Lee, B., & Nunn, S. (2000). Palliative treatments of last resort: Choosing the least harmful alternative. *Annals of Internal Medicine, 132*, 488–493.

Quillman, T. (2012). Neuroscience and therapist self-disclosure: Deepening right brain to right brain communication between therapist and patient. *Clinical Social Work Journal, 40*(1), 1–9.

Quine, S., & Morrell, S. (2007). Fear of loss of independence and nursing home admission in older Australians. *Health and Social Care in the Community, 15*, 212–220.

Raglio, A., & Gianelli, M. V. (2013). Music and music therapy in the management of behavioral disorders in dementia. *Neurodegenerative Disease Management, 3*(4), 295–298.

Ramello, S. (2013). Same sex acts involving older men: An ethnographic study. *Journal of Aging Studies, 27*(2), 121–134.

Read, J., & Harre, N. (2001). The role of biological and genetic causal beliefs in the stigmatisation of mental patients. *Journal of Mental Health UK, 10*, 223–235.

Regidor, E., Franch, J., Segui, M., Serrano, R., Rodriguez-Artalejo, F., & Artola, S. (2012). Traditional risk factors alone could not explain the excess mortality in patients with diabetes: A national cohort study of older Spanish adults. *Diabetes Care, 35*(12), 2503–2509.

Rejeski, W. J., Brawley, L. R., Amrosius, W. T., Brubaker, P. H., & Fox, L. D. (2003). Older adults with chronic disease: Benefits of group-mediated counseling in the promotion of physically active lifestyles. *Health Psychology, 22*, 414–423.

Resser, L., & Epstein, I. (1990). *Professionalization and activism in social work: The sixties, the eighties and the future.* New York, New York, NY: Columbia University Press.

Richards, M., Hardy, R., & Wadsworth, M. E. (2003). Does active leisure protect cognition? Evidence from a national birth cohort. *Social Science and Medicine, 56*(56), 785–792.

Richards, M. A., & Ramirez, A. J. (1997). Quality of life: The main outcome measure of palliative care. *Palliative Medicine, 11*, 89–92.

Richardson, J. P., & Lazur, A. (1995). Sexuality in the nursing home patient. *American Family Physician, 51*(1), 121–124.

Rieker, P. P., & Bird, C. E. (2005). Rethinking gender differences in health: Why we need to integrate social and biological perspectives. *Journals of Gerontology: Psychological Sciences and Social Sciences, 60B*(Special Issue II), 40–47.

Rigler, S. K. (2000). Alcoholism in the elderly. *American Family Physician, 61*, 1710–1716.

Rim Shin, D., Kim, M., & Kim, Y. (2003). Study of the lived experience of aging. *Nursing and Health Sciences, 5*, 245–252.

Ritsher, J. B., Otilingam, P. G., & Grajales, M. (2003). Internalized stigma of mental illness: Psychometric properties of a new measure. *Psychiatry Research, 121*, 31–49.

Roback, A. A., & Kiernan, T. (1969). *Pictorial history of psychology and psychiatry.* New York, NY: Philosophical Library.

Robichaud, L., Duran, P., Bedard, R., & Ouellet, J. (2006). Quality of life indicators in long term care: Opinions of elderly residents and their families. *Canadian Journal of Occupational Therapy, 73*(4), 245–251.

Robinson, W. R., Morris, K., Luck, M., & Pruitt, B. (2002). Hospice utilization by male and female cancer patients in an end-of-life transition program. *Journal of the American Medical Women's Association, 57*, 82–84.

Rodin, J., & Langer, E. J. (1985). The construct of control: Biological and psychosocial correlates. In C. Eisdorfer, M. P. Lawton, & G. L. Maddox (Eds.), *Annual review of gerontology and geriatrics. 1985* (Vol. 5, pp. 3–55). New York, NY: Springer Publishing Company.

Rogers, J. R., Gueulette, C. M., Abbey-Hines, J., Carney, J. V., & Werth, J. L., Jr. (2001). Rational suicide: An empirical investigation of counselor attitudes. *Journal of Counseling and Development: JCD, 79*(3), 365–372.

Romero, L. J., Ortiz, I. E., Finley, M. R., Wayne, S., & Lindeman, R. D. (2005). Prevalence of depressive symptoms in New Mexico Hispanic and non-Hispanic White elderly. *Ethnicity and Disease, 15*, 691–697.

Rosario, M., Scrimshaw, E. W., & Hunter, J. (2004). Ethnic/racial differences in the coming-out process of lesbian, gay, and bisexual youths: A comparison of sexual identity development over time. *Cultural Diversity and Ethnic Minority Psychology, 10*, 215–228.

Rosen, D., Engel, R. J., Hunsakeer, A. E., Engel, Y., Detlefsen, E. G., & Reynolds, C. F. (2013). Just say no: An examination of substance use disorders among older adults in gerontological and substance abuse journals. *Social Work in Public Health, 28*(3/4), 377–387.

Rosen, R. C., & Bachman, G. A. (2008). Sexual well-being, happiness, and satisfaction in women: The case for a new paradigm. *Journal of Sex & Marital Therapy, 34*, 291–297.

Rosen, S., & Erickson, M. H. (1991). *My voice will go with you: The teaching tales of Milton H. Erickson, M.D.* New York, NY: W.W. Norton.

Rowe, J. W., & Kahn, R. L. (1998). *Successful aging.* New York: Dell.

Rowles, G. D., & Bernard, M. (2013). *Environmental gerontolgoy: Making meaningful places in old age.* New York, NY: Springer Publishing Company.

Ruck, C., Karlsson, A., Steele, D., Edman, G., Meyerson, B. A., Kaj, E., et al. (2008). Capsulotomy for obsessive-compulsive disorder: Long-term follow-up of 25 patients. *Archives of General Psychiatry, 65*(8), 914–922.

Rupp, D., Vodanovich, S., & Crede, M. (2005). The multidimensional nature of ageism: Construct validity and group differences. *Journal of Social Psychology, 145*, 335–362.

Rurup, M. L., Onwuteaka-Philipsen, B. D., Pasman, H. R., Ribble, M. W., & van der Wal, G. (2006). Attitudes of physicians, nurses and relatives towards end-of-life decisions concerning nursing home patients with dementia. *Patient Education Counseling, 61*, 372–380.

Ryan, E. D., Giles, H., Bartolucci, G., & Henwood, K. (1986). Psycholinguistic and social psychological components of communication by and with the elderly. *Language and Communication, 6*, 1–24.

Ryff, C. D., Keyes, C. L. M., & Hughes, D. L. (2003). Status inequalities, perceived discrimination, and eudaimonic well-being: Do the challenges of minority life hone purpose and growth? *Journal of Health and Social Behavior, 44*(3), 275.

Sabbadini, G., Travan, L., & Toigo, G. (2012). Elderly women with heart failure: Unseen, unheard or simply forgotten? *Aging Health, 8*(2), 191–204.

Sadavoy, J., & Fogel, B. (1992). Personality disorder in old age. In J. E. Birren, R. B. Sloane, & G. D. Cohen (Eds.), *Handbook of mental health and aging* (2nd ed.). San Diego, CA: Academic Press.

Sadock, B. J., & Sadock, V. A. (2008). *Kaplan & Saddock's concise textbook of clinical psychiatry* (3rd ed.). Philadelphia, PA: Wolters Kluwer/Lippincott Williams & Wilkins.

Sadock, B. J., Sadock, V. A., & Ruiz, P. (2009). *Kaplan and Sadock's comprehensive textbook of psychiatry.* Philadelphia, PA: Wolters Kluver/Lippincott Williams & Wilkins.

Sadovsky, R., Alam, W., Enecilla, M., Cosiquien, R., Tipu, O., & Etheridge-Otey, J. (2006). Sexual problems among a specific population of minority women aged 40–80 years attending a primary care practice. *International Society for Sexual Medicine, 3*, 795–803.

SAGE. (2012). *Services and advocacy for gay, lesbian, bisexual & transgender elders.* Retrieved from http://www.saageuse.org

Saleebey, D. (2009). *The strengths perspective in social work practice.* Boston, MA: Allyn & Bacon.

Salib, E., Tadros, G., & Cawley, S. (2001). Elderly suicide and attempted suicide: One syndrome. *Medical Science and Law, 41*(3), 250–255.

Samuels, S. C. (2004). By way of an introduction: Paving the way for a psychiatric referral. *Geriatrics, 59*(1), 42–43.

Sarisoy, G., Kacar, O. F., Pazvantoglu, O., Korkmaz, I. Z., Ozurk, A., Akkaya, D., et al. (2013). Internalized stigma and intimate relations in bipolar and schizophrenic patients: A comparative study. *Comprehensive Psychiatry, 54*, 665–672.

Satorius, N., Gaebel, W., Cleveland, H. R., Stuart, H., Akiyama, T., Arboleda-Florez, J., et al. (2010). WPA guidance on how to combat stigmatization of psychiatry and psychiatrists. *World Psychiatry, 9*, 131–144.

Savasta, A. M. (2004). HIV: Associated transmission risks in older adults—An integrative review of the literature. *Journal of the Association of Nurses in AIDS Care, 15*(1), 50–59.

Scarmeas, N., Brandt, J., Blacker, D., Albert, M., Hadjigeorgiou, G., Dubois, B., et al. (2007). Disruptive behavior as a predictor in Alzheimer's disease. *Archives of Neurology, 64*, 1755–1761.

Schaie, K. W. (1993). Ageist language in pscyhological research. *American Psychologist, 48*, 49–51.

Scharloo, M., Kaplan, A. A., Weinman, J. A., Wilens, L. N., & Rooijmans, H. G. (2000). Physical and psychological correlates of function in patients with chronic obstructive pulmonary disease. *Journal of Asthma, 37*(1), 17–29.

Scheidt, R. J., & Norris-Baker, C. (2003). The general ecological model revisited: Evolution, current status, and continuing challenges. In H. W. Wahl, R. Wahl, R. J. Scheidt, & P. Windley (Eds.), *Environments, gerontology, and old age. Annual review of gerontology and geriatrics 2003* (pp. 34–58). New York, NY: Springer Publishing Company.

Schiamberg, L., & Gans, P. H. (2000). Elder abuse by adult children: An applied ecological framework for understanding contextual risk factors and the intergenerational character of quality of life. *International Journal of Aging and Human Development, 50*, 329–359.

Schiamberg, L. B., Oehnmke, J., Zhang, Z., Barboza, G. E., Griffore, R. J., von Heydrich, L., et al. (2012). Physical abuse of older adults in nursing homes: A random sample survey of adults with an elderly family member in a nursing home. *Journal of Elder Abuse & Neglect, 24*(1), 65–83.

Schick, V., Herbenick, D., & Reece, M. (2010). Sexual behaviors, condom use, and sexual health promotion for older adults. *Journal of Sexual Medicine, 7*(Suppl. 5), 315–329.

Schick, V., Herbenick, D., Reece, M., Sanders, S. A., Dodge, B., Middlestadt, S. E., et al. (2010). Sexual behaviors, condom use, and sexual health of Americans over 50: Implications for sexual health promotion for older adults. *Journal of Sexual Medicine, 7*, 315–329.

Schmeichel, B. J., Gailliot, M. T., Filardo, E., McGregor, I., Gitter, S., & Baumeister, R. F. (2009). Terror management theory and self-esteem revisited: The roles of implicit and explicit self-esteem in mortality salience effects. *Journal of Personality and Social Psychology, 96*, 1077–1087.

Schneider, E., Glynn, M., Kajese, T., & McKenna, M. (2006). Epidemiology of HIV/AIDS—United States, 1981–2005. *Morbidity and Mortality Weekly Report, 55*(21), 589–592.

Schneiderman, N., Saab, P. G., Catellier, D., Powell, L. H., DeBusk, R. F., Williams, R. B., et al. (2004). Psychosocial treatment within sex by ethnicity subgroups in the Enhancing Recovery in Coronary Heart Disease clinical trial. *Psychosomatic Medicine, 66*, 475–483.

Schnoll, R. A., Harlow, L. L., & Brower, L. (2000). Spirituality, demographic and disease factors and adjustment to cancer. *Cancer Practice, 8*, 298–304.

Schonfeld, L., & Dupress, L. W. (1995). Treatment approaches for older problem drinkers. *International Journal of the Addictions, 30,* 1819–1842.

Schofield, M., Powers, J. R., & Loxton, D. (2013). Mortality and disability outcomes of self-reported elder abuse: A 12–year prospective investigation. *Journal of the American Geriatrics Society, 61*(5), 679–685.

Schonwetter, R. S., Han, B., Small, B. J., Martin, B., Tope, K., & Haley, W. (2003). Predictors of six-month survival among patients with dementia: An evaluation of hospice Medicare guidelines. *American Journal of Hospice and Palliative Care, 20*(2), 105–113.

Schroots, J. J. F., & Birren, J. (1988). The nature of time: Implications for research on aging. *Comprehensive Gerontology, 50,* 1–29.

Schulunberg, S. E., Hutzell, R., Nassif, C., & Rogina, J. (2008). Logotherapy for clinical practice. *Psychotherapy Theory, Research Practice, Training, 45*(4), 447–463.

Schulz, R., & Beach, S. R. (1999). Caregiving as a risk factor for mortality: The Caregiver Health Effects Study. *Journal of the American Medical Association, 282,* 2215–2219.

Schuster, M. A., Colins, R., Cunningham, W. E., Morton, S., Zierler, S., Wong, M., et al. (2005). Percieved discrimination in clinical care in a nationally representative sample of HIV-infected adults receiving health care. *Journal of General Internal Medicine, 20*(9), 807–813.

Scott, K. M., McGee, M. A., & Oakley Browne, M. A. (2006). Mental disorder comorbidity in Te Rau Hinengaro, the New Zealand mental health survey. *Australian and New Zealand Journal of Psychiatry, 40,* 875–881.

Scull, A. (2005). *Madhouse: A tragic tale of megalomania and modern medicine.* New Haven, CT: Yale University Press.

Seale, C., & Addington-Hall, J. M. (1994). Euthanasia: Why people want to die earlier. *Social Science and Medicine, 39,* 647–654.

Seidler, A., Bernhardt, T., Nienhasu, A., & Frolich, L. (2003). Association between the psychosocial network and dementia—A case-control study. *Journal of Psychiatric Research, 37,* 89–98.

Seiler, S., Schmidt, H., Lechner, A., Benke, T., Sanin, G., Ransmayr, G., et al. (2012). Driving cessation and dementia: Results of the Prospective Registry on Dementia in Austria (PRODEM). *PLoS One, 7*(12), 27–41.

Selvin, E., Coresh, J., & Barncati, F. L. (2006). The burden and treatment of diabetes in elderly individuals in the U.S. *Diabetes Care, 29,* 2114–2419.

Sever, B., & Youdin, R. (2006). Police knowledge of older populations: The impact of training, experience, and education. *Professional Issues in Criminal Justice, 1*(2), 35–54.

Severus, W. E., Littman, A. B., & Stoll, A. (2001). Omega-3 fatty acids, homocysteine, and the increased risk of cardiovascular mortality in major depressive disorder. *Harvard Review of Psychiatry, 6,* 280–293.

Seymour, J., Gott, M., Bellamy, G., Ahmedzai, S. H., & Clark, D. (2004). Planning for end of life: The views of older people about advanced care statements. *Social Science & Medicine, 59*(1), 75–86.

Shallcross, L. (2010). Putting clients ahead of personal values. *Counseling Today, 53,* 32–34.

Sharma, M., & Andrade, C. (2012). Behavioral interventions for insomnia: Theory and practice. *Indian Journal of Psychiatry, 54*(4), 359–366.

Shaw, J. (2012). Approaching your highest sexual function in relationship: A reward of age and maturity. In P. J. Kleinplatz (Ed.), *New directions in sex therapy: Innovations and alternatives* (2nd ed., pp. 175–194). New York, NY: Routledge.

Sher, L. (2006). Alcoholism and suicidal behaviour: A clinical overview. *Acta Psychiatrica Scandinavica, 113,* 13–22.

Shifen, J. L., Monz, B. U., Russo, P. A., Segreti, A., & Johannes, C. B. (2008). Sexual problems and distress in United States women. Prevalence and correlates. *Obstetrics and Gynecology, 112*(5), 970–978.

Shippy, A., Cantor, M., & Brennan, M. (2001, November). *Patterns of support for lesbians and gays as they age.* Paper presented at the 54th Annual Scientific Meeting of the Gerontological Society of America. Chicago, Illinois.

Shrivastava, A., Bureau, Y., Rewari, N., & Johnston, M. (2013). Clinical risk of stigma and discrimination of mental illnesses: Need for objective assessment and quantification. *Indian Journal of Psychiatry, 55*(2), 178–182.

Shumaker, S. A., Legault, C., Rapp, S. R., Thai, L., Wallace, R. B., Ockkene, J. K., et al. (2003). Estrogen plus progestin and the incidence of dementia and mild cognitive impairment in postmenopausal women. The Women's Health Initiative Memory study: A randomized controlled trial. *Journal of the American Medical Association, 289*(20), 2651–2662.

Shuster, J. L., Breitbart, W., & Chochinov, H. M. (1999). Psychiatric aspects of excellent end-of-life care. *Psychosomatics, 40*(1), 1–4.

Siegal, J. (2005, July/August). Science's social work. *Bulletin of the Atonic Scientists*, p. 12.

Silveira, M. J., Kim, S. Y., & Langa, K. M. (2010). Advance directives and outcomes of surrogate decision making before death. *New England Journal of Medicine, 362*(13), 1211–1218.

Singer, P. A., Martin, D. K., & Kelner, M. (1999). Quality end-of-life care: Patients perspectives. *Journal of the American Medical Association, 281*, 163–168.

Singer, T., Lindenberger, U., & Baltes, P. B. (2003). Plasticity of memory for new learning in very old age: A story of major loss? *Psychology and Aging, 18*(2), 306–317.

Singh, N. H., Clements, K. M., & Fiatarone Singh, M. A. (2001). The efficacy of exercise as a long-term antidepressant in elderly subjects. *Journal of Gerontology, 56*(8), 497–504.

Sisco, S., Volland, P., & Gorin, S. (2005). Social work leadership and aging: Meeting the demographic imperative. *Health & Social Work, 30*, 344–347.

Slettebo, A. (2008). Safe, but lonely: Living in a nursing home. *Nordic Journal of Nursing Research, 28*(1), 22–25.

Smith, D. L. (2008). Disability, gender, and intimate partner violence: Relationships from the Behavioral Risk Factor Surveillance System. *Sexuality and Disability, 26*(1), 15–28.

Smith, J., Borchelt, M., Maier, H., & Jopp, D. (2002). Health and well-being in the young and oldest old. *Journal of Social Issues, 58*, 715–732.

Smith, K. P., & Christakis, N. A. (2009). Association between widowhood and risk of diagnosis with a sexually transmitted infection in older adults. *Journal of Public Health, 99*, 2055–2062.

Smith, L. J., Mulhall, J. P., Deveci, S., Monaghan, N., & Reid, M. C. (2007). Sex after seventy: A pilot study of sexual function in older persons. *Journal of Sexual Medicine, 4*, 1247–1253.

Solomon, S. H., Avorn, J., Katz, J. N., Finkelstein, J. S., Arnold, M., Polinski, M., et al. (2005). Compliance with osteoporosis medications. *Archives of Internal Medicine, 165*, 2414–2419.

Sorocco, K. H., & Ferrell, S. W. (2006). Alcohol use among older adults. *Journal of General Psychology, 133*, 453–467.

Spira, A. P., Rebok, G. W., Stone, K. L., Kramer, J. H., & Yaffe, K. (2012). Depressive symptoms in oldest-old women: Risk of mild cognitive impairment and dementia. *American Journal of Geriatric Psychiatry, 20*(12), 1006–1015.

Stanley, M. A., Beck, J. G., Novy, D. M., Averill, P. M., Swann, A. C., & Diefenbach, G. J. (2003). Cognitive-behavioral treatment of late-life generalized anxiety disorder. *Journal of Consulting and Clinical Psychology, 71*, 309–319.

Stanley, M. A., Calleo, J., Bush, A. L., Wilson, N., Snow, A. L., Kraus-Schuman, C., et al. (2013). The Peaceful Mind Program: A pilot test of a cognitive-behavioral therapy-based intervention for anxious patients with dementia. *American Journal of Geriatric Psychiatry, 21*(7), 696–708.

Stanley, M. A., Hopko, D. R., Derek, R., Diefenbach, G. J., Gretchen, J., Bourland, S., et al. (2003). Cognitive-behavior therapy for late-life generalized anxiety disorder in primary care: Preliminary findings. *American Journal of Geriatric Psychiatry, 11*(1), 92–96.

Stark, A. C., & Budson, A. E. (2012). Managing memory impairment in patients with Alzheimer's disease. *Neurodegenerative Disease Management, 2*(5), 459–469.

Steffens, D. C. (2013). Exercise for late-life depression? It depends. *Lancet, 382*(9886), 4–5.

Steger, M. F., & Kashdan, T. B. (2007). Stability and specificity of meaning in life and life satisfaction over one year. *Journal of Happiness Studies, 8*, 161–179.

Steger, M. F., Mann, J. R., Michels, P., & Cooper, T. C. (2009). Meaning in life, anxiety, depression, and general health among smoking cessation patients. *Journal of Psychosomatic Research, 67*, 353–358.

Steinhauser, K. E., Christakis, N. A., Clipp, E. C., McNeilly, M., McIntyre, L., & Tulsky, J. A. (2000). Factors considered important at the end of life by patients, family, physicians, and other care providers. *Journal of the American Medical Association, 284*(19), 2476–2482.

Steinhauser, K. E., Clipp, E. C., McNeilly, M., Christakis, N. A., McIntyre, L. M., & Tulsky, J. A. (2006). In search of a good death: Observations of patients, families, and providers. *Annals of Internal Medicine, 132*(10), 825–832.

Stevenson, D., & Grabowski, D. (2010). Sizing up the market for assisted living. *Health Affairs, 29*, 39–43.

Stewart, D., & Olsin, D. (2001). Recognition and treatment of late-life addictions in medical settings. *Journal of Clinical Geropsychology, 7*, 145–158.

Stoller, E. P., & Gibson, R. C. (1994). *Worlds of difference: Inequality in the aging experience.* Thousand Oaks, CA: Pine Forge Press.

Stoller, E. P., & Gibson, R. C. (2000). *Worlds of difference* (3rd ed.). Thousand Oaks, CA: Pine Forge Press.

Storr, A. (1988). *Churchill's black dog, Kafka's mice.* New York: Ballantine Books.

Straka, S. M., & Montminy, L. (2006). Responding to the needs of older women experiencing domestic violence. *Violence Against Women, 12*(3), 251–267.

Stratford, T., Lal, S., & Meara, A. (2012). Neuroanalysis of therapeutic alliance in the symptomatically anxious: The physiological connection revealed between therapist and client. *American Journal of Psychotherapy, 66*(1), 1–21.

Street, A., & Kissen, D. (1999–2000). Dispensing death, desiring death: An exploration of medical roles and patient motivation during the period of legalized euthansia in Australia. *Omega, 4,* 231–248.

Street, D., & Desai, S. (2011). Planning for old age. In R. A. Settersten & J. Angel (Eds.), *Handbook of sociology of aging.* New York, NY: Springer.

Strik, J. J., Denollet, J., Lousberg, R., & Honig, A. (2003). Comparing symptoms of depression and anxiety as predictors of cardiac events and increased health care consumption after myocardial infarction. *Journal of the American College of Cardiology, 42,* 1801–1807.

Stroebe, M. S., & Schut, H. (1999). The dual process model of coping with bereavement: Rationale and description. *Death Studies, 23,* 197–224.

Stroebe, M. S., & Schut, H. (2001). Meaning making in the dual process model of coping with bereavement. In R. A. Neimeyer (Ed.), *Meaning reconstruction and the experience of loss.* Washington, DC: American Psychological Association.

Stroebe, M. S., Schut, H., & Stroebe, W. (2005). Attachment in coping with bereavement: A theoretical integration. *Review of General Psychology, 9,* 48–66.

Stuck, A. E., Walthert, J. M., Nikolaus, T., Bula, C. J., Hollmann, C., & Beck, J. C. (1999). Risk factors for functional status decline in community-living elderly peolpe: A systematic literature review. *Social Scientce & Medicine, 48,* 445–469.

Sudore, R. L., & Fried, T. R. (2010). Redefining the "planning" in advance care planning: Preparing for end-of-life decision making. *Annals of Internal Medicine, 153,* 256–261.

Sullivan, T. A., Warren, E., & Westbrook, J. L. (2006). Less stigma or more financial distress: An empirical analysis of the extraordinary increase in bankruptcy filings. *Stanford Law Review, 59*(2), 213–256.

Sumerskill, B. (2012). *Lesbian, gay and bisexual people in later life.* London, UK: Stonewell.

Suominen, K., Isometsa, E., & Lonnqvist, J. (2004). Elderly suicide attempters with depression are often diagnosed only after the attempt. *International Journal of Geriatric Psychiatry, 19,* 35–40.

Swartz, M. S., Wagner, H. R., Swanson, J. W., Burns, L. K., George, L. K., & Padgett, D. K. (1998). Comparing use of public and private mental health services: The enduring barriers of race and age. *Community Mental Health Journal, 34*(2), 133–144.

Tabnak, F., & Sun, R. (2000). Need for HIV/AIDS early identification and preventive measures among middle-aged and elderly women. *American Journal of Public Health, 90*(2), 287–288.

Takahashi, T., & Matsushita, H. (2006). Long-term effects of music therapy on elderly with moderate/severe dementia. *Journal of Music Therapy, 43*(4), 317–333.

Takkinen, S., Gold, C., Pederson, N. L., Malmberg, B., Nilsson, S., & Rovine, M. (2004). Gender differences in depression: A study of older unlike-sex twins. *Aging and Mental Health, 8*(3), 187–195.

Tatara, T. (2001). Characteristics of victims and perpetrators. In T. Tatara (Ed.), *Elder abuse.* Tokyo, Japan: Chuohoki Shuppan.

Taylor, D. H., Jr., Osterman, J., Acuff, S. W., & Ostbye, T. (2005). Do seniors understand risk of moving to a nursing home? *Health Services Research, 40*(3), 811–828.

Taylor, M. E., Delbaere, K., Close, J. C. T., & Lord, S. R. (2012). Managing falls in older patients with cognitive impairment. *Aging Health, 8*(6), 573–588.

Teaster, P. B. (2003). *A response to the abuse of vulnerable adults: The 2000 Survey of Adult Protective Services.* Washington, DC: National Center on Elder Abuse.

Teno, J. M., Clarridge, B. R., Casey, V., Welch, L. C., Wetle, T., Shield, R., et al. (2004). Family perspectives on end-of-life care at the last place of care. *Journal of the American Medical Association, 291*(1), 88–93.

Teresi, J. A., Ramirez, M., Ellis, J., Silver, S., Boratgis, G., Kong, J., et al. (2013). A staff intervention targeting resident-to-resident elder mistreatment (R-REM) in long-term care increased staff knowledge, recognition and reporting: Results from a cluster randomized trial. *International Journal of Nursing Studies, 50*(5), 644–656.

Teri, l., & Wagner, A. (1991). Assessment of depression in patients with Alzhiemer's disease: Concordance between informants. *Psychology and Aging, 6,* 280–285.

Ternesterdt, B. R., & Franklin, L. L. (2006). Ways of relating to death: Views of older people resident in nursing homes. *International Journal of Palliative Nursing, 12*(7), 334–340.

Thomas, S. B. (2001). The color line: Race matters in the elimination of health disparities. *American Journal of Public Health, 91*(7), 1046–1048.

Thomson, K. (2010). *Once a spy.* New York, NY: Doubleday.

Thornicroft, G., Brohan, E., Kassam, A., & Lewis-Holmes, E. (2008). Reducing stigma and discrimination: Candidate interventions. *International Journal of Mental Health Systems, 2*(1), 3.

Thorson, J. A., & Powell, F. C. (2000). Death anxiety in younger and older adults. In A. Tomer (Ed.), *Death attitudes and the older adult: Theories, concept, and applications.* Philadelphia, PA: Taylor & Francis.

Tien-Hyatt, J. L. (1986–1987). Self-perceptions of aging across cultures: Myth or reality? *International Journal of Aging and Human Development, 24,* 129–148.

Tiernann, E., O'Connor, M. O., O'Siorain, L., & Kearney, M. (2002). A prospective study of preferred versus actual place of death among patients referred to a palliative care homecare service. *Irish Medical Journal, 95,* 232–235.

Tierney, M. C., Snow, W. G., Moineddin, C. J., & Kiss, A. (2007). Neuropsychological predictors of self-neglect in cognitively impaired older people who live alone. *American Journal of Geriatric Psychiatry, 15*(2), 140–148.

Tilden, V. P., Tolle, S. W., Garland, M. J., & Nelson, C. A. (1995). Decisions about life-sustaining treatment: Impact of physicians' behaviors on the family. *Archives of Internal Medicine, 155,* 633–638.

Tinker, A. (1997). *Older people in modern socieity.* London, UK: Addison Wesley.

Tonrey, D. A. (2007). Telling family stories: The family building proojective technique. *Families in Society, 88*(4), 645–649.

Treas, J., & Marcum, C. S. (2011). Diversity and family relations. In R. A. Settersten & J. Angel (Eds.), *Handbook of sociology of aging.* New York, NY: Springer.

Tressel, L. S., Schumm, L. P., Laumann, E. O., Lewinson, W., Muircheatraigh, C. A., & Waite, L. J. (2007). A study of sexuality and health among older adults in the United States. *New England Journal of Medicine, 357,* 762–774.

Tsatali, M. S., Tsolaki, M. N., Christodoulou, T. P., & Papaliagkas, V. T. (2011). The complex nature of inappropriate sexual behaviors in patients with dementia: Can we put it into a frame? *Sexuality and Disability, 29*(2), 143–156.

Tse, M. (2010). Therapeutic effects of an indoor gardening programme for older people living in nursing homes. *Journal of Clinical Nursing, 19,* 949–958.

Tuckett, A. (2007). The meaning of nursing home: "Waiting to go up to St. Peter, OK! Waiting house, sad but true"—An Australian perspective. *Journal of Aging Studies, 21*(2), 119–133.

Tung, E. E., Chen, C. Y. Y., & Takahashi, P. Y. (2013). Common curbsides and conundrums in geriatric medicine. *Mayo Clinic Proceedings, 88*(6), 630–635.

Turner, A., Hochschild, A., Burnett, J., Zulfiquar, A., & Dyer, C. B. (2012). High prevalence of medication non-adherence in community dwelling older adults with substantiated self-neglect. *Drugs Aging, 29*(9), 741–749.

United Nations Organization. (2002). *World population ageing 1950–2050.* New York, NY: Author.

Vaccarino, V., Krumholz, H. M., Yarzebski, J., Gore, J. M., & Goldberg, R. J. (2001). Sex differences in 2–year mortality after hospital discharge for myocardial infarction. *Annals of Internal Medicine, 134,* 173–181.

Valente, S. M., & Trainor, D. (1998). Rational suicide among patients who are terminally ill. *AORN Journal, 68*(2), 252–264.

Vallelly, S. (2002). Extra care housing; A review of the effectiveness of extra care housing for older people. *Housing, Care and Support, 5*(1), 7–11.

Van der Kooy, K., van Hout, H., Marwijk, H., Stehouwer, C., & Beekman, A. (2007). Depression and the risk of cardiovascular diseases: A systematic review and meta analysis. *International Journal of Geriatric Psychiatry, 22*(7), 613–626.

van Heugten, K. (2002). Social workers who move into private practice: Ideological considerations as a factor in the transition. *Families in Society, 83*(5/6), 465–473.

Van Voorhis, R., & Wagner, M. (2001). Coverage of gay and lesbian subject matter in social work journals. *Journal of Social Work Education, 37*, 147–159.

Vance, S. R., Cohen-Kettenis, P. T., Drescher, J., Meyer-Bahoburg, H. F. L., Friedman, P., & Zucker, K. J. (2010). Opinions about the DSM gender identity disorder diagnosis: Results from an international survey administered to organizations concerned with the welfare of transgender people. *International Journal of Transgenderism, 12*(1), 1–10.

Verghese, J., Lipton, R. B., Katz, M., Hall, C. B., Derby, C. A., & Kuslansky, G. (2003). Leisure activities and the risk of dementia in the elderly. *New England Journal of Medicine, 348*, 2508–2516.

Verkerk, M. A. (2001). The care perspective and autonomy. *Medical Health Care Philosophy, 4*.

Vernooij-Dassen, M. J., Moniz-Cook, E. D., Woods, R. T., De Lepeleire, J., Leuschner, A., Zanetti, O., et al. (2005). Factors affecting timely recognition and diagnosis of dementia across Europe: From awareness to stigma. *Journal of Geriatric Psychiatry, 20*(4), 377–386.

Victor, C. R. (2012). Loneliness in care homes: A neglected area of research? *Aging Health, 8*(6), 637–646.

Vilhelmsson, A., Svensson, T., & Meeuwisse, A. (2013). A pill for the Ill? Patients reports of their experience of the medical encounter in the treatment of depression. *PLoS One, 8*(6), 1–8.

Vioeberghs, E., Van Dam, D., Franck, F., Staufenbiel, M., & De Deyn, P. P. (2007). Mood and male sexual behaviour in the APP23 model of Alzheimer's disease. *Behavioural Brain Research, 180*(2), 145–146.

Vittica, M., Grassi, M., Barbano, L., Galavotti, G., Sturani, C., Vianello, A., et al. (2010). Last 3 months of life in home-ventilated patients: The family perception. *European Respiratory Journal, 35*, 1064–1071.

Volicer, L., Harper, D. G., & Manning, B. C. (2001). Sundowning and circadian rhythms in Alzheimer's disease. *American Journal of Psychiatry, 158*, 704–711.

von Heydrich, L., Schiamberg, L. B., & Chee, G. (2012). Social-relational risk factors for predicting elder physical abuse: An ecological bi-focal model. *International Journal of Aging and Human Development, 75*(1), 71–94.

Votova, K., Blais, R. G., Penning, M. J., & Maclure, M. K. (2013). Polypharmacy meets polyherbacy: Pharmaceutical, over-the-counter, and natural health product use among Canadian adults. *Canadian Journal of Public Health, 104*(3), e222–228.

Wachtel, P., & Messer, S. (1997). *Theories of psychotherapy: Origins and evolution.* Washingtom, DC: American Psychological Association.

Waern, M., Beskow, J., & Skoog, I. (1999). Elderly suicides' contact with their general practitioner before death. *International Journal of Geriatric Psychiatry, 9*(12), 1008–1009.

Waern, M., Runeson, B. S., Allebeck, P., Beskow, J., Rubenowitz, E., Skoog, I., et al. (2002). Mental disorder in elderly suicides: A case-control study. *American Journal of Psychiatry, 159*(3), 450–455.

Wagner, L. S., & Wagner, T. H. (2003). The effect of age on the use of health and self-care information: Confronting the stereotype. *The Gerontologist, 43*(3), 318–324.

Wahl, H., & Weisman, G. D. (2003). Environmental gerontology at the beginning of the new mellennium: Reflections on its historical, empirical, and theoretical development. *The Gerontologist, 43*, 616–627.

Walker, D. (2005, December 25). *White House Conference on Aging: Day one opening plenary.* Retrieved from http://www.kaisernetwork.org/health_cast/uploaded_files/121205_whcoa_open_transcript.pdf

Wallace, B., Carter, R., Nanin, J., Keller, R., & Alleyne, V. (2002). Identity development for "diverse and different others." Integrating stages of change, motivational interviewing, and identity theories for race, people of color, sexual orientation, and disability. In B. Wallace & R. Carter (Eds.), *Understanding and dealing with violence: A multicultural approach* (pp. 41–91). (Roundtable series on psychology and education.) Thousand Oaks, CA: Sage.

Walmsley, R. (2000). *World prison population list* (2nd ed.). London, UK: Home Office Research, Development and Statistics Directorate.

Walsh, C. A., Olsen, J. L., Ploeg, J., Lohfield, L., & MacMillan, H. L. (2011). Elder abuse and oppression: Voices of marginalized elders. *Journal of Elder Abuse & Neglect, 23*(1), 17–42.

Walter, C. A., & McCoyd, J. L. M. (2009). *Grief and loss across the lifespan: A biopsychosocial perspective.* New York, NY: Springer Publishing Company.

Wampold, B. E. (2010). The research evidence for common factors models: A historically situated perspective. In B. L. Duncan, S. D. Miller, B. E. Wampold, & M. A. Hubble (Eds.), *The heart and soul of change* (2nd ed., pp. 49–82). Washington, DC: American Psychological Association.

Wang, H. X., Karp, A., Winblad, B., & Fratiglioni, L. (2002). Late-life engagement in social and leisure activities is associated with a decreased risk of dementia: A longitudinal study from the Kungsholment Project. *American Journal of Epidemiology, 155*, 1081–1807.

Wang, P. S., Berglund, P., Olfson, M., Pincus, H. A., Wells, K. B., & Kessler, R. C. (2005). Failure and delay in initial treatment contact after first onset of mental disorders in the National Comorbidity Survey Replication. *Archives of General Psychiatry, 62*, 603–613.

Wang, P. S., Lane, M., & Olfson, M. (2005). Twelve-month use of mental health services in the United States: Results from the National Comorbidity Survey replication. *Archives of General Psychiatry, 62*, 629–640.

Wang, T., & Biederman, S. (2012). Enhance the accuracy of medication histories for the elderly by using an electronic medication checklist. *Perspectives in Health Information Management, 9*, 1–15.

Wapner, S., & Demick, J. (2005). Critical person-in-environment transitions across the lifespan. In J. Valsiner (Ed.), *Heinz Werner and developmental science* (pp. 285–305). New York, NY: Kluwer Academic/Plenum Publishers.

Watt-Watson, J., Garfinkel, P., Gallop, R., Stevens, B., & Streiner, D. (2000). The impact of nurses' empathic responses on patients' pain management in acute care. *Nursing Research, 49*, 191–200.

Webster, J. D. (1995). Adult age differences in reminiscence functions. In B. K. Haight & J. D. Webster (Eds.), *The art and science of reminiscencing: Theory, research, methods, and applications* (pp. 89–102). Bristol, PA: Taylor & Francis.

Wein, S. (2000). Sedation in the imminently dying patient. *Oncology, 14*, 585–598.

Weinberg, D. (2000). "Out There": The ecology of addiction in drug abuse treatment discourse. *Social Problems, 47*, 606–621.

Weiner, B. (1995). *Judgements of responsiblity: A foundation for a theory of social conduct.* New York, NY: Guilford Press.

Weinick, R., Jacobs, E., & Stone, L. (2004). Hispanic healthcare disparities: Challenging the myth of a monolithic Hispanic population. *Medical Care, 42*, 313–320.

Weinstein, E. (1981). Woodrow Wilson: A medical and psychological biography. In D. M. Oshinsky, *Polio: An American Story.* New York, NY: Oxford University Press.

Weisman, A. D., & Worden, J. W. (1976–77). The existential plight in cancer: Significance of the first 100 days. *International Journal of Psychiatry in Medicine, 7*, 1–15.

Weiss, I., Gal, J., Cnaan, R. A., & R., M. (2002). Where does it begin? A comparative perspective on the professional preferences of first year social work students. *British Journal of Social Work, 32*, 589–608.

Weiss, I., & Kaufman, R. (2006). Educating for social action: An evaluation of the impact of a fieldwork training program. *Journal of Policy Practice, 5*(1), 5–30.

Weiss, M. G., & Ramakrishna, J. (2006). Stigma interventions and research for international health. *Lancet, 367*, 536–538.

Weiss-Gal, I. (2008). The person-in-environment approach: Professional ideology and practice of social workers in Israel. *Social Work, 53*, 65.75.

Werner, P., & Heinik, J. (2008). Stigma by association and Alzheimer's disease. *Aging & Mental Health, 12*(1), 92–99.

West, E., Holmes, J., Zidek, C., & Edwards, T. (2013). Intraprofessional collaboration through an unfolding case and the Just Culture Model. *Journal of Nursing Education, 52*(8), 470–474.

Westerhof, G. J., Bohlmeijer, E. T., & Webster, J. D. (2010). Reminiscence and mental health: A review of recent progress in theory, research, and intervention. *Aging & Society, 30*, 697–721.

Westfield, J. S., Range, L. M., Rogers, J. R., Maples, M. R., Bromley, J. L., & Alcorn, J. (2000). Suicide: An overview. *Counseling Psychologist, 28*, 445–510.

White, B., Driver, S., & Wrren, A. M. (2010). Resilience and indicators of adjustment during rehabilitation from a spinal chord injury. *Rehabilitation Psychology, 55*, 23–32.

White, M., & Epston, D. (1990). *Narrative means to therapeutic ends.* New York, NY: W.W. Norton.

Whitehead, B., O'Brian, M., & Jack, B. (2011). Experiences of dying, death, and bereavement in motor neurone disease: A qualitative study. *Palliative Medicine, 26*, 368–378.

Whittington, K. T., & Briones, R. (2004). Prevalence and incidence study: 6–year sequential acute care data. *Advances in Skin Wound Care, 17*, 490–494.

Wiegel, M., Scepkowski, I. A., & Barlow, D. H. (2006). Cognitive and affective processes in female sexual dysfunctions. In I. Goldstein, C. M. Meston, S. R. Davis, & A. M. Traish (Eds.), *Womens' sexual function and dysfunction.* Abingdon, UK: Taylor & Francis.

Wieland, D. (2000). Abuse of older persons: An overview. *Holistic Nursing Practice, 14*(4), 40–50.

Wieland, G. D. (2005). From bedside to bench: Research in comorbidity and aging. *Science of Aging Knowledge Environment, 39,* 29.

Wiktorsson, S., Runeson, B., Skoog, I., Ostiing, S., & Waern, M. (2010). Attempted suicide in the elderly: Characteristics of suicide attempters 70 years and older and a general population comparison group. *American Journal of Geriatric Psychiatry, 18*(57–67).

Wilcox, H. C., Connor, K. R., & Caine, E. D. (2004). Association of alcohol and drug use disorders and completed suicide: An empirical review of cohort studies. *Drug and Alcohol Dependence, 76,* 11–19.

Wilkinson, P. (1997). Cognitive therapy with elderly people. *Age and Ageing, 26*(1), 53–58.

Will, G. F. (1998). A jail break for geriatrics. *Newsweek, 132*(3), 70–71.

Williams, A., Ylanne, V., & Wadleigh, P. M. (2007). Selling the "elixir of life": Images of the elderly in an Olivio advertising campaign. *Journal of Aging Studies, 27,* 1–21.

Williams, D. R., & Harris-Reid, M. (1999). Race and mental health: Emerging patterns and promising approaches. In A. V. Horwitz & T. L. Scheid (Eds.), *A handbook for the study of mental health: Social contexts theories and systems* (pp. 295–314). New York, NY: Cambridge University Press.

Williams, D. R., & Mohaemd, S. A. (2009). Discrimination and racial disparities in health: Evidence and needed research. *Journal of Behavioral Medicine, 32,* 20–47.

Williams, D. R., & Wilson, C. M. (2001). Race, ethnicity, and aging. In R. Binstock & L. George (Eds.), *Handbook of aging and the social sciences* (5th ed., pp. 160–178). San Diego, CA: Academic Press.

Williams, J. W., Barrett, J., Oxman, T., Frank, E., Katon, W., Sullivan, M., et al. (2000). Treatment of dysthymia and minor depression in primary care. *Journal of the American Medical Association, 284*(12), 1519–1526.

Williams, M. V., Davis, T., Parker, R. M., & Weiss, B. D. (2002). The role of health literacy in patient–physician communication. *Family Medicine, 34*(5), 383–389.

Williams, M., Ballard, M. B., & Alessi, H. (2005). Aging and alcohol abuse: Increasing counselor awareness. *Adultspan, 4,* 7–18.

Willis, S. L., & Schaie, K. W. (1999). Intellectual functioning in midlife. In S. L. Willis & K. W. Schaie (Eds.), *Life in the middle: Psychological and social development in middle age* (pp. 233–247). San Diego, CA: Academic Press.

Wilson, D. M., Ross, C., Goodridge, D., Davis, P., Landreville, A., & Roebuck, K. (2008). The care needs of community-dwelling seniors suffering from advanced chronic obstructive pulmonary disease. *Canadian Journal of Aging, 27*(4), 347–357.

Wilson, M. (1993). *DSM-III* and the transformation of American psychiatry. *American Journal of Psychiatry, 150,* 339–410.

Wilson, R. S., Arnold, S. E., Beck, T. L., Bienias, J. L., & Bennett, D. A. (2008). Change in depressive symptoms during the prodromal phase of Alzheimer's disease. *Archives of Gerontology and Geriatrics, 65*(4), 439–446.

Windielman, P., & Berridge, K. C. (2004). Unconscious emotion. *Current Directions in Psychological Science, 13,* 120–123.

Wink, P., & Dillon, M. (2002). Spiritual development across the adult life course: Findings for a longitudinal study. *Journal of Adult Development, 9,* 74–94.

Winnick, C. (1962). Maturing out of narcotic addiction. *United Nations Bulletin on Narcotics, 14,* 3–9.

Winnie, H. J. (2013, October 28). To combat elder abuse, doormen are enlisted to keep a watchful eye. *New York Times,* p. A22.

Witherington, D. C. (2007). The dynamic systems approach as metatheory for developmental psychology. *Human Development, 50,* 125–153.

Won, A. B., Lapane, K. I., & Vallow, S. (2004). Persistent nonmalignant pain and analgesic prescribing patterns in elderly nursing home residents. *Journal of the American Geriatrics Society, 52,* 867–874.

Wood, J., Storey, L., & Clark, D. (2007). Preferred place of care: An analysis of the "first 100" patient assessments. *Palliative Medicine, 21,* 449–450.

Wooddell, V., & Kaplan, K. J. (1998). An expanded typology of assisted suicide and euthanasia. *Omega, 36,* 201–208.

Woodford, M., & Bella, L. (2003). Are we ready to take a stand? Education and heterosexism: Fostering anti-oppressive practice. In W. Shera (Ed.), *Emerging perspectives in anti-oppressive practice.* Toronto, Canada: Canadian Scholars' Press.

Woodruff, L. (2012). *Dementia: Caring for parents with Alzheimer's and coping with grief.* Retrieved from http://www.huffingtonpost.com/lee-woodruff/dementia-grief-and-guilt_b_1231581.html

Woods, B. (2003). Evidence-based practice in psychosocial intervention in early dementia: How can it be achieved? *Aging and Mental Health, 7,* 5–6.

Wordon, J. W. (2008). *Grief counseling and grief therapy: A handbook for the mental health practitioner* (4th ed.). New York, NY: Springer Publishing Company.

World Health Organization. (2000). *Home-based long-term care: Report of a WHO study group Technical Report Series.* Geneva: Author.

Wouts, L., Oude Voshaar, C., Bremmer, M. A., Buitelaar, J. K., Penninx, B. W., & Beekman, A. T. F. (2008). Cardiac disease, depressive symptoms, and incident stroke in an elderly population. *Archives of General Psychiatry, 65*(5), 596–602.

Wright, A. A., Zhang, B., Ray, A., Mack, J. W., Trice, E., Balboni, T., et al. (2008). Associations between end-of-life discussions, patient mental health, medical care near death, and caregiver bereavement adjustment. *Journal of the American Medical Association, 300*(14), 1665–1673.

Wright, R. G. (2002). AIDS caregiving stress among HIV-infected men. In B. J. Kramer & E. H. Thompson Jr. (Eds.), *Men as caregivers: Theory, research, and service implications* (pp. 190–212). New York, NY: Springer Publishing Company.

Yale, R., & Snyder, I. (2002). The experience of support groups for persons with early-age Alzheimer's disease and their families. In P. B. Harris (Ed.), *The person with Alzheimer's disease and their families* (pp. 228–245). Baltimore, MD: John's Hopkins University Press.

Yalom, I. D. (1980). *Existential psychotherapy.* New York: Basic Books.

Yedidia, M. J., & MacGregor, B. (2001). Confronting the prospect of dying: Reports of terminally ill patients. *Journal of Pain Symptom Management, 22,* 807–819.

Yevchak, A. M., Steis, M. R., & Evans, L. K. (2012). Sundown syndrome: A systematic review of the literature. *Research in Gerontological Nursing, 5*(4), 294–303.

Yohannes, A. M. (2012). General practitioners views and experiences in managing depression in patients with chronic obstructive pulmonary disease. *Expert Review of Respiratory Medicine, 6*(6), 589–595.

Youdin, R., & Cleaveland, C. (2006 Fall). Religious affiliation/non-affiliation: A predictor of social work students' attitudes toward old poor people. *Social Work Forum, 39,* 5–19.

Zarit, S., & Femia, E. (2008). Behavioral and pscyhosocial interventions for family caregivers. *American Journal of Nursing, 108*(9), 47–53.

Zarit, S. H. (1980). *Aging and mental disorders: Psychological approaches to assessment and treatment.* New York, NY: The Free Press.

Zarit, S. H., Famia, H. H., Watson, L., Rice-Oeschger, L., & Kakos, B. (2004). Memory club: A group intervention for people with early stage dementia and their care partners. *The Gerontologist, 44,* 262–269.

Zautra, A. J., Reich, J. W., & Newsom, J. T. (1995). Autonomy and sense of control among older adults: An examination of their effects on mental health. In L. A. Bond, S. J. Cutler, & A. Grams (Eds.), *Promoting successful and productive aging* (pp. 153–170). Thousand Oaks, CA: Sage.

Zeiss, A. M., & Steffen, A. (1996). Behavioral and cognitive-behavioral treatments: An overview of social learning. In S. Zarit & B. G. Knight (Eds.), *A guide to psychotherapy and aging* (pp. 35–60). Washington, DC: American Psycholgoical Association.

Zeng, Y., & Vaupel, J. W. (2002). Functional capacity and self-evaluation of health and life of the oldest old in China. *Journal of Social Issues, 58,* 733–748.

Zhang, Y., Niu, J., Kelly-Hayes, M., Chaisson, C. E., Aliabadi, P., & Felson, D. T. (2002). Prevalence of symptomatic hand osteoarthritis and its impact on functional status among the elderly: The Framingham study. *American Journal of Epidemiology, 156*(11), 1021–1027.

Zimmerman, S., Sloane, P., Eckert, J., Gruber-Baldini, A., Morgan, L., Hebel, J., et al. (2005). How good is assisted living? Findings and implications from an outcomes study. *Journal of Gerontology: Social Sciences, 60*(4), S195–S204.

Zimmermann, C. (2007). Death denial: Obstacle or instrument for palliative care? *Sociology of Health and Illness, 29*(2), 297–314.

Zisook, S. (2000). Understanding and managing bereavement in palliative care. In H. M. Chochinov & B. William (Eds.), *Handbook of psychiatry in palliative medicine* (pp. 321–334). New York, NY: Oxford University Press.

Zunzunegui, M. V., Minicuci, N., Blumstein, T., Noale, M., Deeg, D. J. H., & Jylha, M. (2007). Gender differences in depressive symptoms among older adults: A cross-national comparison. The CLESA project. *Social Psychiatry and Psychiatric Epidemiology, 42*(3), 198–207.

Zuurmond, W., Davis, C., & Vergidis, D. (2002). Transdermal fentanyl shows a similar safety and efficacy profile in elderly and non-elderly patients with cancer pain. *Annals of Oncology, 13 (Suppl. 5)*, 171.

Zweig, R. A., & Hillman, J. (1999). Personality disorders in adults: A review. In E. Rosowsky, R.C. Abrams, & R. A. Zweig (Eds.), *Personality disorders in older adults: Emerging issues in diagnosis and treatment* (pp. 31–54). Mahwah, NJ: Lawrence Eribaum Associates.

Index

abuse. *See* older adult abuse
acetylcholine, 102, 103
acetylcholine esterase, 103
acetylcholine synapse, 103
acetylcholinesterase inhibitors, 103
active euthanasia, 199
active-passive communication, 186
addictive type (purpose substitution), 54
ADRD. *See* Alzheimer's disease-related
    disorders
adult day care services, 182–183
advanced care planning (ACP), 194
advanced directives, 194, 195, 198
affect, 29
Affordable Care Act, 71
African Americans. *See also* race and ethnicity
    diabetes, 117–118
    Internet access, 69, 77
    life satisfaction, 69
    nursing homes, 185
    psychotherapy services, 23
age stages
    centenarians, 7–8
    middle-old, 7
    old-old, 7
    super-centenarians, 8
    young-old, 6–7
ageism, 49–50
aging in place, 157, 181–182
AIDS. *See* HIV/AIDS
alcohol abuse/dependence, 130–131
alcohol use disorder, 131
Aldrin, Buzz, 75
Alpert, Richard (Ram Dass), 169

Alzheimer's disease. *See also* dementia
    early detection, 99–100
    fall risk, 108
    medications, 101–102
    psychoeducational support groups, 105–106
    stages, 100–101
Alzheimer's disease-related disorders, 97, 98
anorexia nervosa tardive, 86
anosmic, 35
antiaging hormone treatment, 161
antiaging medical interventions, 161–162
anxiety disorders, 86–87
Aricept, 103
arthritis, 113–114
aspirin, 119
assessing an older adult, 19–45
    appearance, 27
    attitude, 27
    checklist assessment form, 44
    clinician's speaking voice, 20
    collateral interviews, 36
    developmental history, 24–25
    DSM-5 diagnosis, 36–37
    environmental and demographic
        information, 24
    example (Dr. Frank), 37–44
    gender, age, sexual orientation, ethnicity,
        22–23
    homicidal assessment, 32–33
    levels of assessment, 19–20
    medical status, 25
    mental status exam, 33–35
    mood/affect, 28–29
    motor status, 27–28

cocaine, 128. *See also* older adult substance
abuse
Cognex, 103
cognitive behavioral therapy, 48
anxiety disorders, 86–87
cardiovascular disease, 116
dementia, 105
dying adults, 201
mood disorders, 89
pain, 120–121
personality disorders, 91
sleep disorders, 121
substance abuse, 136–137
theory, 55–56
cognitive restructuring, 55
cognitive training, 107
collateral interviews, 36
collateral joining, 58
coming out, 168–169
community living assistance services and
supports program, 71
conductive hearing loss, 119
constructivist theory, 52
continuing care facilities, 183–184
COPD. *See* chronic obstructive pulmonary
disease
Cotton, Harry, 85
coupling, 68
courtesy stigma, 65, 72, 73, 76
cringe factor, 141
cube metaphor, 48–49
cyclic phenomenon (substance abuse), 134, 135

Dass, Ram, 169
death and dying. *See* dying and death
death anxiety, 67, 194
decubitus ulcer, 121
delusional disorder, 88
demands, environmental, 12
dementia, 97–111. *See also* Alzheimer's
disease
caregiver support groups, 105
case study, 108–110
cognitive training, 107
depression, and, 89
falls, 108
frontal lobe, 99
imprisoned older adults, 108
Korsakoff syndrome, 99
leisure activities, and, 106

Lewy body, 98
long-term care, 108
mild cognitive impairment, 97–98
overnight camps, 105
Parkinson's disease, 99
Pick's disease, 99
psychotherapeutic interventions, 105
recreation therapy, 107
sexual behaviors, inappropriate, 108
sexuality, and, 146–147
stigma, 76
sundowning, 104
suspension of driving privileges, 107
therapeutic recreation, 106–107
vascular, 98
dementia with Lewy bodies, 98
demoralization syndrome, 116
depression
arthritis, and, 114
cardiovascular disease, and, 115, 116
co-occurring disorders, 88
dementia, and, 89
famous sufferers, 75
gender, 70
LGBT populations, 174–175
nursing homes, 185–186
personality disorders, and, 90
self-neglect, and, 161
transgender individuals, 174
unequal treatment, and, 88
weight training, and, 90
depressive disorder NOS, 88, 89
developmental stage theory (Erikson), 8–9
diabetes, 117–118
diabetic retinopathy, 118
disability, 180
disabled older adults, 159
disorders of sex development (DSD), 168
DLB. *See* dementia with Lewy bodies
donepezil, 103
double effect, 197, 198
double jeopardy, 76
driving privileges, suspension of, 107
dual process model of coping with
bereavement, 202, 203
dying and death, 193–205
advanced directives, 194, 195, 198
bereavement effect, 198–199
case study, 204–205
end-of-life planning, 193–195
euthanasia, 199–200